Developing Mathematical Ideas
Algebra

Patterns, Functions, and Change

Facilitator's Guide

A collaborative project by the staff and
participants of Teaching to the Big Ideas

Principal Investigators

Deborah Schifter

Virginia Bastable

Susan Jo Russell

With
Christopher Fraley
Virginia Stimpson

And teacher collaborators

DALE SEYMOUR PUBLICATIONS

Pearson Learning Group

This work was supported by the National Science Foundation under Grant Nos. ESI-9254393 (awarded to EDC), ESI-9731064 (awarded to EDC), ESI-0095450 (awarded to TERC), and ESI-0242609 (awarded to EDC). Any opinions, findings, conclusions, or recommendations expressed here are those of the authors and do not necessarily reflect the views of the National Science Foundation.

Additional support was provided by a grant from the ExxonMobil Foundation.

Art & Design: Evelyn Bauer, Kamau DeSilva
Editorial: Margie Richmond, Jennifer Chintala, Jennifer Serra
Production/Manufacturing: Nathan Kinney
Marketing: Kimberly Doster

The classroom activities Staircase Towers, Penny Jar, Magic Marbles, and Fastwalker, described in classroom cases and seen in classroom episodes on the DVD, are from the second edition of the mathematics curriculum, *Investigations in Number, Data, and Space*, developed at TERC and published by Pearson Scott Foresman (2008).

Dale Seymour Publications® is a trademark, in the U.S. and/or other countries, of Pearson Education, Inc. or its affiliate(s).

ISBN-13: 978-1-4284-0521-9
ISBN-10:   1-4284-0521-6

Printed in the United States of America
1 2 3 4 5 6 7 8 9 10   11 10 09 08 07

Dale
Seymour
Publications
Pearson Learning Group

1-800-321-3106
www.pearsonlearning.com

Teaching to the Big Ideas

The *Developing Mathematical Ideas* series was conceived by Teaching to the Big Ideas, an NSF Teacher Enhancement Project. *Patterns, Functions, and Change* was developed as a collaborative project by the staff and teacher collaborators of the Teaching to the Big Ideas and Investigations Revisions Projects.

PROJECT DIRECTORS: Deborah Schifter (Education Development Center), Virginia Bastable (SummerMath for Teachers at Mount Holyoke College), and Susan Jo Russell (TERC).

CONSULTANTS: Virginia Stimpson (University of Washington), Christopher Fraley (Lake Washington Public Schools), Thomas Carpenter (University of Wisconsin at Madison), Herbert Clemens (Ohio State University), Mark Driscoll (Education Development Center), Benjamin Ford (Sonoma State University), Megan Franke (University of California at Los Angeles), James Kaput (University of Massachusetts at Dartmouth), Jill Lester (Mount Holyoke College), James Lewis (University of Nebraska), Stephen Monk (University of Washington), Jean Moon (National Academy of Sciences), Loren Pitt (University of Virginia), Janice Szymaszek (Smith College Campus School), Erna Yackel (Purdue University at Calumet).

TEACHER COLLABORATORS: Beth Alchek, Barbara Bernard, Nancy Buell, Rose Christiansen, Lisette Colon, Kim Cook, Fran Cooper, Pat DeAngelis, Pat Erikson, Marcia Estelle, Nikki Faria-Mitchell, Trish Farrington, Tom Fisher, Mike Flynn, Elaine Herzog, Kirsten Lee Howard, David Jesser, Liliana Klass, Melissa Lee, Jennifer Levitan, Kathe Millett, Florence Molyneaux, Elizabeth Monopoli, Robin Musser, Christine Norrman, Deborah Carey O'Brien, Mary Beth Cahill O'Connor, Anne Marie O'Reilly, Mark Paige, Margaret Riddle, Rebeka Eston Salemi, Karen Schweitzer, Lisa Seyferth, Shoshy Starr, Susan Bush Smith, Liz Sweeney, Janice Szymaszek, Danielle Thorne, Karen Tobin, JoAnn Traushke, Ana Vaisenstein, Yvonne Watson-Murrell, Michelle Woods, and Mary Wright, representing the public schools of Amherst, Boston, Brookline, Holyoke, Lincoln, Natick, Newton, Northampton, South Hadley, Southampton, Springfield, Sudbury, Westwood, and Williamsburg, Massachusetts, and the Smith College Campus School in Northampton, Massachusetts.

DVD DEVELOPMENT: David Smith (David Smith Productions)

FIELD TEST SITES: Bismarck Public Schools (North Dakota), Boston Public Schools (Massachusetts), Buncombe County Public Schools (North Carolina), Eastern Washington University (Washington), Lake Washington School District (Washington), Northampton Public Schools (Massachusetts), Stafford County Schools (Virginia), and Teacher's Development Group (Oregon).

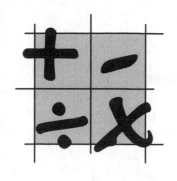

C O N T E N T S

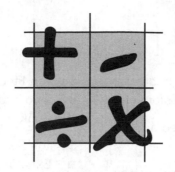

Orientation to the Materials

Patterns, Functions, and Change

The Patterns, Functions, and Change (PFC) seminar provides the opportunity for teachers from Kindergarten through middle school to

- examine how repeating patterns and number sequences can lead to the ideas of functions

- learn how to represent functional relationships using tables, graphs, expressions, and models

- explore the connections between constant and non-constant change and various types of functions (linear, quadratic, and exponential)

- consider how the different attributes of functions appear in tables, graphs, expressions, and models, and what they mean in a context

- interpret and create tables and graphs that are derived from data-based phenomena of change such as temperature or growth over time

Components of the PFC Developing Mathematical Ideas Materials

Each DMI module consists of a Casebook, a Facilitator's Guide, and a DVD. In a DMI seminar, each participant needs a Casebook; facilitators need the Casebook, the Facilitator's Guide, and the DVD. Facilitators will duplicate materials from the guide for use in each seminar session.

Casebook The Casebook includes an introduction and eight chapters. The first seven chapters include cases written by actual classroom teachers detailing classroom discussions and the thinking of their students. Chapter 8 is an essay that provides an overview of the mathematical ideas of the whole seminar.

Participants prepare for each session by reading one chapter of the Casebook. Prior to the first session, participants should read the Introduction to the Casebook, as well as Chapter 1.

Facilitator's Guide For each seminar session, the Facilitator's Guide is made up of the components listed below. A description of each component follows the list.

- Session overview—an overview of the session, including how to prepare for it

- Facilitator Notes—notes that provide mathematical background for facilitators

- Maxine's Journal—a narrative account of each session from the point of view of a facilitator

- Homework responses—samples of participants' written assignments and Maxine's responses

- Detailed agenda—a thorough description of the activities of the session

- Handouts—sheets to be copied and distributed to the participants

Session Overview The session overview summarizes the main goals of the session and provides a chart suggesting the order of the activities, format, and timing for each activity. In addition, a list is provided indicating what to do to prepare for the session.

Facilitator Notes Facilitator Notes, indicated by frames, provide mathematical background for facilitators. The main Facilitator Note follows the session overview and addresses a major mathematical theme of the session. Other notes are inserted into the text where they are most relevant. The topics covered in the Facilitator Notes are

Maxine's Journal "Maxine's Journal" is a session-by-session narrative account of the PFC seminar written from the point of view of a facilitator (Maxine). It is designed to provide additional support for PFC facilitators. For each session, Maxine records small- and whole-group discussions, considers comments made by participants, and shares her thoughts, questions, concerns, and decisions. Reading "Maxine's Journal" as preparation for a session allows facilitators to envision the key mathematical issues that are likely to emerge, provides examples of questions that facilitators can use to drive discussion, and presents probable interactions between facilitators and participants.

Homework responses In addition, "Maxine's Journal" includes examples of participants' writing assignments and Maxine's responses, as well as her comments about what she was trying to accomplish with those responses.

Detailed Agendas These agendas describe each activity of a session and provide suggestions for questions that can be used to shape each discussion. When posters are to be prepared prior to a session, the agenda specifies what should be on the poster.

Some sessions include a DVD component as well, and the agenda includes a summary of the DVD cases. The DVD summaries are not full transcripts; rather, they are brief narrative descriptions of the content of the DVD segments. Facilitators should not rely solely on the narrative summaries but watch the DVD segments and take notes in preparation for leading a session.

Handouts These pages are located at the end of the agenda and are indicated by a grey strip along the edge of the page. They are to be duplicated and distributed to participants during the seminar session. The following types of handouts are included:

- Focus Questions that guide the small- and whole-group discussions of the Casebook chapters

- "Math activities" that participants work on to deepen their mathematical understanding

- Homework pages that describe the reading and writing assignments for the sessions

DVD Segments While written cases allow users to examine student thinking at their own pace and to return as needed to ponder and analyze particular passages, the DVD segments offer users the opportunities to listen to real student voices in real time. They allow participants to see students' gestures and provide rich images of classrooms organized around student thinking. These segments show a wide variety of classroom settings, with children and teachers of different ethnic and language groups.

PFC Seminar Activities

In preparation for each session, participants complete a homework assignment. The 3-hour session typically consists of two or three major activities.

Homework assignments: Before each session, participants read one chapter of the Casebook and complete regular written portfolio assignments. Three times during the seminar, the portfolio assignment has participants explore their students' mathematical thinking. When participants have written such "student-thinking assignments," they share and discuss these writings with one or two other participants during the session. Other portfolio assignments ask participants to reflect on what they are learning in the seminar. Responding to participants' written assignments is an important part of the work of facilitating a DMI seminar. "Maxine's Journal" includes examples of participants' writing and a facilitator's responses.

Case discussions: In discussions of the Casebook, participants examine students' thinking, work on mathematical ideas for themselves, and consider the types of classroom settings and teaching strategies that support the development of student understanding.

Viewing DVD segments: Through video, teachers see episodes that capture both classroom atmosphere and students' gestures. Unlike the print cases, which allow for reading and rereading, these segments provide practice in listening to students in real time.

Math activities: Through activities designed for adult learners, the seminar participants develop, share, analyze, and refine their own mathematical thinking. PFC participants create tables, graphs, and expressions to represent functions; identify features that define particular kinds of functions from situations, tables, graphs, models, and expressions; examine the impact of constant and non-constant change and how it is seen in tables, graphs, situations, expressions, and models; interpret phenomena of change using tables and graphs; and become familiar with categories of functions such as linear, quadratic, and exponential.

Discussing the Chapter 8 essay: This discussion at the last session of the seminar creates an integrated picture of the mathematical themes under consideration, connecting the events observed in the cases and in participants' own classrooms to more formal mathematics. Some facilitators prefer to assign sections of Chapter 8 during the course of the seminar instead of assigning all of it after Session 7.

Preparing to Facilitate the PFC Seminar

Become familiar with PFC as a whole To become familiar with the flow of mathematical ideas in a seminar, we suggest that a facilitator read the introduction to the Casebook, the introduction to each Casebook chapter, and the Chapter 8 essay, "The Mathematics of Patterns, Functions, and Change for the K–8 Classroom." You should also read all of the eight sessions of "Maxine's Journal" to get an image of the seminar experience from the point of view of a facilitator. In addition, you may find it useful to examine some of the cases and look through the detailed agendas and handouts.

Identify connections between goals for the seminar and goals for each session Once you are familiar with the goals and components of the PFC curriculum as a whole, the next step is to prepare for individual sessions. For each session, read the cases, the related entry of "Maxine's Journal," and the agenda. Work through the activities in the session yourself; for example, do the math activity, view the DVD segment, think about the focus questions, and familiarize yourself with any additional handouts. As you do this work, think through the issues raised by that set of activities. What are the goals of the session as a whole? What ideas about mathematics, learning, and teaching should emerge as teachers participate in the investigations and discussions? How are these ideas illustrated in the cases? How might they arise in the other activities? What questions might you pose to call attention to these ideas?

Prepare the logistics Besides planning for issues likely to arise during discussions, you must think through the order of the activities and review the suggested timetable. Organize the materials so everything is ready for each session; having the readings, handouts, DVD, DVD equipment, and manipulatives at hand before a session saves time and allows you to concentrate on seminar participants. Suggestions for time allotments and the order of activities are given in the session agendas, along with lists of the materials you will need for each session.

Note: The homework assignment distributed in Session 4 includes lessons from the NCTM Navigating through Algebra series (See pp. 162–163.) Make sures you have copies of these lessons available to distribute at the appropriate time.

Comments from Other Facilitators

Those who field-tested the PFC seminar had recommendations for other facilitators. Several commented about planning.

I realize now more than ever how important it is to be really prepared and to have thought through the issues, mathematical and otherwise, that might arise. Having a sense of the important points that you want people to be exploring and the direction in which you want them to be headed is crucial. However, it is important to realize that sometimes "the way there" might turn out to be different from the route you anticipate.

In conducting the PFC seminar, it is important to keep in mind both the goals for the whole seminar and how the goals for each individual session fit together to make a coherent whole. One facilitator suggested:

Make an overall outline of the whole course. Each time you plan a session, consider how that session fits into the overall outline of the course so you can sense how the ideas are building.

Several field-test facilitators offered suggestions about how to become familiar with the mathematics of the PFC seminar and the power of building models and looking for connections between the models, the situations, the tables, and the graphs.

Work all of the mathematics before the session, taking the time to build several models and write several story contexts. This will be beneficial as you facilitate discussions about the relationship between the models, the context, and the symbols. It is very difficult to anticipate what the participants might come up with or to help them make connections if you haven't done this yourself.

Some facilitators were concerned about whether their background in algebra was strong enough to address issues that would arise in their seminar. They found that it was important to have identified a person familiar with formal mathematics whom they could go to with questions

between seminar sessions. In the words of one facilitator:

Identify a person who has experience with algebraic thinking that you might use as a resource when issues arise in your seminar that you haven't yet had time to think about yourself. When issues arise that participants want to know more about, but you haven't thought about, give yourself permission to say that all of you can think further about those issues for the next session. You can decide if the issues are essential to discuss with the whole group at a later session or whether they can be addressed with a few people during a break.

Some facilitators wrote about how to address participants who had preconceptions about the role of models in a mathematics class.

During the sessions, insist that participants develop models to illustrate the ideas of the sessions. Models assist in mathematical communication, but they aren't just about "sharing your ideas." Rather, the model brings concrete expression to the idea. Participants might come to the seminar thinking the models are for the less adept students or that they are ways to demonstrate that you understand. Coming to see that creating models is an important part of mathematical reasoning is a goal of the seminar.

Another facilitator offered advice about how to help participants make connections among the various activities in the seminar.

Have posters up front to keep the goals of each session to the forefront and continue to make connections to those goals during each experience of the session.

First Homework

This assignment is to be completed before the first session of the seminar. In that first session, you will have the opportunity to share your thinking about algebra with other participants. You will also be discussing Casebook readings in that session.

Writing assignment: Staircase Towers, Penny Jars, and Cube Trains

Within Chapter 1 of the Casebook are three problems related to the mathematics content of the cases. Explore these problems and be prepared to give your work on them to your facilitator at the first session.

Reading assignment: Starting the Casebook

In preparation for the first session, read the introduction to the Casebook, *Patterns, Functions, and Change*. Then read Chapter 1, "Using Patterns to Determine What's Ahead," including both the introductory text and Cases 1–4.

Maxine's Journal

February 1

Preseminar reflections

I am about to start the seminar Patterns, Functions, and Change. I had set as a requirement that participants have taken at least one DMI seminar prior to this one. The content is likely to be unfamiliar to many, so I want them to know how to pursue their mathematical inquiries and how to learn from studying cases of student thinking. However, once word of the seminar got out, there were several people who requested to be admitted even though they have not taken a prior DMI seminar. A few had participated in a project with a similar format to DMI. One is a middle-school teacher, a former colleague of someone who will be in the class. The grade span of the educators in the group represents Kindergarten through Grade 8.

Because of the prerequisite (and including my few exceptions), I expect that participants in this seminar already view mathematics as being about *ideas* and recognize that they have mathematical ideas, as do the students they teach. I expect them to have some practice with analyzing students' thinking, to be able to follow the reasoning of students' thought process, and to identify the conceptual issues students are working through. They have been figuring out how to help students build on their ideas as well as the ideas of their classmates.

The goals specific to Patterns, Functions, and Change include coming to understand a function as involving a set of inputs, a set of outputs, and a correspondence from each input to one output. Almost all of the functions we study will be derived from some kind of context—familiar, everyday situations, imaginary contexts, or arrangements of tiles or cubes. A good portion of the seminar will concentrate on linear functions, but we will also spend some time on nonlinear functions that can be defined by formulas as well as functions derived from data that do not have an underlying formula. As we work with different kinds of functions, we will explore how they can be represented. We will consider conventional forms of representations—tables, graphs, and formulas written algebraically—as well as representations invented by students to keep track of a phenomenon of change.

We will explore a variety of features of a function and examine how these features appear in the different representations. Is the function increasing, decreasing, or staying the same? Is it increasing at a steady rate, or is the rate of change varying? How can we use the representations to reason about the situation from which the function is derived and communicate our thinking to others?

Through our work on linear functions, participants will learn to recognize situations of constant rate of change compared to situations that do not have that property. We will discuss the slope and *y*-intercept, consider how these relate to the context from which the function is derived, and identify how they appear in a table, in a graph, and in an algebraic formula. We will compare linear functions and figure out if two lines intersect and where that intersection occurs. We will also examine the difference between linear and proportional relationships.

I expect that many participants will have their hands full as they work on these mathematical ideas. However, there are some important issues about student learning to examine as well: the challenge to young students of coordinating multiple units, moving from additive to multiplicative reasoning, learning the conventions of representation, and recognizing when two linearly related quantities are directly proportional. I would like participants to work at interpreting students' unconventional representations, to find the meaning students intend to convey, and to see what some of the conventions provide for us. I would also like participants to recognize how learning is enhanced by connecting multiple representations and how the mathematics is often made clearer by keeping in mind the context that the representations describe.

I want teachers to develop a sense of the potential coherence and continuity of a patterns and functions strand from Kindergarten through middle school. The study of repeating patterns from the primary grades can be set up to work directly with sequences and functions. Students' study of functions can support learning content traditionally taught in the elementary grades (particularly multiplication and multiplicative relationships), at the same time that it leads them smoothly into content traditionally taught in secondary grades.

There will also be opportunities in the seminar to specifically examine the actions of a teacher. Sometimes a focus question will ask participants about decisions they would make if they were the teacher facing particular constraints in the case. At other times, participants will examine a case for the moves the teacher did make. As always, the three student-thinking assignments will provide opportunities to work on planning, enacting, and reflecting on a lesson. However, in this seminar, the third such assignment will be based on materials from NCTM's Navigations Series, which I will provide. Participants will have opportunities to prepare to teach a lesson and discuss their plans with colleagues who plan to teach the same lesson before they actually bring it to their students. After they teach the lesson, they will have time to discuss the results with those same colleagues.

I am aware that many of the participants will arrive at our first session with a sense of trepidation. The content addresses territory of their high-school algebra classes, which were painful experiences for some. On the other hand, many of the participants enjoyed high-school algebra, and the challenge for

them will be to explore content more deeply and to investigate how students $\quad$ 80
encounter these ideas. Part of my task is to help *all* participants figure out how
to work together, to support each other's learning, and to learn as much as
they can from the seminar experience.

I have already given the participants a preseminar assignment: As they
read the first chapter of the Casebook, they were to explore the functions in $\quad$ 85
the cases, themselves. Now I am anxious to see their work and to hear their
reactions to these first cases.

PATTERNS, FUNCTIONS, AND CHANGE

Using Patterns to Determine What's Ahead

Mathematical themes:

■ Developing tables and expressions for repeating patterns

■ Examining how different contexts can yield the same number sequence

Session Agenda

Introductions: Norms for Learning and Seminar Goals	Whole group	20 minutes
Math activity and discussion: Cube Trains Generating arithmetic expressions from repeating patterns	Whole group Small groups Whole group	10 minutes 35 minutes 25 minutes
Break	Whole group	15 minutes
DVD: Developing new skills	Whole group	20 minutes
Case discussion: Developing new skills/looking across contexts	Small groups Whole group	30 minutes 15 minutes
Homework and exit cards	Whole group	10 minutes

Background Preparation

Read

- the Casebook: "Introduction" and Chapter 1
- "Maxine's Journal" for Session 1
- the agenda for Session 1
- the Casebook: Chapter 8, Sections 1 and 2

Work through

- the Math activity: Cube trains (p. 39)
- the Focus Questions for Session 1 (p. 40)

Preview

- the three DVD segments for "Developing new skills" and choose which segments or segments to show

Materials

Duplicate

- "Math activity: Cube trains" (p. 39)
- "Focus Questions: Chapter 1" (p. 40)
- "The Portfolio Process" (p. 41)
- "If You Have to Miss a Class" (p. 42)
- "Second Homework" (p. 43)

Obtain

- DVD player
- cubes
- index cards

Prepare one poster

- Tables for Red, Blue, and Green, the Answer to Math Activity Question 5 (p. 38)

Introducing Functions

Function is a mathematical term that refers to a certain kind of relationship between two sets. One set is called the domain and the other set is the range. A function is a correspondence from each element in the domain to exactly one element in the range.

While the functions examined in PFC are correspondences between sets of numbers, the domain and range do not have to consist of numbers. For instance, a set of colored cubes with a repeating pattern can be used to define a function that maps each of the counting numbers to a color. Consider a pattern based on a repeated 3-color unit: red, blue, and green. This repeating pattern (R, B, G, R, B, G, R, B, G, ...) can define a function with the domain {1, 2, 3, 4, 5, 6,...} and range {red, blue, green}. The 1st cube is red, the 2nd cube is blue, the 3rd cube is green, etc. This function can be expressed as a set of ordered pairs: [(1, red,), (2, blue), (3, green), (4, red), (5, blue), (6, green), (7, red),....]. Note that while each element in the domain is mapped to one and only one element in the range, the reverse is not true; for instance, red is associated with 1, 4, 7, ...

In PFC, participants work with a variety of functions, and as their experience with types of functions increases, the more formal aspects of the definition are gradually introduced. In Session 1, participants encounter the idea of forming a mapping or correspondence from one set of numbers to another and expressing this relationship in a table.

Unlike the function described above that maps numbers onto colors, the functions in Session 1 have the counting numbers as both domain and range. Consider the red, blue, green, red, blue, green, red, ... repeating pattern, only this time identify all of the cubes of a particular color, say red. The 1st cube that is red is associated with the number 1, the 2nd red cube is associated with the number 4, the 3rd red cube is associated with the number 7, and so on.

1st			2nd			3rd			4th
R	B	G	R	B	G	R	B	G	R...
1	2	3	4	5	6	7	8	9	10...

This association defines a function. Written as a set of ordered pairs the function is expressed as [(1, 1), (2, 4), (3, 7), (4, 10), ...]. It can also be expressed in a table. By convention, input values are placed in the left column and the output values in the right.

Position Among the Red Cubes	Position Among All Cubes
1	1
2	4
3	7
4	10
5	13

Detailed Agendas   These agendas describe each activity of a session and provide suggestions for questions that can be used to shape each discussion. When posters are to be prepared prior to a session, the agenda specifies what should be on the poster.

Some sessions include a DVD component as well, and the agenda includes a summary of the DVD cases. The DVD summaries are not full transcripts; rather, they are brief narrative descriptions of the content of the DVD segments. Facilitators should not rely solely on the narrative summaries but watch the DVD segments and take notes in preparation for leading a session.

Handouts   These pages are located at the end of the agenda and are indicated by a grey strip along the edge of the page. They are to be duplicated and distributed to participants during the seminar session. The following types of handouts are included:

■ Focus Questions that guide the small- and whole-group discussions of the Casebook chapters

■ "Math activities" that participants work on to deepen their mathematical understanding

■ Homework pages that describe the reading and writing assignments for the sessions

DVD Segments   While written cases allow users to examine student thinking at their own pace and to return as needed to ponder and analyze particular passages, the DVD segments offer users the opportunities to listen to real student voices in real time. They allow participants to see students' gestures and provide rich images of classrooms organized around student thinking. These segments show a wide variety of classroom settings, with children and teachers of different ethnic and language groups.

PFC Seminar Activities

In preparation for each session, participants complete a homework assignment. The 3-hour session typically consists of two or three major activities.

Homework assignments: Before each session, participants read one chapter of the Casebook and complete regular written portfolio assignments. Three times during the seminar, the portfolio assignment has participants explore their students' mathematical thinking. When participants have written such "student-thinking assignments," they share and discuss these writings with one or two other participants during the session. Other portfolio assignments ask participants to reflect on what they are learning in the seminar. Responding to participants' written assignments is an important part of the work of facilitating a DMI seminar. "Maxine's Journal" includes examples of participants' writing and a facilitator's responses.

Case discussions: In discussions of the Casebook, participants examine students' thinking, work on mathematical ideas for themselves, and consider the types of classroom settings and teaching strategies that support the development of student understanding.

Viewing DVD segments: Through video, teachers see episodes that capture both classroom atmosphere and students' gestures. Unlike the print cases, which allow for reading and rereading, these segments provide practice in listening to students in real time.

Math activities: Through activities designed for adult learners, the seminar participants develop, share, analyze, and refine their own mathematical thinking. PFC participants create tables, graphs, and expressions to represent functions; identify features that define particular kinds of functions from situations, tables, graphs, models, and expressions; examine the impact of constant and non-constant change and how it is seen in tables, graphs, situations, expressions, and models; interpret phenomena of change using tables and graphs; and become familiar with categories of functions such as linear, quadratic, and exponential.

Discussing the Chapter 8 essay: This discussion at the last session of the seminar creates an integrated picture of the mathematical themes under consideration, connecting the events observed in the cases and in participants' own classrooms to more formal mathematics. Some facilitators prefer to assign sections of Chapter 8 during the course of the seminar instead of assigning all of it after Session 7.

Preparing to Facilitate the PFC Seminar

Become familiar with PFC as a whole To become familiar with the flow of mathematical ideas in a seminar, we suggest that a facilitator read the introduction to the Casebook, the introduction to each Casebook chapter, and the Chapter 8 essay, "The Mathematics of Patterns, Functions, and Change for the K–8 Classroom." You should also read all of the eight sessions of "Maxine's Journal" to get an image of the seminar experience from the point of view of a facilitator. In addition, you may find it useful to examine some of the cases and look through the detailed agendas and handouts.

Identify connections between goals for the seminar and goals for each session Once you are familiar with the goals and components of the PFC curriculum as a whole, the next step is to prepare for individual sessions. For each session, read the cases, the related entry of "Maxine's Journal," and the agenda. Work through the activities in the

session yourself; for example, do the math activity, view the DVD segment, think about the focus questions, and familiarize yourself with any additional handouts. As you do this work, think through the issues raised by that set of activities. What are the goals of the session as a whole? What ideas about mathematics, learning, and teaching should emerge as teachers participate in the investigations and discussions? How are these ideas illustrated in the cases? How might they arise in the other activities? What questions might you pose to call attention to these ideas?

Prepare the logistics Besides planning for issues likely to arise during discussions, you must think through the order of the activities and review the suggested timetable. Organize the materials so everything is ready for each session; having the readings, handouts, DVD, DVD equipment, and manipulatives at hand before a session saves time and allows you to concentrate on seminar participants. Suggestions for time allotments and the order of activities are given in the session agendas, along with lists of the materials you will need for each session.

Note: The homework assignment distributed in Session 4 includes lessons from the NCTM Navigating through Algebra series (See pp. 162–163.) Make sures you have copies of these lessons available to distribute at the appropriate time.

Comments from Other Facilitators

Those who field-tested the PFC seminar had recommendations for other facilitators. Several commented about planning.

I realize now more than ever how important it is to be really prepared and to have thought through the issues, mathematical and otherwise, that might arise. Having a sense of

- Detailed agenda—a thorough description of the activities of the session

- Handouts—sheets to be copied and distributed to the participants

Session Overview   The session overview summarizes the main goals of the session and provides a chart suggesting the order of the activities, format, and timing for each activity. In addition, a list is provided indicating what to do to prepare for the session.

Facilitator Notes   Facilitator Notes, indicated by frames, provide mathematical background for facilitators. The main Facilitator Note follows the session overview and addresses a major mathematical theme of the session. Other notes are inserted into the text where they are most relevant. The topics covered in the Facilitator Notes are

Maxine's Journal   "Maxine's Journal" is a session-by-session narrative account of the PFC seminar written from the point of view of a facilitator (Maxine). It is designed to provide additional support for PFC facilitators. For each session, Maxine records small- and whole-group discussions, considers comments made by participants, and shares her thoughts, questions, concerns, and decisions. Reading "Maxine's Journal" as preparation for a session allows facilitators to envision the key mathematical issues that are likely to emerge, provides examples of questions that facilitators can use to drive discussion, and presents probable interactions between facilitators and participants.

Homework responses   In addition, "Maxine's Journal" includes examples of participants' writing assignments and Maxine's responses, as well as her comments about what she was trying to accomplish with those responses.

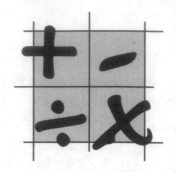

Orientation to the Materials

Patterns, Functions, and Change

The Patterns, Functions, and Change (PFC) seminar provides the opportunity for teachers from Kindergarten through middle school to

- examine how repeating patterns and number sequences can lead to the ideas of functions

- learn how to represent functional relationships using tables, graphs, expressions, and models

- explore the connections between constant and non-constant change and various types of functions (linear, quadratic, and exponential)

- consider how the different attributes of functions appear in tables, graphs, expressions, and models, and what they mean in a context

- interpret and create tables and graphs that are derived from data-based phenomena of change such as temperature or growth over time

Components of the PFC Developing Mathematical Ideas Materials

Each DMI module consists of a Casebook, a Facilitator's Guide, and a DVD. In a DMI seminar, each participant needs a Casebook; facilitators need the Casebook, the Facilitator's Guide, and the DVD. Facilitators will duplicate materials from the guide for use in each seminar session.

Casebook The Casebook includes an introduction and eight chapters. The first seven chapters include cases written by actual classroom teachers detailing classroom discussions and the thinking of their students. Chapter 8 is an essay that provides an overview of the mathematical ideas of the whole seminar.

Participants prepare for each session by reading one chapter of the Casebook. Prior to the first session, participants should read the Introduction to the Casebook, as well as Chapter 1.

Facilitator's Guide For each seminar session, the Facilitator's Guide is made up of the components listed below. A description of each component follows the list.

- Session overview—an overview of the session, including how to prepare for it

- Facilitator Notes—notes that provide mathematical background for facilitators

- Maxine's Journal—a narrative account of each session from the point of view of a facilitator

- Homework responses—samples of participants' written assignments and Maxine's responses

1

Maxine's Journal

February 3

As always, the first session was very interesting. There was a lot of good energy, and I am excited to be working with this group.

In this first session, we worked with arithmetic sequences, exploring how different contexts can have the same mathematical structure, and seeing how the regularity of the sequence allows us to determine values. By defining the *position* of the term in a sequence as a variable and the *value* of the term as another variable, we worked with the functions associated with the sequence and began the task of developing a repertoire of representations for functions. This will take several sessions, starting with tables, but I also encouraged the use of physical and pictorial representations to help participants make connections between the contexts, the patterns in the table, and the arithmetic expressions that allow one to derive the value of a term from its position in the sequence. We explored these ideas through a math activity, viewing two DVD segments from first- and second-grade classrooms, and discussing print cases from teachers of Kindergarten through Grade 4.

Introductions

I was concerned that not everyone could arrive on time, so I decided to start half an hour later than I did in previous seminars—at 4:30 instead of 4:00. However, many teachers finish school early enough to arrive at 4:00, and I wanted to provide a setting in which they could use the time productively. So I invited participants to arrive at 4:00 for snacks and a quiet reading time to review the cases; the seminar then began at 4:30. Before participants arrived, I created seating assignments by approximate grade level. As people came in, I pointed out where the snacks were and directed them to their seat.

Promptly at 4:30, I began the seminar by welcoming everyone to Patterns, Functions, and Change, "I promise that we are about to get into some very interesting mathematics—mathematics that will be challenging but accessible for all of you. However, I expect it will not necessarily start out feeling that way to everyone. As a preseminar assignment, I asked you to work on the mathematics that's in the cases, knowing that the ideas are quite new to some of you and familiar to others. So first, to those of you for whom the ideas are new, I want to say that you will have an opportunity to sort out those ideas in the sessions and through the homework assignments. The thing is, you'll need to be open with me and your colleagues about what is confusing to you, so we can sort it out together.

"And to those of you for whom the ideas are familiar, there will be opportunities for interest and challenge. What's required of you is to seek out questions that will lead you to new insights. Sometimes that might come from listening to your colleagues for whom the ideas are new. It's important to *listen* to them, because most likely, they will offer a new perspective on the content, allowing you to enrich your understanding. Sometimes that will mean digging more deeply into the cases, seeking out the conceptual challenges for students. Sometimes that will mean extending the mathematical questions beyond those that I pose.

"I know that most of you, though not all, have attended at least one DMI seminar before. Those who have taken a DMI seminar know that we periodically discuss group norms—behaviors to keep in mind to promote the learning of everyone in the group. The learning that takes place here isn't completely in the hands of the facilitator and each individual learner. It's the whole group that contributes to the learning of every participant. Today, from the very start, I want you to think about group norms, particularly keeping in mind the different backgrounds of people in the group, the different attitudes people have toward algebra and functions, and the different levels of confidence. So we are about to introduce ourselves. As you do, I want you to state two norms: one that you believe would support your learning in this seminar, the second that you want to keep in mind to be responsible to others' learning."

I gave everyone a moment to think. Then as participants were ready to speak up, they stated their name, where they work, what they teach (or what role they have), and the norms they have in mind today.

I was quite impressed by the thoughtfulness of the group and their willingness to be open in front of many people they did not know. Elinor talked about how important it is to her to be told what is right about her ideas even if some of it is incorrect, and several people concurred. Robin explained that sometimes she gets so focused on analyzing group process that she loses track of the content being discussed. Ivan expressed concern about being a lower-grade teacher and not having relevant classroom experience to share. Georgeann told us that anything related to algebra makes her anxious.

Mariam said that she had enjoyed her algebra experience in high school, but having taken the DMI seminar Reasoning Algebraically About Operations a year ago, she now realizes what it means to understand the content in a deeper, more connected way. She said she is looking forward to making those connections. Dina said that she had experiences similar to Mariam's. She added that when she has new insights, she gets very excited and tends to talk too much; she needs to be careful not to trample on other people's opportunities to think.

By the end of the discussion, we had the following list.

- Keep a sense of humor; humor helps to relieve stress.
- Be comfortable with being direct about your learning needs.
- Come to each session prepared.

- Be open to new ideas.
- Recognize your ideas as viable.
- Know that perspectives from *all* grades are enriching.
- Manage your self-judgment.
- Focus on whole-group discussions; refrain from side conversations.
- Value different ideas.
- Assume best intentions.
- Respect everyone's level of understanding.
- Respect all group members' ideas.
- Rein yourself in when you are very excited by new insights; leave room for others to make discoveries.
- Listen to ideas completely before responding.
- Pay attention to the amount of air time you take.

Throughout this discussion, several cell phones went off, and so I added a couple of items.

- Turn off cell phones!
- Be ready to start at 4:30.

With regard to the last item, I said how much I appreciated that everyone was ready to start on time today and how important that would be throughout the seminar. Each session is quite packed, and we really need the 3 hours that we have allotted for these meetings.

I pointed out that we would turn our attention back to this list periodically, just to be sure that we are living up to these expectations and also to see if there is anything else we should add to the list.

The group is comprised of teachers from Kindergarten through eighth grade. I will see what kind of a challenge it is to work through this content with this grade range. Those who teach algebra might already be familiar with formulas, and my challenge is to help them dig more deeply into the ideas—make new connections for themselves and acquire insight into what can help their students connect the ideas. I will also try my best not to let the teachers for whom these ideas are new slip into listening to the older-grade teachers instead of thinking problems through for themselves. For this reason, I started the first activity in grade-level groups.

Math activity: Generating arithmetic expressions from repeating patterns

Already as a preseminar assignment, everyone completed the task in Case 4 that involved a cube-train pattern. Now they would dig into a more extended exploration of these patterns. I pointed out that some might have found the work interesting; others, confusing. For now, we would start a little further back than the task in Case 4, with a pattern of two-element units.

From the outset, I wanted to make sure everyone in the group felt comfortable using a mathematical table. So I started out by defining the yellow-black Cube Train. I held up a train of cubes and said, "This train starts us off with a repeating pattern with yellow-black as the repeating unit: yellow, black, yellow, black, yellow, black, and it goes on. I can also assign a value to each cube, which is the same as its position in the train—1, 2, 3, 4, 5, 6, ... So, let's look at the black cubes. The first black cube has what value? " $\qquad$ 120

Several people said, "2," so I went on and asked for a few more. Then I produced the following table:

Position Among Black Cubes	Position Among All Cubes
1	2
2	4
3	6
4	8

I asked if there were any questions about how to read the table or what the table showed. Because there were none, I asked if someone would just talk us through what it meant. I wanted to take the time to make sure that everyone in the seminar was on board. $\qquad$ 125

Then I continued. "What color is the cube whose value is 29?"

Yan said, "It has to be yellow. The black values are all even, and since 29 is odd, it has to be yellow." $\qquad$ 130

Ivan added, "The yellow cubes are all the odd numbers."

I nodded, and we quickly made up a table for the yellow cubes.

Pointing back to the table for black cubes, I asked the next question, "What do you see as you look at the two columns? If we were to extend the table, could you tell me what the value of the 9th black cube will be?" $\qquad$ 135

Meg said, "The 9th black will be 18. You just multiply 9 by 2."

I asked, "What about the 100th cube?"

Peggy said, "That would be 200."

I asked for a bit more detail. "What is the arithmetic expression that gives you 200?" $\qquad$ 140

Peggy was not sure what I was asking for, so Mariam spoke up instead. "100 × 2."

"Good," I said. "That's enough to get you started. As you work on this Math activity, I want you to work with tables like this one. When I ask for an $\qquad$ 145

Using Patterns to Determine What's Ahead

arithmetic expression for the value of the 100th cube of a particular color, it's that kind of expression I'm asking for—show the calculation you used to find the value."

Small groups

Even though we had done a good amount of Part A as a whole group, I asked that everyone start with Problem 1. I wanted to make sure those who were feeling timid got a solid footing. Most groups worked through those problems pretty quickly and moved onto the more challenging questions. | 150

Part B, based on repeating patterns that most people recognize, tends to capture everyone's interest. It seems to give them new insights into the number system that are accessible and intriguing. This seminar group was no exception. Soon, the room was humming with activity. | 155

After a few minutes, I sat down with a group. Nazir, Ivan, and Georgeann were working on the red-blue-green pattern and seemed to be stuck. Georgeann said to me, "The numbers they're coming up with just don't seem right to me." Nazir and Ivan showed me their tables, and they looked to me to | 160 be correct. I asked Geogeann to tell me what she thinks is wrong. "Blue can't be 5; it has to be 4 or 6." When I asked why, she said, "The blues are even." And when I asked why again, she said, "Look, the 1st blue is 2, so blues are the even numbers." I suggested she lay out the cubes in the pattern—red, blue, green, red, blue, green—and once Georgeann had created the train, I asked | 165 her to count the cubes. I was not sure if she understood the way the task is defined, so as she counted, I said, "The 1st red has a value of 1; the 1st blue has a value of 2; the 1st green has a value of 3; the 2nd red has a value of 4." Before we continued, Georgeann let out an "Ohhhhhh." Then she explained, "OK. I see it now; blue has a value of 5. For some reason, I got it in my head that this | 170 is all about even and odd numbers. I just had this block—if the 1st blue is even, then all blues are even. But that doesn't work for this pattern."

When I got to Dina, Robin, and April, they were working on expressions for the 100th red, blue, and green cubes. They all agreed that the 100th green cube is 300, and their arithmetic expression was 100×3. What they weren't sure about | 175 is whether the 100th red cube would be $(100 \times 3) + 1$ or $(100 \times 3) - 2$. Robin said, "I know that both 301 and 298 are red cubes, I just don't know which one is the 100th red cube." I told them that would be a good thing to think about.

Elinor, Bill, and Sandy were also focused on the red-blue-green pattern, and were discussing the color of the 100th cube. They all agreed it must be red but | 180 had different ways of thinking about it. Elinor explained, "Since $30 \times 3 = 90$, the 90th cube is green. Then you count on 10 more from there—red, blue, green, red, blue, green, red, blue, green, red. So, it's red." Sandy said, "You don't multiply to do it; you have to divide. You take $100 \div 3$ and get 33, remainder 1. Since the remainder is 1, it has to be red." I asked Bill what he thought, and | 185 he shrugged and said, "They both make sense to me." I suggested that they keep trying both Elinor's and Sandy's methods to see if they always come out the same. If they do, they should figure out *why* they always give the same result.

By the time I got to Ariel, Celeste, and Violet, the middle-school teachers in the seminar, I found that they were taking the task a step further. They had made a table for each of the colors, red, blue, and green, and under each table had written a function rule. For red: $3n - 2$; for blue: $3n - 1$; for green: $3n$. Celeste said, "At first we thought the rules for red and blue were $3n + 1$ and $3n + 2$, but that wasn't working out right." Violet added, "It's because, when you look at the 1st red, it comes before the 1st green; the 2nd red comes before the 2nd green; so the nth red comes before the nth green. That means, you go to the nth green, and then you have to go back to get to the nth red. That's why you subtract."

Ariel added, "The nth red is $(n - 1)$ steps after the first red, so its value is $3(n - 1) + 1$. That comes out the same as $3n - 2$."

I told this group that they have good ways of thinking about this problem, and they can check out those same ideas looking at the 4-color pattern. However, I also asked that, during the whole-group discussion, they hold off sharing these ideas. I explained that I want the ideas from other groups to get out in the air first. I told them next time we'd be working on the general rules, but first I want to make sure everyone feels solid with the arithmetic expressions for particular numbers.

Flor, Lamis, and Yan had also taken the task in a different direction. They were now investigating patterns in which a color appears twice in the unit: *R, R, B, R, R, B* and *B, B, Y, Y, B, B, Y, Y*. Flor looked up and said, "This is more complicated. Every multiple of 4 is yellow, but the yellows aren't all multiples of 4."

Whole group

Just before we began the whole-group discussion, I posted the three tables for red, blue, and green cubes, which I had prepared earlier, alongside the posters for black and yellow, which were already hanging up. When we came together, I made sure everyone agreed with the information presented in the tables. After that, the main point of the discussion was the different ways people viewed the cubes to create arithmetic expressions. To begin, I asked for the arithmetic expressions people wrote for the 100th yellow cube and the 100th black cube.

Georgeann said, "We already said that the 100th black cube is 2×100. The thing we really needed to think about in our group was whether the 100th yellow cube is $(2 \times 100) + 1$ or $(2 \times 100) - 1$. We think it's $(2 \times 100) - 1$, but we're not sure why it works out that way."

Dina responded, "We thought about that, too, and we think it's $(2 \times 100) - 1$. Because, let's say you just want to find the 5th yellow cube. Look at the table, and

Using Patterns to Determine What's Ahead

it's 9. $(2 \times 5) - 1 = 9$. If that's the rule that works for 5, it must be the rule that works for 100. So the 100th yellow cube is 199."

Flor added, "Here's another way to think about it. We sometimes talk about the part that repeats in a Cube Train as a car, so for this pattern, each car is yellow-black." She held up a train of yellow and black cubes and then pulled out one yellow-black pair.

Flor continued, "You know that you have 200 cubes in 100 cars. But, you also see that the 100th yellow comes before the 100th black. Since the 100th black is 200, the 100th yellow is 199. "

I pointed out that we could also use the word *unit* for what Flor was calling a car.

Bill said, "I have another way to look at it, kind of like Flor's, but I change the unit. Take the 1st yellow cube, and let it sit alone. Then you start adding on black-yellow pairs—those are the units."

Bill explained, "In order to get to the 100th yellow, you have to add on 99 of those black-yellow pairs. So, it's $1 + (2 \times 99)$. And that's the same as $(2 \times 100) - 1$." I nodded to Ariel to indicate to her that this was the same idea she talked about in her small group, but in terms of a variable. I also took a moment to make sure everyone agreed that $(2 \times 100) - 1 = 1 + (2 \times 99)$.

Robin then took our discussion to a more general level. "I figured out an expression that works for all the patterns. You take the row number and multiply it by the 'step up.' Then you add the starting number and subtract the step up."

Most people in the room were unable to follow what Robin was saying, but there were several interesting components of her claim. First, she borrowed the language of the Staircase Towers in Cases 2 and 3 to talk about Cube Trains. In those problems, the "starting number" is the number of cubes in the 1st tower. After that, the number of cubes in each tower increases by the "step up" number. For example, if the starting number is 1 and the step up number is 2, the number of cubes in a sequence of towers is 1, 3, 5, 7, ... Robin had evidently seen that both contexts, Staircase Towers and these Cube Train problems, involve the same numerical structures. Then she found a way to relate the patterns in the two problems.

We spent some time taking apart Robin's idea. Translating to the language of Cube Trains, by *row number* she meant the value in the left column, the position of a cube among its own color. By *step up* she meant the length of the unit, what Flor called a "car." By *starting number* she meant the position of the first cube of a particular color.

I wrote out Robin's rule in terms of the language we have been using for Cube Trains:

(row number) × (length of unit) + (starting number) − (length of unit)

I suggested we go back to finding the 100th yellow and see how Robin's rule works:

$$(100 \times 2) + 1 - 2$$

That gave us 199. And so we went on to check the 100th red cube.

$$(100 \times 3) + 1 - 3$$

That gave us 298. I asked, "Does this expression look like anyone else's?"

Meg said, "It's kind of close to ours, but a little different. Our group said $(100 \times 3) - 2$. It comes out the same."

Most people said that their expression was the same as Meg's.

Trudy said, "I came up with a different expression, but I first want to show you how I thought about it." She then came up and wrote out this table.

Unit Number	Position	Pattern
1	1	1
2	4	1 + 3
3	7	1 + 3 + 3
4	10	1 + 3 + 3 + 3
5	13	1 + 3 + 3 + 3 + 3

Trudy explained, "I could see the pattern better if I wrote out all the steps to getting any value. Like, to get 4 for the 2nd red, you start at 1 and add 3. To get to 7 for the 3rd red, you start at 1 and add 3 and add 3 again. I noticed that the number of 3s you add is always one less than the row number. So my expression for the 100th red is $1 + (99 \times 3)$."

I suggested that we write the expression to include the first step she took, subtracting 1 from 100, and the expression became

$$1 + (100 - 1) \times 3.$$

I turned to the group. "What do you think?"

Yan said, "It gives the same answer. Trudy's expression is also 298."

Dina said, "I can see that it gives you the same answer, but I don't really see *why* they're equal."

This question of "why" is always an interesting one. Some people are satisfied to say that two expressions are equivalent because they're both equal

Using Patterns to Determine What's Ahead

to 298, period. However, some people, like Dina, look for a different kind of connection or relationship to feel satisfied.

Celeste said, "Look, if you think of it as a rule for the nth term, you can see it." She went to the board and wrote:

$$1 + 3(n - 1) = 1 + 3n - 3 = 3n + 1 - 3$$

I registered that Celeste chose to present this identity even though, in small group, I had asked that she and her partners not share it with the class. Perhaps she felt that it was appropriate at this point in the discussion. Certainly what Celeste showed us was correct, but I was worried about those participants who have not developed the skill of thinking in terms of algebraic notation. Besides, I still had the feeling that Celeste's equations would not satisfy Dina's question. I acknowledged Celeste's work, and then asked if anyone else had a different way of thinking about it.

Georgeann said, "I do. Most of us focused on the size of the unit, then found the position of the 100th green, 3 × 100, and then worked backward from there to find the red or blue. But Trudy went in the other direction. She started with the 1st red and then figured out how many units she has to skip up to get to the 100th red. She didn't first find the 100th green. Using Trudy's method, the 100th blue would be 2 + 3(100 − 1) because it's 99 units after 2, and the 100th green would be 3 + 3(100 − 1) because it's 99 units after 3. Trudy worked forward from the 1st red, and the rest of us worked backward from the 100th green."

As Georgeann talked, I saw Dina begin to smile. Everyone else was listening carefully. I looked at Bill and smiled to acknowledge that this was similar to the way he thought about the yellow-black pattern. Once Georgeann finished, a lot of people said "Oh, yeah."

Georgeann's way of describing the two approaches is something that we'll all be working on in later sessions. When we work on rules for the functions, we'll think about how the expressions are derived from the structure of the situation the function describes. Certainly Celeste's way of demonstrating the equivalence of two algebraic expressions is valid; not only is it valid, but it's the method that, eventually, I would like all teachers (and students) to use fluently. However, at this stage of the process, looking for how each component of an expression relates to the context deepens our understanding of the symbols we are learning to use. I wonder if Celeste registered the difference between Georgeann's explanation and her own, and how different participants responded to each.

DVD and Case discussion: Developing new skills/looking across contexts

After the break, I brought the group together to watch two DVD segments. I did not want to spend a long time on the segments, but it felt important to provide images of students working on these ideas in the context of regular classrooms. The first segment showed a teacher, Kirsten, and her first-grade class working on the Staircase Towers activity: start with 1 cube and add 3 to each successive tower.

(In the language of the first-grade activity, "start with 1, step up 3.") After viewing the segment, I asked about the math ideas the students were engaged with.

Yan said, "The children need to keep packets of 3 in their head. That's different from counting by 1."

Sandy pointed out that some students held onto the number in one tower to figure out the number in the next. "They didn't start over again and again. They could count on from the previous tower."

April referred to the girl who talked about counting by 2s. "Did she just mean skip-counting in general? Maybe to that girl, counting by 2s means skip-counting."

Mariam said, "You know, counting by 3s, starting at 1 is not a familiar sequence. Those children were working hard in that task."

Before showing the second DVD segment, I needed to explain one of the activities the second graders had been working on. "In this segment, you'll see there are tables posted all over the room. The tables were generated from two different activities. One of them was the Cube Train pattern, like the activity we just did. In the second activity, students create buildings out of cubes. In a building, every floor has the same number of rooms." I held up a row of 5 cubes. "So if the buildings have 5 rooms on each floor, the building with 1 floor has 5 rooms." Then I attached another row of 5 cubes on top of the first. "A building with 2 floors has 10 rooms." Then I moved to create the table, talking the group through each row.

Number of Floors	Number of Rooms
1	5
2	10
3	15
4	20
5	25

Now we were ready to watch the DVD of the teacher, Mike, leading a discussion with his second graders. Observations of this segment addressed both what the teacher and students were doing.

Ivan started the discussion: "It's really important to have posted past work around the room while you are doing this unit. It kept the work from previous days alive and available for students."

Celeste said, "It's clear Mike wanted them to compare situations. He isn't just focused on getting the work done for this one day's activity, but in bringing their attention to larger issues."

Ariel added, "You can see the students are able to use the idea of unit as an organizing tool. In one table, the unit is the colored cubes that repeat; in

Using Patterns to Determine What's Ahead

the other table, it's the rooms on a floor. Even though the units are different things, they could use the idea of a unit to see what's the same."

While Ivan's and Celeste's comments were important, Ariel's point was getting to the heart of the mathematics, so I wanted to pause here and let her comment sink in. I nodded and asked someone to paraphrase what Ariel had said. Lamis stepped up to the task, "The students are pointing out the similarity in the list of numbers but are also quite conscious of the situations that generated them."

I concurred, "Yes, they are seeing what is the same in these different contexts. Ariel made the point that they use the idea of a unit to describe what is the same."

I transitioned to the case discussion by pointing out that the group now had several significant experiences since they had read the cases. "You've had a chance to do some pretty deep thinking about the Cube Train activity, and you've now seen and discussed these DVD segments of students working on the Staircase Tower task and second graders thinking about two activities together. As you return to the cases and work from the focus questions I'm giving you, you might also find it useful to refer back to your homework about the Penny Jar and Staircase Towers activities."

Small groups

As I listened in on the small-group discussions, I noticed that people were engaged with each of the activities. The Kindergarten and first-grade teachers were particularly interested in Catherine's case. Meg said, "Before I read this case, it never occurred to me that patterns like dog, cat, dog, cat had anything to do with numbers. I just thought it was good mentally for children to be able to continue patterns. I guess I never really knew why that kind of work was part of the curriculum."

Flor said, "Yeah, and think about all we did with the red-blue-green pattern. The question Catherine asked her Kindergarten students is getting them started with that."

Nazir began to think about her own practice, "I didn't think children that young could be asked to look ahead in a pattern. I always just asked what comes next. I'll need to ask my students to imagine something further down the line."

Flor took this idea a bit further. "I noticed this is a routine the teacher uses. The class does this kind of pattern work over and over again. It's not just something you do once and get it. I like the idea of having something like this as a class routine."

When I got to Georgeann, Peggy, and Trudy, they were discussing the third case. Trudy said, "I think Elizabeth could see the connection between the Penny Jar and Staircase Towers because of the previous work on graphing the class had done. It was in her head as a way to look at things and so even if the teacher wasn't trying to get them to see what was the same about them, Elizabeth was in the habit of thinking of graphs and so she could do that." | 405

Georgeann connected this back to the math work she had done in the pre-seminar assignment, "This case brought out something I noticed when I did the math activities. The 1 for the Penny Jar and the 1 for the Staircase Towers are not the same. The number sequences get to be the same but not at the beginning. A situation that starts with 4 and add 3 would be 7, 10, 13 for the Penny Jar and 4, 7, 10, 13 for the Staircase Tower. That confused me when I did the problems for homework. So, wouldn't the graph of the Penny Jar be different than that of the Staircase Tower?" | 410 ... 415

Georgeann was pointing out that, when building the staircase towers, the start number was the first number in the sequence, but for the Penny Jar, the sequence started with the number of pennies after the 1st day. Peggy caught on to that and pointed out that the Staircase Towers can be considered a graph of the Penny Jar situation that included the number of pennies in the jar before the 1st day's pennies were added. | 420

Whole group

For the whole-group discussion, I decided to draw everyone's attention to Case 3.

Ariel said, "What Elizabeth saw in first grade was like what we saw on the DVD, what the second graders could see in their two activities." | 425

I think I knew exactly what Ariel meant. However, again, because I wanted to make sure everyone understood Ariel's point, I asked another question. "The case tells us that Elizabeth saw the Staircase Towers as a representation of the Penny Jar. What is it that she needs to recognize in order to make that connection?" | 430

I was not surprised that Robin spoke up. After all, she was the one to use the language of Staircase Towers to describe the Cube Trains. "Elizabeth must have seen that the number of pennies you start with is like the first tower, and the number of pennies you add each day is like the step up."

Peggy pointed to Trudy's table from the math activity (as seen on p. 20) in which she had written out the arithmetic for each step. "That same table could describe what happens with the Staircase Tower, where you start with a tower of 1 cube and step up 3 each time. And, it could describe the Penny Jar, where you start with 1 penny in the jar and add 3 pennies every day. I think that's what Elizabeth sees." | 435 ... 440

Time was just about up, and I felt we were at a good place to stop for the day. However, before we ended the session, I wanted to make sure everyone

Using Patterns to Determine What's Ahead

began to develop meaning for the word *function* as a mathematical term. I explained that a function is a correspondence from one set to another—it frequently tells what happens to one quantity as another quantity varies. For example, in all of those Penny Jar situations, the number of pennies in the jar varies with the number of days. The number of cubes in a tower varies with the tower number. From the Cube Train tables, we can say the position of a red cube among *all* the cubes varies with its position among the red cubes. Also, in each of those situations, for each value of the first quantity, there is assigned one corresponding value of the second. Then I added, "Clearly, we will have plenty of time to work on this idea. If the idea of what a function is seems fuzzy now, don't worry about it. By the eighth session, I bet you will feel comfortable with it."

Returning to group norms

I distributed the homework assignment and asked if there were any questions. Because most participants have been in a DMI seminar before, they were already familiar with the assignment and could answer the questions posed by those who were new.

Before closing, I brought the group back to the norms we had specified in the beginning of the session. "So, how did we do? Did it feel like we were following these norms? Are there any other norms you would like to add?"

Yan said, "I think we did pretty well."

Meg added, "I'm new to these ideas, and it feels safe to be here."

Peggy agreed, "I think we could all share ideas without worrying."

Georgeann chuckled as she said, "My group members were very patient with me," to which Ivan said, "I learned a lot from Georgeann's thinking."

Elinor said, "I'd like to add something: Be prepared to be both a learner and a teacher."

I added Elinor's norm to the list, and then posted the exit-card questions: What math ideas did this session highlight for you? What was the session like for you as a learner? Anything else you want to tell me?

Exit cards

Looking through the exit-card responses, it seemed that the first session went pretty smoothly.

Bill's response was representative of the group as a whole: "It was interesting to rethink the ideas of how tasks can be related (or not) and how students make connections if we let them. I am also struck, again, by how difficult it is to follow their thinking! I liked the work with patterns—it was a good balance for me—of safe and risky things! There was enough I could work out, and then a stretch to what *might* work!"

I had been concerned about the lower-grade teachers, but they seemed pretty happy with the way the first class went, too. Meg, a Kindergarten teacher, wrote, "It was important to understand what could be noticed in progressing from a list to a table to a formula. Without formulas, this work is very time consuming and daunting, yet the creation of formulas comes from that process—hmmm.... It was challenging, yet not overwhelming. It's great to be back in DMI. Thank you for creating professional development that allows me to make sense of my high-school algebra learning."

I was also concerned about the middle-school teachers and how they would approach this content. Ariel's response was very interesting: "As a learner, it was great to move from reasoning to some use of algebra. Algebra began to have a purpose. Building those connections with algebra and the real world is so useful. It was especially important to understand the different ways of thinking about the Cube Train problem."

Ariel's response gives me an important key to what may be happening with many middle-school teachers. They may be quite fluent with algebraic manipulation and formulas, but they do not see it connected to reasoning or any real-world contexts. I expect this seminar will be very satisfying for Ariel.

Several participants wrote about how important the visual representations were, some specifically mentioning Flor's image of the train cars. April said that she was hesitant to use a table, afraid that putting numbers in a table would constrain her thinking. I will need to address that thought.

Responding to the first homework

February 5

The day after our session, I read through the homework participants did on the Staircase Towers, Penny Jar, and Cube Trains to prepare for their reading of the cases. This was very illuminating, giving me a sense of where each participant was mathematically. I could group the work into four categories.

1. Some participants wrote out number sequences for each task but did not generalize.
2. One participant wrote out the number sequences and then wrote a recursive rule (e.g., add 3 to get the next term).
3. Some participants wrote out an arithmetic expression after looking at the number sequence.
4. Several wrote out an algebraic expression after looking at the number sequence.

It did not seem appropriate to write individual responses to this homework. After all, this was work people did before they even arrived at the first session, and then they had more opportunity to work on these ideas in class. I found myself writing short notes to just a few people. For example, Ivan had worked very hard and some of the rules he discovered for the sequences were quite complicated but correct. I wanted to make sure he knew that, even though in class he would have found other ways to think about the sequences, his reasoning on his homework was still correct.

A few people wrote something on their exit cards that I wanted to respond to individually, so there, too, I responded with a short note on their homework sheet.

However, overall, I wanted the whole group to think about some issues that arose for me as I looked over both their homework and their exit cards, and so I wrote the following letter.

> *Dear PFC seminar group,*
>
> *I found it very interesting to look over your homework to see how you thought about the problems before the seminar began. As you did for Chapter 1, you will find it very useful to do the mathematics problems in the cases before actually reading each chapter. Knowing first how you approach a math problem will help you better interpret what students are doing.*
>
> *I also appreciated reading the exit cards. There were several points that were raised that I would like to share with all of you.*
>
> *Many of you wrote about the importance of having physical representations or pictures to work from. To do the Cube Train problems, it was helpful to actually have the cubes in front of you to sort out the mathematical relationships. To think about the Staircase Towers, it was important to draw out the towers (or to build them with cubes). Similarly, many people drew jars with pennies in them to think about the Penny Jar problems.*
>
> *However, it is not only a matter of having a physical representation to look at. It is also important to have in mind a way to organize what you see. For example, when discussing the Cube Train, Flor mentioned that when she looks at the train of cubes, she thinks in terms of "cars," the set of cubes that make up a unit. Several people mentioned in their exit cards that Flor's image of cars helped them interpret the different expressions we had created for describing the position of the 100th red (or blue) cube. This idea of organizing the physical or pictorial representation will be particularly important in the work to create rules that we will begin toward the end of Session 2.*
>
> *In the homework, I noticed that some people, while working on the Penny Jar problems, drew pictures of the penny jar after Day 1, Day 2, Day 3, ... and were very careful in the way they organized the pennies in the jar each day. The organization helped to reveal the mathematical relationship between the day number and the number of pennies in the jar. We will all be able to take a look at this when we discuss Abigail's case in Chapter 2.*

Some exit cards also talked about the use of tables. Some people found it very helpful to organize their work into tables; others were afraid that tables would "stifle" their thinking. During this seminar, we will learn how to look at a variety of representations of functions, including the conventions of tables, graphs, and formulas (expressed arithmetically or algebraically), but not leaving behind physical or pictorial representations or other kinds of models you might find helpful. We do not want you to hesitate to use tables or graphs; nor do we want you to feel that you are "done" as soon as you have written out or drawn one or another—or several—of these representations. Some of the work is to be able to look across representations and see connections. If you see a pattern in the table, how does that connect to the physical representation or drawing? How do you see the same phenomenon in the graph? Where does it show up in the algebraic formula?

Overall, you indicated that you felt comfortable and safe working together in our first session. Many of you commented that people in your group were respectful of everyone's ideas and that each person listened carefully to try to understand the different ways people had of modeling and explaining their ideas. I'll give you a list of the norms you came up with, and hope you will continue to refer to it from time to time as a reminder throughout the seminar. There are always, as in any classroom, a range of preferences for pace and style of working, but it seems like you are all focusing on how to support both your own and your colleagues' learning. Thanks for such a productive first class.

Maxine

Detailed Agenda

Introductions: Norms for learning and seminar goals (20 minutes)

Whole group

The first activity of the seminar is designed so that participants may introduce themselves and begin to feel comfortable doing mathematics together. As individuals enter the room, arrange them in small groups in preparation for the first math activity. If you have information about the grade levels they teach, you might want to form groups that represent grade bands (K–2, 3–5, and 6–8).

Welcome the whole group by talking about the goals you have for participants' work in the seminar. Let them know that they will be exploring mathematics for themselves, examining how students develop these ideas through print and DVD cases, and also investigating and sharing their students' work. Point out that the seminar title, Patterns, Functions, and Change, may not carry much meaning for them at this point and assure them that they will have opportunities to make meaning for these terms in the context of the seminar work.

Acknowledge that the group is diverse, including participants who have had a variety of experiences with algebra. Some may have enjoyed this aspect of mathematics and some may not. Suggest that this range of past experiences will enhance the seminar because each participant's ideas will contribute to the learning of the group as a whole. Tell them that it will be important to keep in mind this range of backgrounds and comfort with the content as they work together. Let them know that now, as they begin this work together, you want them to think about the kind of atmosphere that makes it possible for everyone to learn. Ask them to think of two statements regarding group norms: one which they believe will support their learning in the seminar and one that they want to keep in mind in order to support the learning of others. Let them know that you will collect the statements and begin to create a poster of group norms.

During the introductions, participants should state their name, the grade level they teach, and their school. In addition, participants should share the norm they had thought about to support the learning of their colleagues. Collect these statements on a poster for all to refer to throughout the seminar.

Previous seminar groups have generated statements such as

- Allow time in small-group work for individuals to think before talking.
- Be prepared for sessions—everyone should have something to contribute.
- Listen carefully to take in another participant's ideas.
- Find ways to disagree without being disagreeable.

- Start and end each session on time.
- Be open to a new idea or perspective.

Math activity and discussion: Cube Trains (70 minutes)
Generating arithmetic expressions from repeating patterns

Whole group (10 minutes)

Groups of three (35 minutes)

Whole group (25 minutes)

There are two important mathematical goals for this activity:

- Becoming familiar with tables to represent a repeating-pattern situation
- Writing arithmetic expressions for particular terms in a sequence

To address the first goal, participants work with number sequences that are produced in the context of repeating patterns of color, such as yellow, black, yellow, black or red, blue, green, red, blue, green, which are modeled by trains of colored cubes. Identifying the placement of cubes of a particular color in the cube train forms the sequences; e.g., the sequence for the black cubes is 2, 4, 6, 8, 10, ... and the sequence for the red cubes is 1, 4, 7, 10, 13, ...

The table is created by matching the counting numbers to the sequence derived from the color pattern. For example, this is the table for the black cubes:

Position Among the Black Cubes	Position Among All the Cubes
1	2
2	4
3	6
4	8
5	10

To achieve the second goal of this activity, participants develop arithmetic expressions for determining values in the sequence beyond those given; e.g., to find the 100th black, multiply 100 by 2 (100×2); to find the 100th red, multiply 100 by 3 and then subtract 2 ($100 \times 3 - 2$). Forming arithmetic expressions is the precursor to writing algebraic formulas, a topic explored in detail in Sessions 2 and 3.

This activity lays the groundwork for the use of tables and writing arithmetic expressions, some of the basic mathematical tools for representing functions used in the seminar. While some participants might be familiar with writing algebraic formulas or graphing, keep this session focused on

Using Patterns to Determine What's Ahead

having all participants develop familiarity with making tables and writing arithmetic expressions so these tools will become accessible to all. In Session 2, participants will extend this work to graphing and writing formulas using algebraic notation.

The Math activity sheet is divided into three parts. Use the questions in Part A as a way to introduce the whole group to this work and to establish a system for creating tables from the number sequences generated by the repeating patterns. Part B will be the focus of the small-group work and the subsequent whole-group discussion. Part C is optional and is included to provide a challenge for participants who want more opportunities to work on similar problems.

Begin the activity with the whole group by building a cube train using a two-color repeating pattern: yellow, black, yellow, black, ... Generate the table representing the black cubes and then a table for the yellow cubes with the whole group. Pose a few questions such as "What color will the 18th cube be?" "What position in the cube train will the 15th black cube be?" "What arithmetic expression would you write to express the value of the 100th black, the 100th yellow?" See "Maxine's Journal" for Session 1, pages 15–17, for an example of such a discussion.

Organize participants into small groups and distribute "Math activity: Cube trains." Announce that participants will have 35 minutes to work in their small groups. Suggest they spend a few minutes discussing the work the group did on Part A, the yellow, black pattern, and then turn to Part B. Let them know they should work on the questions at a pace that feels comfortable to them. "Don't feel you have to rush to get to all of the questions on the sheet. Before the small-group work time is over, I will let you know what questions we will discuss in whole group so you will have time to explore those. It is OK if you do not work on all of the questions on the sheet during this small-group time."

After 5 minutes, suggest that the groups move to Part B if they have not already done so.

As you listen in on the small groups, pay particular attention as participants articulate their methods for addressing Problems 6 and 7 to support participants as they work with each arithmetic expression. Ask questions to help them articulate the difference between questions about the 100th cube and the 100th green cube, for example. Some groups may have to work through how different expressions can be matched to the same color. For instance, $(100 \times 3) + 1$ and $(100 \times 3) - 2$ both produce a red cube; the first expression matches the 101st red cube, and the second matches the 100th red cube. During the small-group work, decide on two or three participants' explanations that you want to be included in the whole-group discussion.

After 25 minutes, announce that the whole-group discussion will be based on Problems 6 and 7 and invite all groups to take the last 5 minutes to focus on those two questions.

The whole-group discussion should include three components:

- Comparing the tables for red, blue, and green cubes
- Examining the thinking of Angela and Bob as they each express the position of the 50th red cube
- Explaining how to find the color for the 100th cube, and the number associated with the 100th red cube, 100th green cube, and 100th blue cube

Start the whole-group discussion by posting tables for red, for blue, and for green cubes, invite participants to compare their tables with the ones posted, and allow time for any questions. Then turn to Question 6 by asking, "What does Angela's arithmetic expression indicate about her thinking?" and "What is Bob's method?" Finally ask, "How can it be that two different expressions both represent the position of the 50th red cube?" Use the last 10 minutes of the whole-group discussion to solicit responses to Question 7 and to allow participants to explain the differences among the four parts of that question.

If there is time and several small groups worked on Question 8, add the observations they made to the posters with the tables for red, blue, and green. Let the participants know that while they may want to think about the questions in Part C, there will not be a specific time in the seminar to discuss them.

Break   (15 minutes)

DVD: Developing new skills   (30 minutes)

Whole group

There are two options of DVD segments for this discussion. The first option contains two clips that feature first and second graders. The second option features a class of middle-school students. After viewing all the segments, choose which option is most appropriate for your seminar participants, either the two short segments of primary-grade students or the set of segments of middle-school students. DVD segments of math classrooms provide practice for participants in listening to students describe their thinking in real time. The images from a classroom where students are sharing and building on each other's ideas can help bring to life the children in the print cases.

First and second graders develop skills at looking across contexts

The first 6-minute DVD segment is of first graders working with a Staircase Towers situation. The DVD provides images of a first grade class working with mathematical ideas similar to those in the cases; however, it also provides an opportunity for participants to listen to student thinking. On the DVD, the students explore how to build and record a Staircase Tower situation where the first tower has 2 cubes and 3 are added for each step. Ask the participants to take notes during the DVD so they will be able to discuss the thinking of each child. After viewing the segment, ask the group to explain the thinking of the students on the DVD.

The second 2-minute DVD segment shows a class of second graders who have created tables for two activities: 1) Building Buildings—"Buildings" are built from cubes, each "floor" with the same number of "rooms." For instance, a building with 5 rooms on each floor results in a table that includes values (1, 5), (2, 10), (3, 15). 2) Cube Trains—"Cube Trains" are created with the five-cube repeating unit, Yellow, Yellow, Orange, Orange, Brown. Then students discuss the corresponding table for the position of the brown cubes. Suggest that participants take note of the questions the teacher, Mike, poses and the students' responses.

During the discussion, focus the group's attention on the idea that different situations can give rise to the same table. The discussion should include how the students make connections between the various situations and the number sequences that are generated.

 ### Middle-school students look for connections among tables, models, and equations

In this set of segments, a middle-school class is working on the Math activity: Cube trains. (This is the same activity that seminar participants just worked on.) Before showing the DVD, let participants know they will be discussing the following questions and suggest that they take notes:

- What are the connections these students make among tables, equations, and models of the repeating patterns?
- What moves does the teacher make to draw their attention to these connections?

Stop the DVD when Discussion Break is indicated. Ask for comments on these questions.

The whole-group discussion should include references to the following ideas:

- The equations for yellow and black both include a $2x$ term and how that matches the data.
- The table and the equation can be verified by referring back to the model of the repeating pattern they represent.

Then suggest participants continue to take notes on the next three short segments. Again, the whole-group discussion should highlight the connections among the table, the equation, and the model of the repeating pattern.

The DVD segments and cases also highlight the differences between questions posed to the adult seminar participants or secondary students and to the elementary-aged students. On the one hand, the first graders work to build and count the cubes in the Staircase Towers; they are not asked to write arithmetic expressions for the 100th tower. The second graders are asked to determine the numbers associated with the last color in the cube train and to explain how the same number sequence is generated by different situations; they are not asked to find number sequences for the other colors in the patterns or to write arithmetic expressions for the 100th case. On the other hand, the middle-school students are asked to determine both arithmetic and algebraic expressions. These distinctions might be useful when participants are asked to explore the thinking of their own students for the homework.

Case discussion: Developing new skills/looking across contexts   (45 minutes)

Small groups (mixed grade level; 30 minutes)

Whole group (15 minutes)

The cases in Chapter 1 allow participants to consider four major questions:

- What mathematical tools do students use to explore number sequences?
- What mathematical ideas can they encounter through this work?
- What do they learn by comparing different situations that produce the same number sequence?
- What kinds of questions can teachers pose to draw students' attention to these ideas?

Organize participants into groups of 3 or 4 and distribute the Focus Questions for Chapter 1. Let them know they will have 30 minutes for small-group discussion.

Focus Question 1 refers to Lucy's case, Case 2. Participants should discuss the approaches students in the case use to examine a Staircase Towers situation and the mathematical ideas that each approach calls upon. Focus Question 2 draws participants' attention to Case 3 and the insights offered by Anna who notices the connections between the Staircase Towers and Penny Jar problems. Focus Questions 3 and 4 draw attention to questions that the teachers in Case 4 and Case 1 posed to their students and invite participants to consider the impact of those questions on student thinking. Focus Question 5 invites participants to compare two students' methods for working with Cube Trains. Participants should also compare the work of these students with their own thinking on the Cube-Train work.

The whole-group discussion should primarily address Focus Question 2 to highlight two points: One, that different situations might have the same mathematical structure, and two, how previous experiences may have contributed to Anna's insight. Use the last few minutes to turn to the question of teacher moves by asking, "What do you see teachers in these cases doing to make these ideas more visible to their students?" Tie the DVD and case discussion together by eliciting comments about the role the teachers' questions played in these cases and on the DVD.

Homework and exit cards (10 minutes)

Whole group

Before assigning the homework, take a few minutes to ask participants to examine the list of group norms they generated. "How did we do? Is there anything you want to add?" Let the group know the list will be posted at each session and that they may suggest additions to it at any time.

Distribute the "Portfolio Process" handout and answer any questions participants have about maintaining a portfolio. The portfolio can be a binder, a folder, or any other means of keeping a collection of their written work and your responses. Explain how important reading and responding to papers are for you as the seminar facilitator; knowing their thinking helps you plan for the next session. They should also understand the portfolio assignments are carefully designed to move their ideas forward and will often be used as a basis for class discussion. Establish a routine for collecting and returning assignments.

You should also distribute the handout "If You Have to Miss a Class" or orally explain your expectations about attendance. Emphasize the ideas of the seminar build from session to session. Missing any session will jeopardize their continued understanding and active participation in class activities.

Distribute the "Second Homework" sheet and have participants read the portfolio assignment. Say, "Sometimes people read the cases in the chapter and wonder if their own students think about math ideas in similar ways. This assignment is a chance to check that out." Explain that these papers will be the basis for discussion with another participant at the next session. Let them know this kind of assignment will be given three times over the course of the seminar.

Suggest they include their own analysis of the class or students in the paper "Tell us what you make of what the students did. What did *you* learn about your students' thinking by looking closely at their work or comments? What questions does their thinking raise for you?" Finally, ask if there are any questions about the assignment.

As the first session ends, distribute index cards and pose these exit-card questions:

1. What mathematical ideas did this session highlight for you?
2. What was the session like for you as a learner?

Explain this procedure by announcing that each session will end with a period of reflective writing, known as "exit cards." This is an opportunity for participants to think about the experience of being in the seminar and sharing their thoughts and learning with you. Emphasize that their responses are invaluable as you plan future sessions. Exit-card questions are of two types; one is about the math content of the seminar and the other is about the seminar experience. As participants are using the exit cards as a way to communicate with you, they should sign their names.

Before the next session...

In preparation for the next session, read what participants wrote in their preseminar writing assignment in response to the math activities embedded in the Chapter 1 cases. Write a response to the whole class, taking note of common themes you see in the mathematical approaches. Be sure all participants' ideas, if not their exact words, are represented in your response. You might also choose to respond to any issues or ideas that came up in the exit-card activity. For more information, see the section in "Maxine's Journal" (p. 26) on responding to the first homework. Make copies of both the papers and your response for your files before returning the work.

DVD Summary

Session 1: Choice One

Segment One: First-grade students with teacher Kirsten (6 minutes)

In this segment, first-grade students are explaining to their teacher how they are building and recording a Staircase Towers activity that starts with 2 and adds 3 each time.

The first student explains that she makes towers of alternating colors of the same height and then adds 2 extra cubes. The teacher, Kirsten, questions her and the student corrects herself indicating that she adds 3 on each time. Kirsten asks the student to explain why she is adding 3 each time, and the student refers to the Staircase Towers situation.

The next student has towers of 2, 5, 7, 10, and has just counted out 13. The teacher calls his attention to the fact that he started counting the new tower from 10 on, 11, 12, 13. The student recounts the tower.

Another student says this is "counting by 2s." When the teacher asks her to explain, the student says, "It goes 1, 4, 8, 10, 13." The teacher questions this and another student offers an example of counting by 2s, "2, 4, 6, 8, 10, 12."

The teacher turns to Jamarie, who had asked for help. Jamarie explains the towers should go up by 3 and not 2. The teacher reminds him of the work he had done previously with the penny jar. The student counts by 3s with his fingers.

Segment Two: Second-grade class with teacher Mike (2 minutes)

In this segment, a second-grade class is finishing a discussion of a color-cube-repeating pattern. The unit that repeats is yellow, yellow, orange, orange, brown. They have built a table showing the numbers associated with the brown cubes.

Using Patterns to Determine What's Ahead

1	5
2	10
3	15
4	20
5	25

Posters are displayed around the room showing tables from other pattern work. The teacher asks students to look at the table for the colored-cube pattern and to see if they can find other tables with similar values.

A student, Sam, indicates that the table for Building B has the same numbers. The teacher asks Sam to explain what the numbers in the table for Building B represent. Sam explains that the numbers on the table go up by 5s, and they stand for the total number of rooms for buildings of 1, 2, 3, 4, and 5 floors.

The teacher, Mike, asks why the two tables have the same numbers, and two different students explain that both patterns are built around 5. In the cube train, the pattern repeats after 5; i.e., 5 is the unit and in the building, each floor has 5 rooms.

Session 1: Choice Two

Eighth-grade class with teacher Chuck (11 minutes)

In the first segment the students are working with the repeating pattern: yellow, black, yellow, black, yellow, black... Since some students are having difficulty creating equations for the contexts, the teacher calls the class together. They first generate the table for the position of the black tiles and determine the equation that matches this situation. Then they generate the table and equation for the position of the yellow tiles.

Discussion Break

The next three short segments are clips of small groups working with the three-color repeating pattern: red, blue, green, red, blue, green...

One pair of students calls the teacher over saying some of their values in the different tables repeat. The teacher listens to them explain and then suggests they get tiles, build the pattern, and then re-create the table.

In the next segment, two students are working to determine the color of the 42nd tile. In order to do this, they laid out 42 tiles in the pattern. The teacher asks them if that is the way they will do the 67th or the 100th case. One student says they are going to find an equation.

In the final short segment, a pair of students are examining the table for the position of the red tiles. They generate the equation by examining the number pattern in the table and then connect it to the model they built with tiles.

Poster to prepare for Session 1:

Tables for Red, Blue, and Green, the Answer to Math Activity Question 5

Position Among the Red Cubes	Position Among All Cubes
1	1
2	4
3	7
4	10
5	13

Position Among the Blue Cubes	Position Among All Cubes
1	2
2	5
3	8
4	11
5	14

Position Among the Green Cubes	Position Among All Cubes
1	3
2	6
3	9
4	12
5	15

PATTERNS, FUNCTIONS, AND CHANGE

Math activity: Cube trains

| 1 | 2 | 3 | 4 | 5 | 6 | 7 | 8 | 9 | | | | |

This is what we are calling a number strip. The numbers can be extended for as long as you choose. You can make your own number strips on graph paper to help you with the following exercises.

A. Represent this repeating pattern—yellow, black, yellow, black—by building a cube train and then recording it on a number strip

1. The 1st black cube corresponds to 2; the 2nd black cube corresponds to 4. List some other numbers that correspond to the black cubes. Organize this list into a table.

2. The 1st yellow cube corresponds to 1; the 2nd yellow cube corresponds to 3. List some other numbers that correspond to the yellow cubes. Organize this list into a table.

3. What color is the 100th cube? What number is the 100th black cube? What number is the 100th yellow cube? Explain the differences among these questions and how you solved them.

B. Represent this repeating pattern—red, blue, green, red, blue, green—by building a cube train and then recording it on a number strip.

4. Experiment with this pattern by posing questions such as, What color is the 25th cube? What number is the 13th green cube?

5. Make tables that show the sequence of green numbers; the sequence of blue numbers; the sequence of red numbers.

6. To express the 50th red cube, Angela wrote 3(50) − 2. Bob wrote 3(49) + 1. What are they each thinking? With whom do you agree and why?

7. What color is the 100th cube? What number is the 100th green cube? What number is the 100th blue cube? The 100th red cube? Explain the differences among these questions and how you solved them.

8. Consider the tables you made for Question 5, and compare those three tables with the tables the group generated for the yellow, black pattern. What do you notice in the table? How is what you noticed connected to the repeating pattern of colored cubes?

C. Experiment with repeating patterns using four or five colors. Consider orange, pink, violet, brown, or yellow, yellow, orange, orange, brown.

9. Once you have experimented with a given sequence, make tables and observations and compare those with your previous work.

Focus Questions: Chapter 1

1. In Case 2, lines 166 to 179, the teacher explains the approaches of Stanley, Burt, Jeff, and Barry. Analyze each of these three approaches. What understanding about the mathematics might each approach indicate?

2. What do you see in the thinking of Anna in Case 3? What experiences might have contributed to her understanding?

3. Consider the teacher's question in Case 4, line 330. What does that question highlight? Discuss student responses after that question was posed.

4. What is the impact of the question that Catherine poses in Case 1, line 41? What do students need to understand in order to determine what will be in a later position in a repeating pattern?

5. In Case 4, lines 295 to 300, explain Dora's method of finding color for the 16th cube. What does her method indicate about her understanding? Explain Juanita's method in lines 305 to 314. What does her method indicate about her understanding? How is Dora's method the same or different from Juanita's?

The Portfolio Process

As a participant in the DMI seminar Patterns, Functions, and Change, you will complete writing, reading, and sometimes mathematics assignments for each session. In fact, you already did the first of these in the preseminar homework, as you wrote about the mathematics content and read the cases in the first chapter.

You will write a paper for each class session. Some of these writings will be read and considered in group discussion; all are opportunities to communicate with the facilitator of the seminar. The facilitator will collect your paper at the end of each session. During the following session, your paper will be returned to you with a written response from the facilitator. Please save both your writing and these responses in a folder that will serve as your seminar portfolio.

There will be a total of nine papers, one to be turned in at each session and one—the final portfolio review—to be completed at the end of the seminar. In all cases, the purpose of the assignments and written responses is to stimulate your thinking. The portfolio will be a record of your work and will also serve as a tool for reflection. Particularly toward the end of the seminar, you will be able to look back over your work and think about how your ideas changed.

If You Have to Miss a Class

DMI seminars are highly interactive, providing many opportunities for you to express your own ideas and to listen to the ideas of your colleagues. Much of what you learn in the seminar is developed through small-group and whole-group discussions. You will get the most from the seminar and will be able to contribute positively to the learning of everyone in the group if you make every effort to prepare for each session and attend the entire time.

Frequently, ideas that are introduced in one session are expanded upon and developed more fully in later sessions. Thus, every session is important. If you find that you are unable to attend a particular session or might miss a part of a seminar (by coming late or leaving early), please contact the facilitator as soon as possible. Make arrangements to turn in assignments and to obtain copies of the assignments that you will miss.

When you are absent, you are also responsible for turning in a reflective paper describing your reaction to the cases that were discussed at the session you missed. This is in addition to the regularly assigned work. You also need to turn in your work on the math activity that was completed while you were absent. If at all possible, meet with a classmate to discuss the session you were not able to attend.

These requirements are designed to ensure that a missed session will minimize any loss of learning.

Second Homework

Reading assignment: Casebook, Chapter 2

Read Chapter 2 in the Casebook, "Representing Situations with Tables, Diagrams, and Graphs," including the introductory text and Cases 5–9.

Writing assignment: Examples of student thinking

It is likely that reading the cases and working on the mathematics in this seminar have made you curious about how your own students might work with number sequences. This assignment asks you to examine the thinking of your students.

Pose a mathematics task to your students related to number sequences. You might pose a question taken directly from one of the cases in Chapter 1. Then think about what happened. What did you expect? Were you surprised? What did you learn? Write up your question, how your students responded, and what you make of their responses (your expectations, your surprises, and what you learned). Include specific examples of student work or dialogue. Examining the work of just a few students in depth is very helpful.

At our next session, you will have the opportunity to share this writing with colleagues in the seminar. Please bring three copies of your writing to share and to turn in to the seminar facilitator.

Note: You will be asked to prepare similar assignments that involve investigating students' thinking for Session 4 and Session 6. Check your classroom schedules and lesson plans to be sure you will be able to complete these assignments.

PATTERNS, FUNCTIONS, AND CHANGE

Representing Situations with Tables, Diagrams, and Graphs

Mathematical themes:

- Creating tables and graphs of data generated by a variety of situations
- Identifying features of graphs
- Analyzing different representations for the same situation to see what each reveals
- Writing arithmetic expressions and formulas for situations involving linear functions

Session Agenda

Sharing student-thinking assignment	Pairs	20 minutes
Math activity: Comparing and contrasting functions	Whole group	15 minutes
	Six groups	15 minutes
	Small groups	25 minutes
	Whole group	20 minutes
Break	Whole group	15 minutes
Case discussion: Representing functions	Small groups	25 minutes
	Whole group	20 minutes
Math activity: Finding formulas	Small groups	20 minutes
Homework and exit cards	Whole group	5 minutes

Background Preparation

Read

- the Casebook, Chapter 2
- "Maxine's Journal" for Session 2
- the agenda for Session 2
- the Casebook: Chapter 8, Section 3

Work through

- the Math activity: Graphing functions (pp. 79–80)
- the Focus Questions for Session 2 (p. 81)
- the Third Homework (pp. 82–83)

Materials

Duplicate

- "Math activity: Graphing functions" (pp. 79–80)
- "Focus Questions: Chapter 2" (p. 81)
- "Third Homework" (pp. 82–83)

Obtain

- graph paper
- cubes or tiles

Prepare

- Poster: Representations from Case 6: Lunch money models (p. 78)

From Penny Jars to Linear Functions

In PFC, sometimes after a function with a discrete domain is graphed, we suggest joining the points in order to see the trend. What is the difference between the graph of discrete points and the graph of the line that joins the points? What can we learn by joining the points?

Consider a Penny Jar situation defined by starting with 5 pennies in the jar and adding 7 pennies each round. A table for this situation might include these values:

Number of Rounds	Number of Pennies
Start	5
1	12
2	19
3	26
4	33

By identifying the Start as 0 rounds, this situation and table define the function represented by the set of ordered pairs [(0, 5), (1, 12), (2, 19), (3, 26), (4, 33), ...] and whose graph is shown below. The number of pennies in the jar can be determined from the number of rounds by the formula $y = 5 + 7x$, where x is the number of rounds and y is the number of pennies.

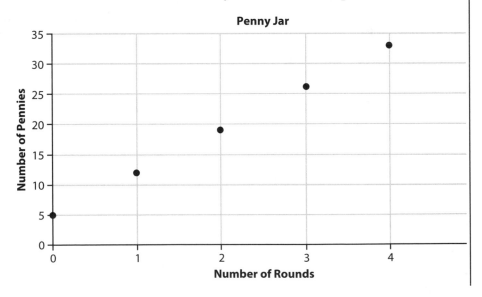

Penny Jar

Representing Situations with Tables, Diagrams, and Graphs

The domain of this function is {0, 1, 2, 3, 4,...} and the range is {5, 12, 19, 26, 33, ...}. The points on the graph (the six shown here and those for domain values larger than 5) constitute the graph. The Penny Jar context limits the domain to the set of whole numbers and consequently the graph is a set of unconnected points. The values between these points make no sense in the context; for example, there is no Round 3.5. The context demands a domain with whole-number points, a discrete domain.

Imagine instead of a Penny Jar, a rectangular container 40 centimeters high to which water is added at a constant rate. At the start (time = 0), the water in the container is at a level 5 centimeters high, and from then on, water is added continuously and at a constant rate so that for each hour the water level rises 7 centimeters. The formula associating each x-value (number of hours) with a y-value (number of centimeters) is the same as that of the Penny Jar: $y = 5 + 7x$. However, now x-values such as 3.5 have meaning in this context; $x = 3.5$ would indicate a time $3\frac{1}{2}$ hours after the start and would map onto $y = 29.5$, indicating the water level is 29.5 centimeters.

This function has a continuous domain from time = 0 to time = 5 hours when the container is full or starts to overflow. The domain is bounded on one side by 0 because x does not take on any negative values and bounded on the other side by the size of the container. Within these bounds on x, the domain is all of the numbers on the number line, and the graph is a solid line segment.

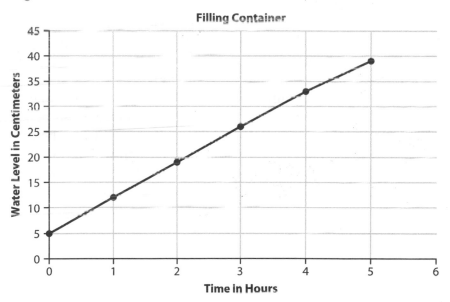

Now consider the formula $y = 5 + 7x$, without any external context associated with it. The domain of this function is all the numbers on the number line. That is, it is both continuous and unbounded. The graph is a line that extends without end in either direction.

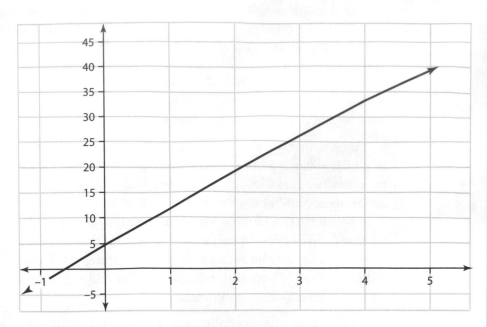

The two functions we have presented in context—the Penny Jar and the water filling a container—are both embedded in this third function whose domain and range are all the numbers on the number line. The discrete set of points that make up the penny jar graph and the continuous line segment that is the graph of water filling a container both fall on this graph.

In PFC, we use contexts (penny jars, arrangements of tiles and cubes, racing crayfish) to reason about functions based on what we know about objects in the world. Our interest is not so much in the particulars of the context (we do not really care about penny jars or sequences of colored cubes), but about the functions the context gives us access to. At times, seminar discussions stay within the specific contexts and the limited or discrete domains they imply. At other times, we may join the points of a graph with a discrete domain, or extend the segment of a graph with a bounded domain, in order to learn about the continuous function with a domain and range of all the numbers on the number line.

Representing Situations with Tables, Diagrams, and Graphs

Maxine's Journal

February 17

A major goal of the seminar is to deepen participants' understanding of functions through multiple representations. In the first session, participants were introduced to tables as one conventional representation of functions. Now for the second session, they read Lucy's and Karl's cases in Chapter 2, which introduced them to graphs, a form of representation at the heart of the first math activity in this session. By the end of the session, participants were also writing out formulas using algebraic notation to represent functions.

However, in order to learn to reason effectively with these representations, it is important to stay close to the context that is being represented. This often involves relying on other, less conventional, representations, as well: drawings or diagrams of the context or the use of physical objects like tiles or cubes. These, too, were featured in Session 2.

Sharing student-thinking assignment

Participants were asked to sit in pairs to read one another's student-thinking papers. Then I gave them time to discuss their assignments. Until they began talking, I, too, read a couple of the papers and then moved around listening to some of their conversations.

Peggy had her students work with a number sequence beginning with 12, adding 11, without offering a context for them to think with. She said that they dutifully extended the sequence—12, 23, 34, 45, 56—and found patterns in the digits, but they did not know what to do when she asked them to find a general rule.

Yan had given her students a Cube Train problem and was surprised that her students found it so difficult. Looking over her paper, I saw that she had given them the task from Lenore's Case 4—for the repeating pattern red, blue, yellow, and green, find a rule for the blue cubes. I asked why she hadn't asked her students to work with the green cubes first, and she said she wanted them to think about other colors because that's what had been challenging for her in the previous session. I suggested that her students might first need to think about how multiples of 4, which are familiar to them, apply to this context, and then they could think about how that sequence is related to the other colors.

Just before it was time to move on, I heard Sandy say how much she and her students enjoyed working on this task. It made me realize that (as always) people in the group had very different experiences working on this assignment, and so as I brought the whole group together, I commented on that. I told them that I was looking forward to reading these assignments and would be thinking with them about how to define tasks that would bring students deeper into the ideas. I suggested we could look at that when we get to the cases, as well.

Math activity: Comparing and contrasting functions

In Session 1, we worked with several sequences that could be viewed as linear functions: Each term was derived by adding a constant to the previous term. All of the functions that appear in the cases of Chapters 2 through 5 are linear. It is not until Chapters 6 and 7 that we read about students exploring nonlinear functions. However, it is important that, early on in the seminar, participants become aware of a variety of functions and recognize that not all functions are linear. The math activity, categorizing functions, gives them an opportunity to see a variety of functions, which will be explored more deeply later in the seminar.

In this math activity, participants were given a list of nine contexts for which they were to create a table and a graph. Each participant would work in a small group on three contexts and then join a different small group with those who had worked on the other contexts. Once they had tables and graphs for the set of nine contexts, they were to look at the characteristics of each and find similarities and differences between them.

Before we began, I wanted to make sure everyone knew how to create a graph. I mentioned that in Case 8, Graphing staircase problems, the teacher, Lucy, wrote about her third graders' early attempts to graph a function, and in Case 9, Karl worked with his seventh graders on graphs. I said, "These cases might have raised some questions for you."

Then I said we would make sure everyone is comfortable with the basics of graphing. "Here's the context we'll start with. We have a penny jar, and we start with 5 pennies in the jar. Each round, we add 7 pennies. So, together, we'll make a table."

Within a minute, we had created the following table:

Number of Rounds	Number of Pennies
Start	5
1	12
2	19
3	26
4	33
5	40

Once the table was up, Ivan raised his hand with a question. "I don't understand why you put 12 at the 1st round. It seems to me that's the 2nd round; the 1st round is 5."

Actually, this was an important question Ivan was bringing up and one that would likely cause more confusion if not addressed. I said, "Ivan, I'm glad you raised that question. There are some situations in which we can choose how we want to define our variables. For example, let's say we have a situation in which we pull the penny jar out of the closet and there are 5 pennies sitting at the bottom. We haven't added any pennies yet; we just have pennies at the start. Then, we put 7 pennies in the jar, and that's our 1st round. We can simply define our rounds that way. Each round, we put 7 pennies in. And even though it might sound strange, we can say that at the 0th round, that is, before we actually get started, there are already 5 pennies in the jar.

"I heard some people say last week that, in this way, the Penny Jar situation is different from Staircase Towers or Cube Trains. But actually, even though it might seem pretty strange, we could decide to talk about a 0th green cube or a 0th tower if that made things easier for us.

"But for now, I just want to make sure we're OK with the Penny Jar situation. Is it OK with you to define the rounds as the times we add 7 pennies to the jar, and so after the first round we have 12 pennies?"

Ivan nodded, and nobody else added anything, so I went on to show the group how to make a graph.

I pointed out that the horizontal axis would show the number of rounds, and the vertical axis, the number of pennies. If we wanted to plot only those points we had now in the table, the horizontal axis needed only extend to 5, but the vertical axis needed to extend to 40. It was OK for the scales to be different—the numbers on the horizontal axis could be more stretched out than on the vertical. What is important, however, is that we marked off equal intervals on each axis.

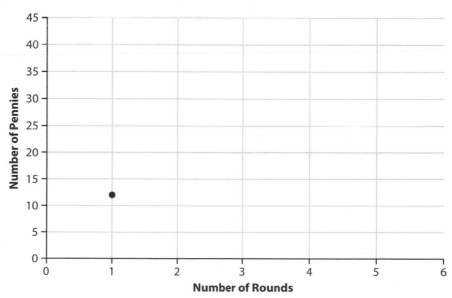

I plotted the point (1, 12) and asked someone to explain what that one dot meant. Robin said that if you look down from the point, you see 1 on the horizontal axis; when you look across to the left, you get to 12 on the vertical axis. I nodded and said, "In that way, the point represents the two corresponding values, 1 and 12."

I plotted the rest of the points and drew in a line connecting them, but that, too, needed an explanation. "I'm sketching in this line, but I want to make sure we all understand what's meant when we do that." I pointed to the place on the line halfway between Rounds 1 and 2. "Does this context have any meaning for the point (1.5, 15.5)? What could that mean?"

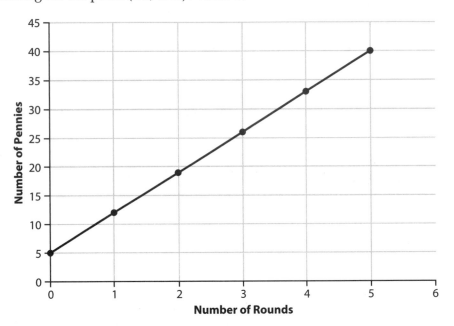

Yan said, "That doesn't make sense. You don't have $1\frac{1}{2}$ rounds or $15\frac{1}{2}$ pennies."

"Right," I said. "When we graph this context, it's really these discrete points, the whole numbers that appear in this table, which could go on to (6, 47), (7, 54), etc. In a situation like this, when we draw in the line, it's just a visual aid for us to see the trend."

I wanted to make sure participants understood the distinction, so I asked if anyone could think of a context in which all the points on the line would be values for the context. Ariel said, "It needs to be a context where both of the quantities can be fractions. What if there's something increasing, like the Penny Jar, but not at a particular time of day? Like what if water is flowing into a tub or some kind of container? At the beginning, there are 5 inches of water in the tub. You turn on a faucet, and the water rises 7 inches every minute. Then in half a minute, it rises $3\frac{1}{2}$ inches, and in a quarter of a minute, it rises $1\frac{3}{4}$ inches."

I was concerned that all of Ariel's halving was confusing for many people, but the context of water flowing into a tub was a good one. So, I pointed to the graph, between 3 and 4 and asked, "Does this point represent values that fit the situation?"

A group was working on the movie-tickets context presented in Set II: *Tickets cost $8 each; the amount of money collected is dependent on the number of tickets sold.* They called me over to explain their discovery. Lamis said, "We had a long discussion about what increments to put in our table, and we finally decided to calculate the money collected for every 10 tickets. So, we graphed it and saw that it came out to be a straight line. Then Mariam said we should see what the graph looks like if we do it in increments of 5 tickets. Nazir suggested we do it right on the same axes. As we started to do it, we realized all the points were already on the graph!"

I smiled and nodded in response. Having their expectation contradicted in that way will help them develop a better understanding of what a graph is. I then asked them to look at Context 5—*a rectangle has a height of 8 centimeters; the area of the rectangle depends on the length of its horizontal sides*—and see how that graph compares.

When participants were finished creating their three graphs, I put them into groups to share what they had done and to examine all nine graphs together.

Most people were interested in the graph of the different-sized groups of people contributing to a gift of $36. Georgeann said, "It swooshes! At the beginning, if you add one more person to the group, see how the cost really drops. But later, if you add one more person, it's like, so what? You save a few cents. But, going from 1 person to 2, it drops $18."

Ivan's group was looking at that same graph and comparing it to the one about having money left from $36 after buying a gift. He commented, "Both graphs are descending, but in one it's a steady change; in the other, it starts with a drastic change and then tapers off." Georgeann and Ivan were hitting on ideas that get right to the heart of the seminar.

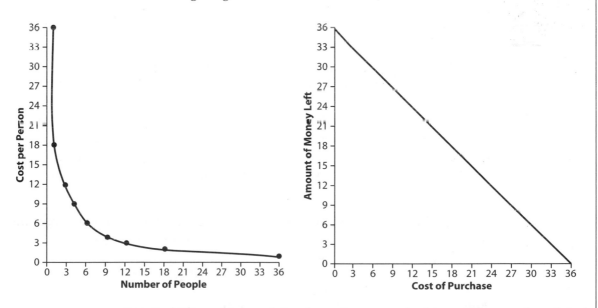

I visited Elinor, Yan, and Sandy, as they were looking at the graphs related to the problems presented in Set III: *The area of a square depends on the length of a side* and *If I fold a paper once, I have two sections. If I fold it again (2 folds) there*

are four sections. What happens if you continue to fold the paper? Elinor pointed out that both graphs curve up. Sandy said, "Yeah, but the numbers for the paper folding got really big."

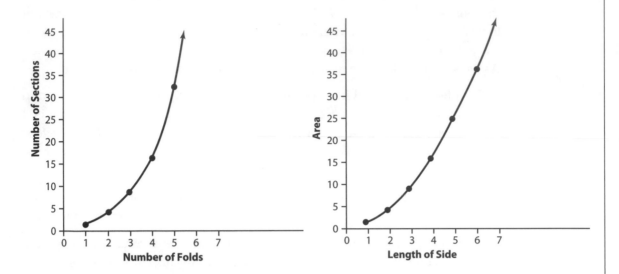

In another group, Violet was explaining to Trudy and Bill what they should be seeing in the graphs. As a middle-school teacher, Violet is familiar with these different kinds of graphs and Trudy and Bill were asking questions. My concern is whether Trudy and Bill had the same opportunity to work on the ideas of this activity as those in groups who had the space to make errors or express their observations. Maybe this will not become a problem, but this is a dynamic I will need to pay attention to. 185 190

Whole group

I brought the whole group together to talk together about participants' observations. Mariam started out talking about graphs in which "all points are relevant" versus those in which there are "no middle values." It took me a moment to understand her language, until I realized she was comparing the contexts presented in Problems 4 (income from movie tickets) and 5 (area of a rectangle). Once you draw a line through the points in Context 4, you end up with a graph that looks the same as that of Context 5. Mariam went on: "All the points on the line are relevant to the rectangle graph but not for the movie tickets." 195

I asked for some examples of such points. Ivan said, "If the length of the rectangle is 1.5 inches, the area is 12 square inches. But, you never sell 1.5 tickets, and the income is never $12." 200

Ariel added, "If the length of the rectangle is $\sqrt{2}$ inches, then the area is $8\sqrt{2}$ square inches. But you never sell $\sqrt{2}$ tickets."

These were both good examples. Ariel particularly illustrated that when the graph is continuous, it includes not only fractions but also irrational 205

Representing Situations with Tables, Diagrams, and Graphs

numbers. I did not comment on the different kinds of numbers at that time. There was plenty of content to get to without taking time to discuss irrational numbers.

April pointed out that some of the graphs are straight lines and some are curves. It's important to be able to characterize the difference between the contexts that are graphed as straight lines and those that are not, and so I said, "Let's take a look at the straight lines. What else can you tell me about them?"

Dina said, "They look like they're steady; they're predictable."

Celeste responded, "If it's predictability you're paying attention to, I want to include all of them."

I asked Celeste to elaborate, so she explained, "For all the contexts, there's some kind of formula that allows us to know what the value of the dependent variable will be for a given value of the independent variable."

Celeste had started to use some terms that not everyone in the class was familiar with, and so I needed to slow things down. "Let's take a minute to make sure everyone is on board with these ideas. When we use the term *independent variable*, we are talking about the quantity that appears on the horizontal axis. It is also the quantity that appears in the left column of our tables, and it is sometimes called the *input variable*. The dependent variable appears on the vertical axis and in the right column of the table, and it's sometimes called the *output variable*. Those are conventions. Now without using those terms, I would like to hear someone else paraphrase Celeste's point."

Robin decided to give it a try. "For any value on the horizontal axis, you know what the corresponding value will be on the vertical axis."

Bill said, "I have another way to think about it. If you look at the function tables we made in our different groups, every table for a given context will have all the same values."

Lamis said, "But it might turn out that some of us put down more values. Our table might be longer than yours."

Bill nodded, "Yeah, but whatever you say corresponds to 2 or 3 or 4, I'll have the same value."

I looked at Dina who was nodding, and then checked with the whole group. "Now I want to go back to what Dina said. Her comment had two parts, and we have talked about one of them—all the graphs are predictable. The other thing she said is that the three straight-line graphs are steady."

Meg said, "Yeah, if you look at the graphs of the area of a square, it goes up by a different amount each time. You can predict it, but it's not steady; it doesn't go up by the same amount each time. The same with those other two, the folding paper and sharing the cost of the present."

I told the group that they were identifying very important characteristics of functions. "These functions are called linear functions because they are graphed as straight lines. You're identifying an important property of a linear function: It increases or decreases at a steady rate. For the next several sessions, we will be exploring linear functions more deeply.

"The other functions we've looked at today, the nonlinear functions, are types that we will be studying in Session 6. As Meg pointed out, for these functions, the change is not constant. But as we'll see in Session 6, there are interesting things to notice about how the change varies for those functions.

"However, I don't want you to think we've exhausted the categories of functions. In fact, there are many, many types of nonlinear functions that are still defined by formulas. There are also functions that aren't defined by formulas. For example, a person's height is a function of time. There are certainly general trends. People start out small when they are born and grow taller until their late teens or early 20s. But there's no way to look at a 5-year-old and determine, definitively, how tall she will be when she's 6. We can call functions like that 'data-based functions.' In Session 7, we'll be working on those."

I reiterated that we would be setting aside the nonlinear functions for a while. After break, we would move into discussion of the cases in which all the students were working on linear functions.

Case discussion: Representing functions

After the break, we got right into the case discussion. Because the math discussion had gone longer than I had anticipated, the time available for the cases was cut short. Most of the small-group time was spent on Question 1: Of the representations developed by Kate's students, which two would you present to the class? Why would you choose those two?

This question is an important one. It allows participants to work on interpreting all the different representations students came up with, to analyze their similarities and differences, and to think about making classroom decisions based on the mathematical ideas they want their students to engage with.

When I spoke with Bill, Elinor, and Mariam, they told me that they liked Eliana's representation, as well as Abigail and Kayla's representation, and so those are the two they would show the class. When I asked why, they said those two were the cleanest and clearest, and so they wanted to encourage the students to create representations like those. I noted to myself that these two representations were essentially the same: The number of lunches was represented by position (the row number or the tower number), and the cost, by the number of cubes in that position. Eventually, I wanted this group to understand what students would learn by investigating two representations that treated the variables differently. However, for now, I wanted them to become more articulate about how their two preferred representations differed from the others. So, I said, "I'd like you to be able to explain more specifically how Abigail, Kayla, and Eliana's representations are the same, and how they are different from the others. For example, you might examine how each representation shows the number of lunches: How do you find 4 lunches—and the cost of 4 lunches—in each representation?"

When I came to Ariel, April, and Lamis, they were talking about the challenge to these second graders to keep track of two different quantities that were changing in relation to each other. April was saying, "Let's look at each representation to see what each cube stands for. Like, when I look at the first representation, 2 cubes stand for $2 at the same time they stand for 1 lunch. Is that the way it is for everyone?" April continued, "No, Anna has one stack stand for the number of lunches and the other stack, the number of dollars. So, Anna's is really different from everyone else's in that way."

Whole group

Before we started the whole-group discussion, I hung a poster that showed six representations created by Kate's students. This would help us keep track of which representation participants were talking about.

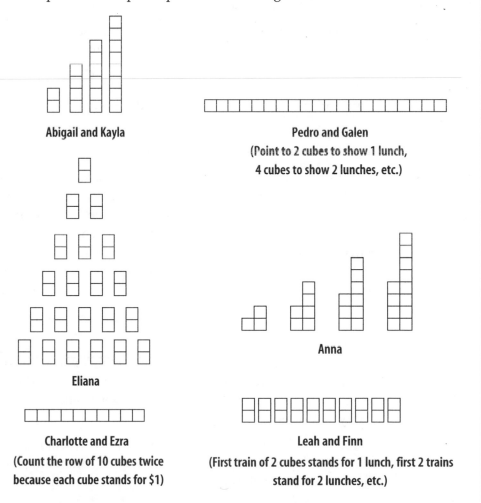

Abigail and Kayla

Pedro and Galen
(Point to 2 cubes to show 1 lunch, 4 cubes to show 2 lunches, etc.)

Eliana

Anna

Charlotte and Ezra
(Count the row of 10 cubes twice because each cube stands for $1)

Leah and Finn
(First train of 2 cubes stands for 1 lunch, first 2 trains stand for 2 lunches, etc.)

I began the discussion by asking, "What is the mathematics these first and second graders are working on as they create their representations?" Participants identified several content areas:

- Counting by 2s
- Developing ideas of multiplication and its links to counting
- Developing representations for multiplication
- Creating representations of their thinking
- Making sense of someone else's representation
- Keeping track of two quantities in relation to each other

In connection to the last item, Flor commented that students were not just answering a single question, like finding the cost of 5 lunches, but were also exploring relationships in the situation.

Then I asked, "Which two representations would you choose to share with a class, and what question would you ask to help them think more deeply about the representations?"

Meg started us off. "I'd focus on Anna's representation and Leah and Finn's. I'd ask, 'What's the connection between how Anna represented the number of lunches and how Leah and Finn did?'"

Georgeann said, "That's interesting. I'd ask the same question, but I'd focus on Anna's and Abigail's representations. It seems to me there's something very similar between Anna's and Abigail's. If you just take away the cubes Anna used to represent lunches, you're left with Abigail's representation. And so it highlights what Anna did differently."

I asked, "What exactly did Anna do differently? I want to hear from someone other than Georgeann."

Bill spoke up. "Abigail and Kayla show the number of lunches by position. The 4th tower stands for the cost of 4 lunches, the 5th tower stands for the cost of 5 lunches. Anna has a tower for the cost of 4 lunches next to a tower that shows 4 lunches. There's something kind of cluttered and confusing in Anna's representation. Sometimes a cube stands for 1 lunch, and sometimes a cube stands for $1. But also, since she organizes the information from left to right, the towers for the number of lunches are redundant. She doesn't need them."

I was pleased with Bill's comments. Clearly he had taken on the question I had posed to his small group.

Ariel now said, "That's precisely why I think it's powerful to have the class look at those two representations together. Those second graders aren't going to be as articulate as Bill, but if they can get a sense of those ideas, those are pretty big ideas."

Flor brought us back to Leah and Finn's representation, but she was interested in comparing it to Abigail and Kayla's. She said, "Once we know that the number of lunches is designated by position, there are different ways to see the number of lunches. For Abigail and Kayla, you look at the one tower in that position. For Leah and Finn, you look at the tower in that position plus all the towers to the left."

Lamis said, "I'd like to compare Leah and Finn's representation with Pedro and Galen's. It seems they were based on the same idea, but Leah and Finn separated out their trains of 2. I'd ask, 'What information can be seen in each of these? Is one easier to see than the other?'"

Robin would compare Pedro and Galen's representation to Charlotte and Ezra's. She'd ask, "How can a train of length 10 and a train of length 20 both represent the same situation?"

Mariam said, "Even though Maxine questioned us in small group, I would still want the class to look at Abigail's and Eliana's representations. And I think I'd ask the same question, 'How can they both represent the same situation?' Students would still need to explain how both representations show the number of lunches and how they both show the cost."

I was very interested in all of these ideas presented by the group. I summarized by pointing out that any of the issues they wanted to go after in the discussion with the first and second graders could get at important ideas. "The main thing is to select representations with intention, with an idea of the important mathematics that is to be mined. I also want to point out that the questions all of you articulated get at how the representations show the number of lunches, the number of dollars, and the relationship between the two."

Math activity: Finding formulas

Time was running out, and I wanted to make sure everyone had a chance to get started on the mathematics they would be doing for homework. That is, I wanted each seminar participant to leave today's session with a sense of confidence that they could write algebraic formulas for the situations presented in the cases of Chapter 3. So I led the group through a review of Abigail's case about the penny jar as a transition.

I drew a picture of a penny jar and reviewed what Abigail said in her case. "Abigail is a fourth-grade teacher who was concerned that some of her students weren't recognizing multiplication in the Penny Jar context. Because her class had been using arrays as a representation for multiplication, she wanted her students to see that, as pennies enter the penny jar, they could be arranged as an array.

"She was working with a context in which there were 7 pennies in the penny jar to start." I drew 7 pennies at the bottom of the jar and then drew a line above it, as Abigail said she had done. "Then 3 pennies are added each round." I drew in 2 rows of 3 pennies, each. "So let's look at what we have so far. If we look just at the pennies above the line, we can think in terms of that array: 2 rounds times 3 pennies, or 2 × 3. Then we can add in the 7 pennies we started with."

I wrote out, "2ⁿᵈ round: (2 × 3) + 7."

Then I continued, "Let's draw in another few rounds." I drew in more pennies until the penny jar showed 5 rounds. "What's the calculation that would give me the number of pennies now?"

Sandy offered, "5 rounds times 3, and then add 7."

I wrote out, "5ᵗʰ round: (5 × 3) + 7."

To introduce the algebraic notation, I said, "We can see the round number by looking at the number of rows. If we multiply that number by 3, we get the number of pennies we've added since the start, and then we still need to add 7 to get the total number of pennies in the jar. We can do that for any round, right?" I looked out to see participants nodding. "So let n stand for the number of rounds."

I wrote out, "nᵗʰ round: (n × 3) + 7."

Participants were still nodding. Just in case, I said, "At the start of our first session, some people said they had had a hard time with algebra when they were in school. Does this make anyone feel nervous? Or are you OK with it?"

Everyone kept nodding, so I assumed they were OK. If not, I could check in with individuals as they started working on the next task.

I then added to what I had already written, "nᵗʰ round: $3n + 7$." I pointed out that when we see $3n$ written that way, with the two symbols next to each other, multiplication is implied. It means $3 \times n$.

Now I was ready to explain the homework assignment. "The next chapter has four cases in which students develop formulas like this one. Before you read the cases, I want you to work with each of the situations and develop your own formula for it. As you do so, I want you to keep in mind that you can manipulate how you look at the situations to help you develop formulas. Just like Abigail arranged the Penny Jar to show an array separated from the starting number of pennies, you might see what you can separate out in these other situations to help you find formulas."

Small groups

Everyone now got started on the first problem, which involved the following arrangements of yellow and blue tiles:

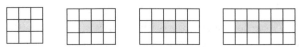

Around a number of blue tiles in a row, there is a border of yellow tiles. The task was to write the formula for the number of yellow tiles as a function of the number of blue tiles.

Representing Situations with Tables, Diagrams, and Graphs

Violet, Robin, and Trudy had made a table and, when I stopped by, they told me that the table goes up by 2, and the formula was $2x + 6$. When I asked what the formula had to do with the arrangement of tiles, they couldn't come up with an answer. I asked that they consider such questions as, Why does it go up by 2? What is it about the way the tiles are arranged that makes that happen? What does the 6 have to do with the tile arrangements? At first I think they were a bit put off by my questions—they felt good and satisfied that they could find the formula so quickly—but as I stayed with them, they did become intrigued by looking for connections between their formula and the patterns in the arrangements.

On the other hand, Joy, Georgeann, and Nazir had pulled apart their figures to show different parts.

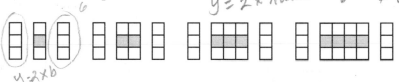

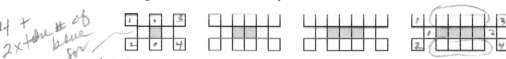

Joy told me she got that idea from the Penny Jar demonstration. She said, "When I pulled it apart like that, I could immediately see the 6 tiles in each arrangement, and it's also clear that in the rest, there are twice as many yellow tiles as blue ones." This was exactly the kind of thinking I was hoping for.

When I got to Meg, Ivan, and Lamis, I saw that they, too, had decomposed their arrangements, but then they felt stuck.

This group had pulled away a tile at each of the four corners and then did not know how to proceed. Then, before I even said anything, they started to see a pattern: 4 (for each of the corners) + 2 × the number of blue tiles (for the rows above and below the blue tiles) + 2 (for the tiles on each end of the blue). That gave them $4 + 2n + 2$. This made me feel satisfied. If they do not see how to simplify their expression on their own, they will certainly see how the student in the case solved the problem.

$$4 + 2n + 2 = 2n + 6$$

By the send of the session, I felt fairly confident that all the groups were on track. So, I concluded by posting the exit-card questions.

Exit cards

- What math ideas struck you in this session?
- What was it like working in a small group?
- Anything else you want me to know?

NAZIR: On the tables, not only is there a relationship between the 2 columns, but also all the way down the second column. I'm becoming much more comfortable with graphing and the tables. All this is so new to me. I'm sure going to find a way to show them in my class.

DINA: In the first activity, I found it interesting to find the similarities among the different graphs. Some of the differences seemed confusing to me at first, but other members at my table helped to clarify it for me. I felt less stressed working in my group today.

GEORGEANN: I was amazed at all the different ways my group worked on the tile problem. It was interesting to compare graphs and have people share their reasoning. I appreciate the support of my group since I am not always confident in my math thinking.

CELESTE: I got to explore connecting a formula I derived from a table to the situation it describes. It is so helpful to see what other people are thinking and the way they explain things. Sometimes I don't know how much to share of what I'm thinking.

I am pleased that Celeste, a middle-school teacher, is finding the satisfaction of making new connections to strategies and formulas already familiar to her, of understanding those strategies and formulas more deeply. I am also grateful that she is attentive to how much she speaks and to what extent her formal knowledge is helpful to others. In a whole group, I try to frame what she says to make it helpful to others. My impression is that it registers for Celeste that I am doing that. I take from her exit card that she monitors accordingly what she says during her small-group discussions.

I am not sure if Violet, also a middle-school teacher, is able to do the same. In her exit card, Violet did not answer the question about the mathematics and said that things were fine in her small group.

Responding to the second homework

February 19

Notwithstanding my first impression when participants shared their assignments in the session, I was quite pleased when I actually read them. Almost everybody had given their students a relevant mathematical task (most of them taken from one of the cases in the first two Casebook chapters), and almost all of them were thoughtful about their students' thinking. Perhaps this is a result of most participants having previously taken a DMI seminar.

Of all the participants, Nazir had the most difficulty, and so I will share her assignment here. She has just recently gotten a mid-year appointment for a class whose teacher is on medical leave, and so she is still getting to know her group.

Nazir
Grade 1

I have to admit, I was a bit concerned when I realized I had to do a number sequence activity with my first graders. Just having observed them over the

Representing Situations with Tables, Diagrams, and Graphs

last few weeks, I could tell that many of them lacked the number-recognition skills needed for first grade.

I decided to proceed with the Staircase Towers activity. In this activity, children create a set of towers (staircases) that match the cards 1–10. I found most of the children were able to do this successfully if they didn't use the number cards.

My class is made up of many ELL students and mostly "attentionally challenged" children. (Although this is not an actual term, it should be.) What I found was that many of these children, who are also academically challenged, had a hard time recognizing the written representation of the number. As long as I worked with them, keeping them on task by recounting with them, they were able to continue their staircase pattern.

During the introduction of the activity, I would purposely ask questions about what they noticed happening. Kayla, Diana, and Antonio noticed that each tower had exactly 1 more cube than the last. They could have easily created any number of towers, following the pattern, without having to count past tower 1 (with 1 cube).

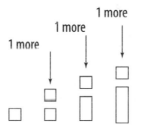

I repeated this activity with the children the next day as a center activity; they were expected to do it independently. As I wandered around the room, I saw that although most children could build the towers following the correct pattern, many of them needed me to keep them on task. I also noticed that Marisel couldn't read the numbers but could tell me what tower would come next if I recounted with her. But I had to recount with her because if she were left to do it on her own, her attention would shut off.

At this point, the attention-deficit issues make it hard to see if they are having difficulty with the math idea of patterning or if they just can't stay focused long enough to complete the task. (Then there are the children who end up building guns, cars, etc.)

I also want to add that I have found, surprisingly so, that my children in first grade often struggle with the idea of patterning. I look forward to discovering, with the help of this seminar, what I can do to help them.

I felt that it was important to communicate to Nazir that I recognized the difficulty of her job. She has a real challenge to teach the content of first grade when her students have not yet learned to count to 10 and do not recognize numerals. On the other hand, I also wanted to emphasize what she *can* do for her students, and what a difference it will make in their lives. I was pleased that, within this report of her struggles, Nazir described an idea that her students took hold of—that each tower in the sequence had 1 more cube than the previous one. I want to emphasize her ability to recognize her students' ideas.

Nazir,

It sounds like you have a challenging class. It is not easy to help children when they are missing the basic knowledge that we usually take for granted. It is also the case that you are in the position of making a difference in these students' lives—helping them to see what they can do instead of always focusing on what they cannot is one way to help them build up their repertoire of skills, both in math and in persistence. It is hard to be persistent when one has never had success in seeing that such persistence pays off. Your students are likely to be in that category when it comes to schoolwork.

Yet you are also noticing that they are capable of ideas. They may not know the number sequence yet or how to write numbers, but I see from your work with them that they are capable of recognizing and continuing patterns. Seeing "1 more cube" in the sequence of towers is significant! So your challenge is to help them develop the skills of counting and writing numbers, while at the same time helping them express the patterns that they see.

From your description, it sounds like the questions you are asking help your students to express their ideas and help you to see what they are thinking. As the year proceeds and you continue to ask such questions, I suspect they will get better at providing answers.

I think one appeal of working with patterns, even with such young children that might not have counting and number writing down yet, is that it provides an arena that math is predictable, that it makes sense, that you can expect it to behave in a certain way. That can help students feel they are in control of the numbers rather than being dominated by them.

Maxine

Ivan began his lesson with a version of Guess My Rule. This game can be played in a variety of contexts. A rule-maker creates a rule and identifies a set of objects that fits his rule. For example, a person might pick the rule "wearing jeans today," and then name two people in the class wearing jeans. Certainly, there are many rules that would include the two people named. However, each time someone guesses a rule different from the one the rule-maker has in mind, the rule-maker identifies another object (or person) that fits his rule but contradicts the guess. In this way, students accumulate evidence until someone can guess the rule-maker's rule. In this lesson, Ivan introduced Staircase Towers with Guess My Rule.

Ivan

I chose the Staircase Towers problem as my first graders had recently explored calculators and colored number patterns on 100s boards (2s, 3s, 5s, and 10s).

Representing Situations with Tables, Diagrams, and Graphs

I used the "starting with 1, add 3" problem to introduce the activity. Later, I asked children to work with a partner on starting with 1, add 2. I made a worksheet to help with directions.

Building Towers: Build 4 towers. The first tower has 1 cube. For each new tower, add 2 cubes more than the one you just made. After you have made 4 towers, answer these questions: What do you notice about your towers? What patterns do you see? Can you predict how many cubes will be in the 10th tower? How do you know?

Part 1: Introduction

We began by playing Guess My Rule. Sitting in a circle, I placed 1 cube in the center and explained that this was my 1st tower. Then placing my 2nd tower of 4 cubes next to it, I asked the class to look at my towers and predict how many cubes would be in the 3rd tower. Marin predicted 5. When I asked her to share how she arrived at 5, she explained that there was 1 cube in tower 1 and 4 in tower 2. She added the cubes together for a total of 5 cubes. I restated her rule and asked the group to think about her rule and see whether the next tower fit her rule or another rule. I went ahead and placed the 3rd tower of 7 cubes next to the other towers. When students disagreed, I asked Kurt to explain the rule he thought I was applying as I built each new tower. Kurt said, "Adding 3." When I asked him how many cubes would be in the 4th tower, he thought for a few seconds and responded, "10." When I asked him to explain, he said, "You started with 1, and then I see 4 and that is 3 more than 1. Then there is 3 more than this (pointing to the tower of 4). And, I think there is going to be 3 more than this."

Cassia used the word pattern *to describe how the consecutive towers differed. When I asked her to talk more about the pattern, she responded, "The pattern of the towers is ... it is kind of like when you compare, but ... you compare like ... here is 4 and 1, and it is 3 more than the 1 and then here 4 and 7 and 7 is 3 more, is ... 10 is 3 more than 7." After Cassia's explanation, I asked her if when she said "you compare" she was referring to the math we do in the morning when we use Unifix cubes to act out lunch-order comparison problems? (One of our daily routines is to use Unifix cubes to act out lunch-order problems; i.e., the students count out cubes to represent the different lunch-order groups [hot, cold, and milk] and lay the towers of cubes side-by-side to explain how many more children ordered hot lunch than cold lunch or milk than hot lunch, etc.) Cassia nodded in agreement. Cassia clearly understands how consecutive towers differ and is able to connect this activity to the related situation that arises when she is solving our lunch-ordering comparison problems.*

Before I sent them off to solve the "start with 1, add 2" problem, I asked two more questions. How many cubes will be in our 6th tower? When Kirsten responded, "16 cubes," I noticed that at least half the class put up their thumb to show they were in agreement with her. When I asked her to explain why she thought it was 16, she said, "I put 3 more and that made 13 and then 3 more and that made 16."

I ended this rather long introduction with one final question, "How many 610
cubes will be in the 10th tower?" After eliciting answers 22, 28, 13, and
18 cubes, we went ahead and built the remaining towers until we had all
10 towers in the middle of the circle. Of note during this last segment was
how the students built the 9th and 10th towers. Marin counted out 22 cubes.
To ensure that she had the correct numbers, she placed her tower next to 615
the 8th tower (22 cubes). When she recognized that they were equivalent,
she added 3 more cubes to her tower and placed it in the staircase line.
Victoria used the same strategy to build the 10th tower. She built a tower
of 25 cubes, compared it, and added more cubes to make 29. When she
placed her tower next to the 9th tower, however, she noticed that she must 620
have miscounted, as her tower was exactly 4 cubes longer. As soon as she
noticed her error, she pulled 1 cube off and replaced it in the line. After
counting the total in the 10th tower, I asked Bruce, a child who originally
answered the question correctly, if he could explain how he arrived at
28 cubes. Unfortunately, he was only able to talk about how he counted the 625
28 cubes in Victoria's tower.

Part 2: Student work

I sent pairs of children off to solve the "start with 1, add 2" problem. After
building the 4 towers with cubes, they were to talk about the three questions
and then answer them in writing.

Observations: A few children built towers counting up from 1 each time. 630
Most children, however, built the 3rd and 4th towers by first building a tower
equivalent to the last tower and then adding 2 more cubes to create the next
tower in the sequence.

As I met with groups, I asked students to tell what they noticed about their
towers and describe any patterns that they observed. Many students abstract- 635
ed the rule that the towers were growing bigger by 2. A few students noticed
the number sequence 1, 3, 5, 7, 9 and predicted that the sequence would repeat
in the next group of numbers (ones digit only). Nicholas and Victoria noted
that the towers represented "all the odd numbers." When I asked Nicholas
to explain further, he added, "You are adding 2. You're skipping all the even 640
numbers."

The biggest surprise during this activity occurred when students thought
about the 10th tower. Few, if any of my students, could make a reasonable
prediction of how many cubes would be in the 10th tower. Although some
students could add 2 twice to arrive at a tower 2 steps away, they seemed 645
unable to keep track of multiple +2 steps to reach the 10th tower. Many of
their solutions referred back to the problem we solved earlier during my
introduction. "When we were adding 3 in the other problem, the 10th tower
was 28 cubes long. Now we are adding 2 each time. Since 2 is 1 less than 3,
the 10th tower must be 1 less than 28—27." The only students who offered 650
a reasonable prediction based on a sound mathematical strategy were Adam

Representing Situations with Tables, Diagrams, and Graphs

and Jane. Adam's answer of 17, while off the mark, used a double counting strategy.

Part 3: Follow Up: "Start with 1, add 2" Staircase Problem

Over the next two days, I returned to my students' explanations both written and those I had recorded as I observed their class work. Looking at their work, I was struck by how many students seemed unsure how to think about the 10th tower. Their attempts to solve this problem surprised me. Although every student in my class had possessed efficient double-counting strategies for adding two numbers (putting out fingers to keep track of each successive number as they counted on), most of my class could not keep track of multiple +2 steps. Very few children thought to use a tool such as the 100s board, pencil marks, or fingers to help them make sense of the problem. Only Adam and Jane tried to solve the problem using a counting strategy. As I considered their solution, I was reminded of Carpenter's work[1] in which he describes the developmental continuum through which children pass as they learn addition and subtraction solution strategies. Children at the Kindergarten and first-grade levels tend to solve problems by using a direct modeling strategy. Given time and opportunities to solve similar problems, children gradually learn to think about the numbers as "abstract entities." Children replace direct modeling with a more efficient counting strategy. Using a double-counting strategy, a child will put out a finger for each number she counts in the sequence. The child uses her fingers to help keep track of the number of steps added to in the sequence.

Adam's solution reflects a capacity to think about numbers more abstractly. After stating that the answer was 17, he described how he began with the 4th tower. "Beginning with the 4th tower, I put out 4 fingers and counted 7." As he extended a 5th finger, he said "9," a 6th finger, "11," a 7th finger, "13," and so on. Although he stops before reaching the 10th tower and his prediction is off by a few, his solution strategy is remarkable. Many of my other students were unable to keep track of the +2 steps in their head without directly modeling their solution with a manipulative.

As I observed my students' work through the "start with 1, add 2" Staircase problem, I gathered considerable information about their thinking and solution strategies. This activity also generated a few questions: Why were my students unable to use the more efficient counting strategy to support their thinking? What activities would lead my students to use the counting-on with fingers strategy to keep track of counts when adding 2s, 5s, or 10s?

---

[1] Carpenter, T.P., Fennema, E., and Franke, M. (1996). Cognitively guided instruction: a knowledge base for reform in primary mathematics instruction. *Elementary School Journal*, 1, 3–20.

I found Ivan's write-up to be very interesting and thorough. Clearly, he is a very careful thinker and pays close attention to the mathematics of his classroom and the thinking of his students. The issue I especially wanted to highlight for him has to do with the cognitive challenge to young students of coordinating multiple units. Double-counting in the Staircase Towers context is very different from double-counting in addition and subtraction in which the units are always the same. The double counting here involves counting by 1s and 2s at the same time.

Dear Ivan,

What an interesting lesson you had with your first graders. There were several important moves you made, and there is much that we can learn about student thinking here.

First, it is interesting that you used the Staircase Towers for Guess My Rule. I gather your students have already had experiences with Guess My Rule, and so that aspect was not new. When Marin predicted that the 3rd tower would have 5 cubes, she provided a perfectly reasonable rule to get that 5. If one were to keep applying the rule, the sequence would turn out to be 1, 4, 5, 9, 14, ... Actually, some mathematicians study that kind of sequence, where each term is the sum of the two previous terms. The most common of these starts with 1, 1 (1, 1, 2, 3, 5, 8, ...) and is called the Fibonacci Sequence.

One thing you should keep in mind is that, even if you have a particular rule in mind, there are many different rules that could begin with the few numbers you present. Marin's guess highlights that for us. When you gave the class the next tower, it was clear that Marin's rule did not fit, but there are many other rules that could have worked. Kurt offered the rule you had in mind.

Cassia's explanation of what she saw in the towers highlights another important issue—that your students make connections between ideas that arise in different discussions. That's a very important disposition to encourage.

I found it very interesting to read about your students' thinking about the next task you gave them, which they were to perform on their own—to predict the height of the 10th tower when they start with 1 cube and add 2 cubes for each step. Because it is new to give these kinds of activities to primary-grade students, we are all learning about what many students can do and what is challenging.

One thing to keep in mind about these types of problems is that they involve multiplicative relationships. As students count the number of steps by 1, the number of cubes goes up by 2 each time. That is, not only do they need to perform a double count, but they also need to hold in mind two different units, 1 step and 2 cubes, in relation to each other.

Some of your students reason that steps of 3 got them to 28 for the 10th tower, so steps of 2 should get them to 27. Here, they are using what they understand about additive relationships and applying it to a multiplicative situation. They do not yet see that, because they had 9 steps of 2 instead of 9 steps of 3, they need to subtract that one 9 times.

This skill of coordinating multiple units is one that most students begin to develop in second grade, though of course, some students develop faster, others slower. It is related to being able to see the equivalence of ten 1s and one group of 10 and coordinate those 10s and 1s when working with two-digit numbers. However, even once they have the cognitive ability, it is still challenging to sort out when the situation involves multiplicative relationships instead of additive ones.

The main thing I am saying is, I think it is **great** *that you are giving your class tasks like this. However, do not feel dismayed that they have difficulty with it. Instead, maintain a stance of inquiry, to try to figure out what the issues are for your students. If you periodically give your students tasks like these, do you see progress as some of your students start to think multiplicatively?*

I see that you go back to Carpenter, et al., to help you interpret what is happening in your class. That is a very good strategy. You might also be interested to return to the research highlights essays in Building a System of Tens (Seeing a ten as "one") and Making Meaning for Operations (Modeling multiplication and division) to see if those essays fill out the ideas any further.

Maxine

Detailed Agenda

It is important that participants have enough time in this session to explore the graphs in the Math activity and to begin the homework task of writing formulas. Therefore, it is important to follow the timing of this session closely. In order to provide time for the math work, the sharing of the student-thinking assignment is done in pairs.

Sharing student-thinking assignment   (20 minutes)

Pairs

Organize participants into pairs to discuss the episodes they wrote examining the thinking of their students. Tell participants to read each other's papers before beginning any conversation so that their discussions will reflect ideas from both papers. They might begin by sharing what surprised them or what they discovered about their students' thinking. The discussion can also include the similarities and the differences between the papers.

At the end of the activity, let the participants know that you will be reading and responding to all of the papers and remind them of the procedure you established for collecting papers.

Math activity: Comparing and contrasting functions   (75 minutes)

Whole group (15 minutes)
Six groups (15 minutes)
Small groups (25 minutes)
Whole group (20 minutes)

This activity has two main goals. One is to introduce the variety of functions that will be examined over the seminar sessions. Another is to introduce graphing as a tool for examining functions. While some seminar participants might be familiar with graphing conventions, others may not. This activity provides the opportunity for all seminar participants to become familiar with the process of making graphs from tables. Creating and interpreting graphs will be an important mathematical tool throughout the seminar.

As a whole group, establish some of the conventions for making a graph. Use the Penny Jar situation, start with 5 and add 7 each time. Solicit values from the participants to complete the first five values in a table. Then make a graph with the *x*-axis labeled "Number of Rounds" and the *y*-axis labeled "Number of Pennies." Ask for suggestions regarding an appropriate scale to show values from 5 to 40 and how to plot the starting amount of 5. Establish (0, 5) as that point. Then plot points up to (5, 40). Finally, ask for comments about connecting the plotted points to raise two ideas. First, in this situation, values such as $3\frac{1}{2}$ or 4.3 do not have meaning; there can only be a whole number of rounds or pennies. Second, even though only whole-number values make sense in the situation, connecting the plotted points with a lightly drawn line can make clear the overall tendency of the situation being graphed.

The following Facilitator Note describes the graphs of the functions found in "Math activity: Graphing functions."

Graphing Functions

Set I includes three decreasing graphs: two that are linear (Graphs 2 and 3) and one that is not (Graph 1). Set I also includes a pair of situations in which one is embedded in the other (Graphs 2 and 3). Because situation 2 is in the context of money, reasonable data is limited to values that can be expressed in terms of dollars and cents such as (1, 35), (2.50, 33.50), or (0.01, 35.99) and technically the graph should be a set of unconnected points. Situation 3 presents the same mathematical relationship but in a context that is not limited to discrete values and consequently the graph is a solid line.

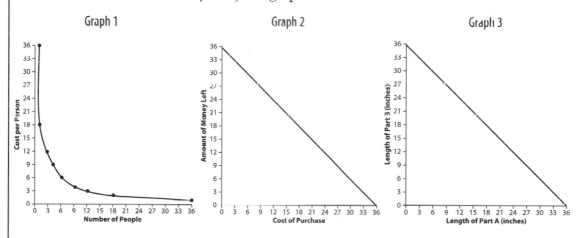

Set II includes two graphs that are increasing (Graphs 4 and 5) and one that is decreasing (Graph 6); all three are linear. Situation 4 illustrates another example of data from a specific context being embedded in a larger mathematical relationship. Graph 4 is a set of unconnected points, while Graph 5 is a solid line. Graph 6 is also a set of unconnected points, but on this scale the points run together and the graph looks as through it is a solid line.

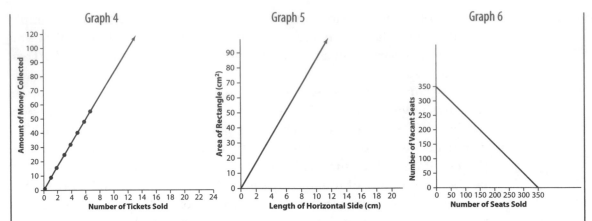

Set III includes three increasing graphs; however, the graphs increase in different ways. Graph 7 is linear; Graphs 8 and 9 represent two different kinds of nonlinear graphs. Graph 8 is an example of an exponential relationship; Graph 9 is quadratic. Participants will have opportunities to examine these kinds of functions in later sessions; you do not need to introduce these terms in this session.

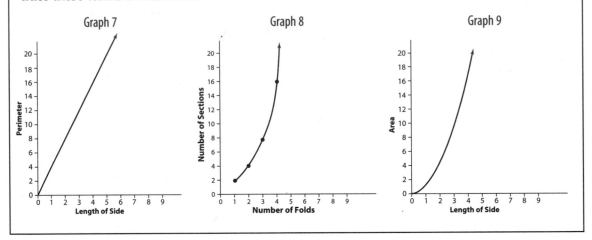

Organize participants into six groups and distribute "Math activity: Graphing functions." To ensure that participants experience a range of functions and also have time to list features of the graphs, the nine problems are organized into three sections. First participants will work with only three of the situations, and then they will regroup and work on all nine graphs. Assign two groups Set I, two groups Set II, and the remaining two groups Set III. Participants should work together to produce tables and graphs for the three situations their group is assigned.

During the small-group work, participants may need support on issues such as these:

■ The scale on each axis must be consistent; however, the scales on the two axes do not need to be the same.

■ The quantity in the left column of the table is generally plotted on the horizontal or x-axis; the quantity in the right column of the table is plotted on the vertical or y-axis.

■ Not all graphs are straight lines; not all graphs go up to the right.

Representing Situations with Tables, Diagrams, and Graphs

- When a graph is a set of unconnected points, a lightly drawn line or curve that connects them can be helpful in looking for general trends.

Once they have created the graphs for three situations (approximately 15 minutes), regroup the participants into groups of three (or four) so each group includes a participant with graphs of Sets I, II, and III. In the first part of the small-group work, participants should explain their graphs to each other so that all will be familiar with the nine situations and graphs. Then they should examine the entire set of nine graphs to articulate features or characteristics of graphs, such as linear, increasing, etc.

Some participants may want to determine algebraic expressions for the situations. Suggest they first make the graphs and compile a list of features and then, only if they have time, consider the algebraic expressions. You should also assure participants who are not familiar with making algebraic expressions that this is *not* the focus of this activity and let them know they will have opportunities to work on creating algebraic expressions later in the session.

In the whole-group discussion, introduce the terms—*linear*, *nonlinear* (curved), *increasing*, *decreasing*—by linking these terms to the features of the graphs offered by participants. You should also contrast either Graphs 2 and 3 or 4 and 5 to establish the idea that when working within a context, some graphs may be a set of unconnected points and others may be a continuous line. In the later case drawing the line or curve that connects discrete points often provides entry into the mathematics that underlie the specific example.

You should also introduce the term *function* if you have not already done so. Without going into a formal definition of function, explain that all nine of these situations represent functions. As participants discuss the functions with graphs that curve (1, 8, and 9), let them know they will have an opportunity to work with these kinds of functions in more detail as the seminar proceeds. You can also let participants know that later in the seminar, they will examine functions based on data generated from real-world phenomena such as temperature at a particular location as a function of time and height of an individual person as a function of age. First, however, they will examine linear functions in the next few sessions.

You can also remind them that they have been working with two particular tools that are used to represent situations, tables and graphs. Other forms of representations such as verbal descriptions and making models to express mathematical ideas are also a part of the seminar work, which, after the break, will be the focus of the case discussion.

"Maxine's Journal" (pp. 50–58) presents one seminar's work on the Math activity: Comparing and contrasting functions.

Break

Case discussion: Representing functions

Small groups (mixed-grade level; 25 minutes)
Whole group (20 minutes)

The cases in Chapter 2 address these main questions:

- What are the ways students create and use models to represent and solve problems that involve functions?
- What can be seen when the same situation is represented in more than one way?

Organize the participants into groups of three or four and distribute the Focus Questions for Chapter 2. Let them know they will have 25 minutes for small-group discussion.

Focus Question 1 addresses the ways students in Case 6 build models for the lunch money situation and what each of those models offers in terms of student understanding. In Focus Question 2, participants continue to examine the role representation plays in supporting student discussion, this time in the context of a Penny Jar situation. Participants are asked to examine the teacher's intention in presenting a certain model to her students in Case 7 and the impact of that teacher's move. Focus Question 3 turns participants' attention to the graphs students make in Case 8 based on a variety of Staircase Towers situations. Question 4 invites participants to examine the teachers' moves in Cases 5 and 9.

As you interact with participants in small groups, note comments that will be useful to bring to the whole-group discussion. In particular, pay attention to participants' responses to Focus Questions 1 and 2, as these will be the focus of the whole-group discussion.

Begin the whole-group discussion by posting a chart with the various models for the lunch money situation from Case 6. Ask, "What mathematics are students working on as they create these representations?" After a few ideas have been gathered, examine each representation by asking, "How does this show both the number of lunches and the cost of the lunches?" Then turn to the question of which two representations they would share and why. (See "Maxine's Journal" pp. 58–61, for a discussion of Case 6.)

Continue to examine representations by focusing on Case 7. Pose questions such as "How does this representation show both the number of rounds and the number of pennies?" "What might this representation offer students?"

Finally turn to the role teachers played in either accepting or presenting various models in this set of cases by asking, "What are some of the moves you see teachers making in these cases to help their students use representations to explore mathematical ideas? What do you see as the impact of those teacher decisions?"

Math activity: Finding formulas

(20 minutes)

Small groups

Let participants know the next activity will begin their work on creating algebraic expressions. You could say, "In the first session, we worked with tables; in this session, we worked with graphs and cube models. These are all ways to represent the relationship in a given situation. Writing arithmetic expressions and the more general algebraic expression is another way."

 To provide an example of this kind of work for your participants, use the Penny Jar situation, graphed earlier in the session, and develop an arithmetic expression for the 10th $(5 + 7 \times 10)$ and the 100th round $(5 + 7 \times 100)$ and the algebraic expression for the nth round $(5 + 7 \times n)$. You may want to use this example as an opportunity to explain some of the conventions for writing algebraic expressions, such as using juxtaposition to express multiplication. Using this convention, the expression becomes $5 + 7n$. See "Maxine's Journal" for Session 2 (pp. 61–63) for an example of such a discussion.

Distribute the "Third Homework" sheet. Remind the group of the value of making models and suggest they actually build the tile arrangements as they work on Question 1. As you interact with small groups, ask questions to ensure that they are making connections between the tile arrangements and the data they collect or the expressions they make.

When the time is up, remind participants to continue to work on these four problems before reading the cases. "It will make the reading of the cases more interesting for you." Also let them know you will be collecting their work at the next session.

Homework and exit cards

(5 minutes)

As the session ends, distribute index cards and pose these exit-card questions:

1. What mathematical ideas struck you in this session?
2. What was it like working in a small group?
3. Is there anything else you want to tell me?

Before the next session...

In preparation for the next session, read what participants wrote in their student-thinking assignment and write a response to each participant. For more information, see the section in "Maxine's Journal" on responding to the second homework. Make copies of the papers and your response for your own files before returning the work.

Poster: Representations from Case 6: Lunch money models

Abigail and Kayla

Pedro and Galen

(Point to 2 cubes to show 1 lunch,
4 cubes to show 2 lunches, etc.)

Eliana

Anna

Charlotte and Ezra

(Count the row of 10 cubes twice
because each cube stands for $1)

Leah and Finn

(First train of 2 cubes stands for 1 lunch, first 2 trains
stand for 2 lunches, etc.)

PATTERNS, FUNCTIONS, AND CHANGE

Math activity: Graphing functions

Each statement below implies a relationship from one quantity to another—a function.

Part A: For each of the functions in the set assigned to your "expert" group:

✓ Find some data points that fit the given context.

✓ Organize the data into a table. Use the quantity identified as the *x*-axis for the left column of the table and the quantity identified as the *y*-axis for the right column.

✓ Organize the data into a graph. Use the quantity identified as the *x*-axis for the horizontal axis and the quantity identified as the *y*-axis for the vertical.

IMPORTANT: Each member of your group will need a copy of your graphs to share with the next group.

Part B: For "jigsaw" groupings:

✓ Share and compare your graphs.

✓ Identify similarities and differences among the various graphs.

Set I

1. A group is getting together to buy a $36 gift. The amount of money each person has to contribute depends of the number of people. (*x*-axis, number of people; *y*-axis, cost per person)

2. I have $36 to buy a gift. The amount of money I have left depends on the price of the purchase. (*x*-axis, price of purchase; *y*-axis, amount of money I have left)

3. A straight line, 36 inches long, is divided into 2 parts, *A* and *B*. The length of Part *B* depends on the length of Part *A*. (*x*-axis, length in inches of Part *A*; *y*-axis, length in inches of Part *B*)

Set II

4. The amount of money collected for a particular show is dependent on the number of tickets sold. Tickets cost $8 each. (*x*-axis, number of tickets sold; *y*-axis, amount of money collected)

5. A rectangle has a height of 8 centimeters. The area of the rectangle depends on the length of its horizontal sides. (*x*-axis, length in centimeters of horizontal side; *y*-axis, area of rectangle in square centimeters)

6. The number of vacant seats in a movie theater that seats 350 people is dependent on the number of seats that are sold. (x-axis, number of seats that are sold; y-axis, number of seats that are vacant)

Set III

7. The perimeter of a square depends on the length of a side. (x-axis, length of side; y-axis, perimeter)

8. If I fold a paper in half once, I have 2 sections. If I fold it in half again (2 folds), I have 4 sections. What happens if I continue to fold the paper? (x-axis, number of folds; y-axis, number of sections)

9. The area of a square depends on the length of a side. (x-axis, length of side; y-axis, area)

Focus Questions: Chapter 2

1. Consider the various ways students in Case 6 represent the lunch money problem in lines 163–185:

   - Explain how each representation illustrates both quantities involved, that is, the number of lunches and the cost of the lunches.
   - If you only had time to introduce two of these representations to the class for the whole-group discussion, which two would you choose and why?

2. Consider the thinking of the teacher, Abigail, in Case 7. In the beginning of the case (lines 222–232), she details the various ways her students were approaching the Penny Jar problems. In lines 232–235, she articulates an idea she wants her students to encounter.

   - What is this idea and why is it important?
   - What does she decide to do and what is the impact of that decision (lines 246–292)?

3. Examine the way students in Case 8 work with the graphs.

   - Explain Adam's work in lines 325–337.
   - Explain what Maria notices in lines 351–357. Why is that significant?
   - How is that idea connected to Adam's comment in lines 381–393?
   - What does the class notice in comparing the graphs in lines 406–456?

4. In these cases, we see teachers helping their students to develop the use of tools such as tables, models, and graphs to represent mathematical situations. Examine Cases 5 and 9 with this point of view. Describe both the teachers' decisions and the impact of each decision on students' thinking.

Third Homework

Reading assignment: Casebook, Chapter 3

Read Chapter 3 in the Casebook, "Finding Formulas," including the introductory text and Cases 10–13.

Writing assignment: Finding formulas for situations

The cases in Chapter 3 provide examples of students working to find ways to express a general relationship. Before you read the cases, spend some time working on the mathematics involved for yourself. Bring your work to the next session so you can use it during a discussion with other participants. You will also hand in your work on these problems to the facilitator.

1. These figures are made up of yellow and blue square tiles with the blue tiles in a row and a border of yellow tiles around them. For 1 blue tile, 8 yellow tiles are needed; for 2 blue tiles, 10 ~~blue~~ *yellow* tiles are needed, and so on. How many yellow tiles are needed for 10 blue tiles? For 100 blue tiles? For *n* blue tiles?

    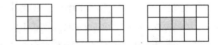

2. In the chicken coop, the hens roost in a line. Each hen has her own roost and in each situation Henrietta's roost is in the middle. If Henrietta is in the 7th position, how many hens are in the line? If Henrietta is in the 10th position, how many hens are in the line? If Henrietta is in the nth position, how many hens are in the line?

3. To change from one figure to the next, the number of square tiles is increased by 1 on each of the 4 sides of the figure. How many square tiles are needed to build Figure 10? Write an expression for the 100th case. Can you write a formula for the nth case? Explain your thinking.

    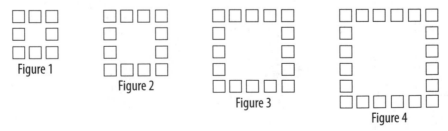

    Figure 1   Figure 2   Figure 3   Figure 4

4. In the pattern below, 5 square tiles are arranged to form a space the size of 1 square tile; 6 square tiles form a space the size of 2 square tiles; and 7 square tiles are arranged to form a space the size of 3 square tiles. Assuming similar arrangements of square tiles, what is the size of the space if you build the arrangement with 12 tiles, 20 tiles, 100 tiles, or *n* tiles?

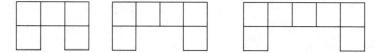

PATTERNS, FUNCTIONS, AND CHANGE

Finding Formulas

Mathematical Themes:

- Generating numeric and algebraic expressions for linear functions ✓
- Considering the role of various representations in making formulas for the nth case ✓
- Identifying features of linear functions

① Math Activity: Penny Jar Problem — create table

Session Agenda — *represent w/ graph*

✗	Case discussion: Finding formulas	Small groups	45 minutes
		Whole group	30 minutes
✗	DVD: Finding formulas for Penny Jars	Whole group	15 minutes
	Break	Whole group	15 minutes
✗	Math activity: Comparing Penny Jars, What to look for in a straight line	Small groups	25 minutes
		Whole group	20 minutes
	Planning for student-thinking assignment	Small groups	20 minutes
	Homework and exit cards	Individual	10 minutes

Background Preparation

Read

- the Casebook, Chapter 3
- "Maxine's Journal" for Session 3
- the agenda for Session 3
- the Casebook: Chapter 8, Sections 1–3

Work through

- the Focus Questions for Session 3 (p. 118)
- the Math activity: Comparing Penny Jars (p. 119)

Preview

- the DVD segment for Session 3

Materials

Duplicate

- "Focus Questions: Chapter 3" (p. 118)
- "Math activity: Comparing Penny Jars" (p. 119)
- "Fourth Homework" (p. 120)
- "Planning for student-thinking assignment" (p. 121)

Obtain

- DVD player
- cubes or tiles
- graph paper
- index cards

Prepare

- Poster: Comparing Penny Jars (p. 117)

What Is a Linear Function?

Consider the following two functions from the Math activity in Session 2:

1. The perimeter of a square depends on the length of a side. (*x*-axis, length of side; *y*-axis, perimeter)
2. The area of a square depends of the length of a side. (*x*-axis, length of side; *y*-axis, area)

A table of values of these two functions might be:

Length of Side	Perimeter	Area
0 cm	0 cm	0 cm²
1 cm	4 cm	1 cm²
2 cm	8 cm	4 cm²
3 cm	12 cm	9 cm²
4 cm	16 cm	16 cm²

The graph of the first function is a straight line; the second, a curve.

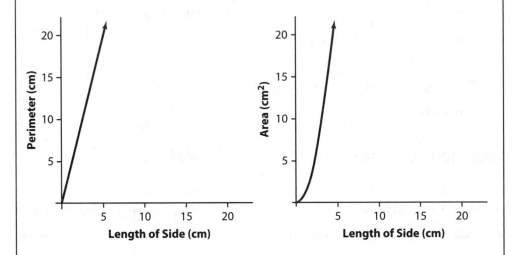

The first graph represents a class of functions referred to as *linear* functions because their graphs are straight lines. Below are graphs of other linear functions.

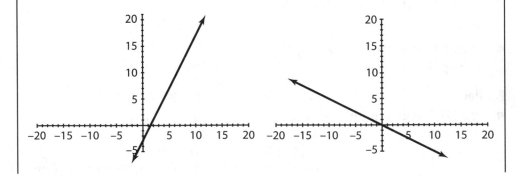

Linear functions have several other special characteristics.

A linear function has a constant rate of change. Whenever the side of a square increases by 1 unit, the perimeter increases by 4 units. Whenever the side of a square increases by 2 units, the perimeter increases by 8. The ratio of the change in perimeter to the change in the length of the side is constant. For any linear function, the "steepness" of the graph is measured by selecting two points on the line and dividing the difference in the y-values by the corresponding difference in the x-values; this ratio is called the *slope*. For the perimeter function, we might choose (0, 0) and (1, 4): $\frac{4-0}{1-0} = 4$; or we might choose (2, 8) and (5, 20): $\frac{20-8}{5-2} = \frac{12}{3} = 4$. The slope of the perimeter function is 4.

In contrast, when the length of a side increases by 1 unit, the change in area is not constant. For example, if the side increases from 1 to 2 units, the area increases from 1 to 4 square units, an increase of 3 square units. However, when the side increases from 2 units to 3, the area changes from 4 to 9 square units, an increase of 5. A variety of nonlinear functions will be examined in later sessions of PFC.

One form of notation for a linear function is $y = mx + b$. For the perimeter function, the formula is $y = 4x$, where x is the length of the side, y is the perimeter. In this case, $m = 4$ and $b = 0$. The slope of the linear function—the rate of change—is m. (Remember, we already determined above that the slope of the perimeter function is 4.) The line intersects the y-axis at b. That is, b is the value of y when $x = 0$ and is called the y-intercept.

The situations from the homework in preparation for Session 3 provide additional examples of linear functions:

Number of yellow tiles (y) as a function of number of blue tiles (x): $y = 2x + 6$; $m = 2$, $b = 6$.

Number of hens (y) as a function of the position of Henrietta's roost (x): $y = 2x + 1$; $m = 2$, $b = 1$.

Number of tiles (y) as a function of figure number (x): $y = 4x + 4$; $m = 4$, $b = 4$.

Area of the missing space (y) as a function of the number of tiles (x): $y = x - 4$, $m = 1$, $b = {}^-4$. (In this context, the domain of the function is whole numbers greater than 4, and the graph doesn't intersect the y-axis. When we consider the embedding function whose domain is all the numbers on the number line, the y-intercept is $^-4$.)

Maxine's Journal

March 3

In this module, participants learn that functions have features that can be represented in a variety of ways. They are learning about what features are especially useful to identify and how those features appear in different representations: in tables, graphs, physical models, and formulas expressed algebraically.

In the first session, we worked specifically on how to represent a function in a table, and in the second, how to represent a function as a graph. At the very end of the second session, we began to look at function formulas. When participants arrived at the third session, they were very excited by the homework they had done, both reading the cases about students finding formulas and the mathematical thinking they did for themselves.

At the end of the session, we turned back to representing functions with graphs.

Case discussion: Finding formulas

Small groups

The work on finding formulas was based on the cases in Chapter 3. As we got started, it was clear that everyone had learned a lot from Drew, the student featured in Case 10, and were excited to be able to see the connections between a formula expressed algebraically and the physical model that defined the function.

As I sat down next to Ariel, she said, "At first I thought the sophisticated way to do this problem was to create the table and see that as the first column goes up by 1, the other column goes up by 2. But later on, when Drew separated the tiles in different ways, I saw *why* it goes up by 2. I needed to do it with the tiles."

I saw Ariel's table, which looked similar to everyone else's.

Number of Blue Tiles	Number of Yellow Tiles
1	8
2	10
3	12
4	14

Then I asked Ariel to show me what she meant, and so she arranged the tiles for Figure 4, pulled it apart, and then added the tiles for Figure 5.

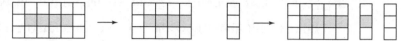

She then continued, "When you insert this new blue tile into the diagram, you have to add 2 new yellow ones, too, 1 above and 1 below the blue tile you just added. That's why the table works like that. You could say that the column in the table increases by 2, just looking at the number pattern. That's not enough for me anymore. I couldn't do that without moving the tiles around; just drawing the picture didn't show that to me."

Peggy said that it wasn't until she read the cases that she realized she could build the figures with different colors: one color for the 6 tiles on the edges, one for the dark center, and a third color for the tiles along the top and bottom. "The color scheme helps me see what changes from one figure to the next and what stays the same."

Celeste said that she had found the rule $2n + 6$ from the table and felt OK with that. "Then I read the case and *saw* the 6 as a physical object, the 3 tiles on each end. So where's the 6 in the table?"

I suggested that Celeste might imagine the table extending in both directions. She wrote in a 0 above the 1 in the first column, and then turned to me and grinned, before filling in the corresponding value for yellow tiles.

Number of Blue Tiles	Number of Yellow Tiles
0	6
1	8
2	10
3	12
4	14

Celeste said, "It's as if you don't have any blue tiles at all, but you still have the ones on the ends. That's the y-intercept. The number of tiles on the ends is the y-intercept. I never thought it would really mean anything."

I was not sure if Ariel and Peggy were seeing exactly what Celeste had just seen, so I asked that they all discuss this before moving on.

Elinor called me over to share what she had just figured out. "When I was alone at home, I just couldn't figure out the formula about multiplying by 3 and subtracting the blue tiles." She was referring to Drew's formula, $3(n + 2) - n$. "Now, with help from Meg and Mariam, it's so clear and I wonder why I couldn't see it before. I am so limited; I could see things only one way."

I talked a bit about how the way we were taught mathematics influences the way we approach math now, but now you have the opportunity to look for other ways, or follow the thinking of other people.

Mariam said, "I'm not sure I ever expected numbers to mean anything that was worth looking for. It was just rules you needed to remember. Drew knows that if he moves the tiles around, he can find the math that fits. I always figured I needed to remember the rules in order to be sure I was right."

Mariam was supporting what Elinor had said, so I added, "Yes, and Drew is showing us a different stance toward the mathematics. We can all learn from Drew. Now you have an opportunity to try out some of those same ways of thinking by looking at the functions in the other two cases."

I want to mention just a couple of points that arose about the other cases. For Case 12, which was based on the growing figures shown below, Bill said that he got the formula $n - 4$. Then he realized he had found the formula for the number of spaces, if n is the number of tiles. When n is the number of spaces, $n + 4$ gives the number of tiles. I registered that Bill had found the inverse function but chose not to go into that with him.

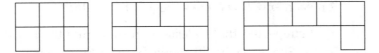

Quite a few groups said the formula for Case 11 was difficult. Some of what was hard was that the number 4 comes up in two different ways. You add 4 tiles each time you go from one figure to the next, but you also always have to deal with the 4 corner tiles. The formula many people got was $4n + 4$. However, others saw it as $(n + 2)^2 - n^2$.

Whole group

When we got to the whole-group discussion, I asked participants to share some of the strategies they used to find formulas for the function in Case 12 and to identify whether it was like a strategy from Case 10.

Lamis gave the first example. "I was interested in what Shaquin did because that's the way I saw it. You always have the 4—2 blocks on either end—so you subtract that 4 to see the connection between the number of spaces and the number of blocks. I learned this from Drew and the way he pulled apart the two 3s on the sides. I approached this problem with that idea."

I asked Lamis to write out the formula she found that way. She wrote,

$$b = s + 4.$$

We specified that b is the number of blocks in a figure and s is the number of spaces. (Although students in the case were thinking of the size of the space as a function of the number of blocks—$s = b - 4$—I left Lamis's function as is.)

Ivan said, "I hadn't seen this before, but what Brian did was like another of Drew's strategies. Brian colored in all the spaces to make a full rectangle and then subtracted the spaces. That's like when Drew multiplied by 3 and then subtracted. This was a new strategy for me."

I asked Ivan to write out the formula he gets using Brian's method. He wrote,

$$b = 2(s + 2) - s.$$

I said, "It sounds like a lot of people are feeling like they have new ways to look at these kinds of problems. Maybe it isn't just Drew who can think flexibly."

Now I wanted to use this opportunity to think a bit about equivalent algebraic expressions. I asked the group to look at the two formulas for the number of blocks. "We know that both expressions give the correct number of blocks. Like, let's say we have a figure with 5 spaces. What do we get for b using each formula?"

There was a pause until David said, "Both formulas give 9."

I asked the group to try a few more values for s, doing the calculation for each formula. Then I went on, "One way to write out what we've been saying is this." I wrote the following equation on the board.

$$s + 4 = 2(s + 2) - s$$

"Let's just do a little bit of algebraic manipulation to use another way to show this has to be true for all values of s. What would be some steps to show this?"

Sandy suggested, "Take the expression on the right, and multiply the 2 times s and times 2." This gave us, "$2(s + 2) - s = 2s + 4 - s$."

I asked, "How do you see this new expression in the figure?"

Peggy said, "It's like what I did with Drew's problem. I used more colors to see what's going on. You can see it if you do it that way."

Once Peggy drew this diagram on the board, she explained, "In this diagram, you have 5 spaces. The 4 blue squares is the 4 in the expression. Then you have two rows of 5, but you have to subtract out the 5 that are just spaces. So that gives you $s + 4$."

I finished by adding "$2s + 4 - s = s + 4$" to the equations on the board. I then suggested we turn to Drew's formulas for the figures in Case 10:

$$2n + 6$$
$$(n + 2)2 + 2$$
$$(n + 2)3 - n$$

I asked, "What does n stand for?"

Georgeann said, "Blue tiles," and then Celeste said, "Number of blue tiles."

The two different responses to my question highlighted an important distinction to note. I said, "Let's pause for a moment to think about what n stands for. Does it matter if we say *blue tiles* or *number of blue tiles*?"

At that moment, a light bulb turned on for Georgeann. She let out a long, "Ohhhh," and then explained, "I was so confused in my homework, I couldn't keep straight what stood for what. It's *not* blue tiles. It has to be the number of blue tiles."

I asked if anyone else would explain the difference. Joy said, "When we say *blue tiles*, we really mean *number of blue tiles*. That's what we're talking about—numbers of tiles."

However, Georgeann said that was precisely what she had been confused about.

Trudy then asked, "Does it have to be n? Does it matter if you use x or y?"

Trudy's was a good question; that was not quite as straightforward as it might seem. I said, "In one sense, we could use any letter to stand for the number of blue tiles. We could use d, and we could use k, and we could use x.

"However, there are also some conventions in the way we use variables. In the problem about blue and yellow tiles, we are finding the number of yellow tiles in terms of the number of blue tiles. The value we consider as the 'input' for the function is conventionally called the *independent variable*; the 'output' is called the *dependent variable*. When we use x and y, the convention is that x is the independent variable and y is the dependent variable."

I showed how we could write the three formulas:

$$y = 2x + 6$$
$$y = (x + 2)2 + 2$$
$$y = (x + 2)3 - x$$

Then we moved on to the next ideas. I asked, "What did you do to show the three expressions are equivalent?"

Sandy said, "We actually did it differently, without algebra. Like let's say we have 3 blue tiles. We created the arrangement of blue and yellow tiles for each expression and laid them on top of each other. That showed us they were all the same."

Lamis said, "But that just shows that you get the same result for 3 blue tiles. That doesn't show that it works for *any* number of blue tiles."

I was pleased to hear Lamis's comment. She had taken the seminar, Reasoning Algebraically About Operations, last year and was now quite articulate with one of the main themes of that module.

Joy said, "That's why I think you need to go to the algebra."

I said it would be useful to go to the algebra, but we could still stay connected to the tiles to think about what is happening with each of the steps.

So, Joy started us off. "Take Drew's second formula, $(n + 2)2 + 2$. We can see the parts by looking at three colors." She got up and drew a picture of the tile arrangement.

Then she explained how the expression describes the tile arrangement. "The number of blue tiles is n. So, the rows above and below, shown in yellow, come to $(n + 2)2$. Then these tiles at either end, which we colored green, are the 2 that need to be added on. But when you multiply through, you get $2n + 4 + 2$."

With that move, Joy used red to shade in the four corner tiles.

Joy continued, "So n still stands for the number of blue tiles. The two rows above and below are $2n$. Then you have the 4 corners in red and the 2 tiles at each end of the blue tiles—that's $4 + 2$."

I wrote out next to Joy's figure, "$(n + 2)2 + 2 = 2n + 4 + 2$," while Joy finished her explanation. "But then, you can just add the $4 + 2$ and you have the 6 tiles in the two end columns."

I added to the algebraic equation, so that it now read,

$$(n + 2)2 + 2 = 2n + 4 + 2 = 2n + 6.$$

I asked if there were any questions, and when there were none, we went to Drew's third expression, $(n + 2)3 - n$.

Ivan volunteered for this one. He said, "You start out looking at all the tiles in the figure. Since each row has $n + 2$ tiles, you multiply by 3 because there are 3 rows, and then subtract out the blue tiles. That's how I looked at it first. You can see all that in Joy's picture. Then we multiply out $(n + 2)3$ to get $3n + 6$." Ivan pointed to Joy's picture, indicating the 3 rows of blue and yellow tiles to show the $3n$, and the green and red tiles at either end to show the 6. While he did that, I wrote out the algebra,

$$(n + 2)3 - n = 3n + 6 - n.$$

Ivan continued, "And then you don't want that row of blue tiles, so you subtract that from the $3n$ and you're left with the 2 rows of yellow tiles, which is $2n$."

The algebraic equation now read,

$$(n + 2)3 - n = 3n + 6 - n = 2n + 6.$$

Robin raised her hand and asked, "Why does everything come down to $2n + 6$? Is there something special about that expression?"

I explained that we could look at the algebraic steps in other ways. We could start with $2n + 6$ and show the steps to make it equivalent to $2(n + 2) + 2$. However, that was not exactly what Robin was thinking of. After trying to explain her thinking a few more times, she then said, "When I was working to find an algebraic expression, the questions that helped me the most were, 'What's changing and what's staying constant?' When I asked myself those questions, then I could find the formulas."

Georgeann picked up on Robin's insight and said, "Wow. That captures it. The tiles at the end columns are staying the same and the inside part keeps growing. The part that stays the same is the 6 tiles, and the inside keeps increasing by 2."

The idea was registering for other people, too. I said, "I want you to hold onto this idea as we look at some DVD segments of a fourth-grade class."

DVD: Finding formulas for Penny Jars

In the DVD, a fourth-grade class is working on some Penny Jar problems and writing formulas for them. Similar to what we had discussed in Session 2, the teacher draws a picture of the Penny Jar showing the starting number of pennies at the bottom with a line over it and then arranging the pennies in an array to show the amount added for any number of rounds. Then students go on to discuss algebraic formulas for specific Penny Jar situations and for the Penny Jar in general.

Before showing the segment, I told participants there were two components that I wanted them to think about. First, I wanted them to consider the role of the teacher's representation and then to pay attention to the kinds of thinking going on as students work to develop verbal and algebraic expressions.

After viewing the segment, Robin said, "Yes, there it is again. She drew the start number of pennies first—that's the constant. And she separated that from the array that shows the part that's changing."

I nodded and said, "Right. You can find those two parts in any linear function." Then I looked around for other comments about the segment.

Peggy said, "The students are relating this situation to something that they have already done. They are making connections to experiences they have already had. They are using models of arrays. The physical model is helping them to see that there is an array in this situation that they use to make this problem easier."

I wanted to pursue this idea for a little bit and asked, "So what makes the array so helpful to them?"

Bill suggested, "It helps them to understand that they can multiply to solve this problem and to know what to multiply to solve other cases or any case."

Lamis said, "I teach fourth grade, and early in the year, we do a lot of work with arrays to understand multiplication. Without that work, I am not sure that this model would have been as helpful."

I asked Lamis to tell us more about what she was thinking, and so she continued, "If they had not done some earlier work with arrays, they may not have been able to make the connection between the array in this model and that multiplication is a helpful operation for this context."

Trudy said, "Models are so powerful. Students need lots of experience with different kinds of models so that they can take advantage of these kinds of opportunities."

I asked, "In what ways are they powerful? Explain."

Trudy elaborated, "Well, they allow students to represent the situation and to create images that help them reason about the problems, like we have been talking about the last two sessions. They also help students to organize information from a problem in a way that allows them to see connections."

I used this as an opportunity to make a point about what is at the heart of the two DMI algebra modules. "I want to highlight that, as Lamis and Trudy are saying, there is an important connection here between the models of situations we're working with in this seminar and the models for operations we talked about in RAO. We want to give students extensive experience with powerful ways to model operations, so they will have the foundation they need to make sense of and connect these operations to algebraic formulas and expressions. Lamis is right, these students most likely have had prior experiences with arrays so that when they come to this work with functions, that representation makes sense to them and helps give them insight into the Penny Jar."

April said, "I also see that this work is helping them to make connections between addition and multiplication. They are seeing a relationship between the two and maybe some students are making the leap from repeated addition to multiplication as a more efficient strategy for these kinds of problems."

Georgeann said, "I see the teacher providing a lot of support for students. But she is helping them to think, not doing the thinking for them."

I asked, "How do you see her doing this?"

Georgeann responded, "She put the model up there for students to help them see the start and the rounds of 4 each time. But she does not tell them what to see. She paraphrases and repeats statements using the model to help make students' words clearer."

Meg added, "She also asks really good questions like 'Can you imagine the 10th round?'"

I asked, "What is the value of this particular question? How does it seem to impact students' ideas?"

Dina said, "It forces students to have to make a prediction."

Mariam offered, "They have to extend the model."

Dina added, "It accentuates how important the 'add 4 each time' is. They have to realize that this adding of 4 each time will continue."

I wanted to highlight what they were saying in terms of the general learning agenda a teacher might have in mind. "So are you saying that the question with the model helps to accentuate an important feature or structure of the situation or function?"

Robin said, "Yes. To answer her question, students have to identify the important features that will allow them to figure it out. It brings us back to what stays the same and what changes. All of that work helps them state a formula or generalization. By seeing how what they add each time is used to answer the question, they are able to develop the formula: number of rounds times 4 gives the array total, and then you have to add 3."

Mariam connected Robin's point to our own mathematical work this evening. "Even though some of us could look at the table of Drew's problem and figure out the formula, we could understand it so much better when we worked with the model of the tiles."

Dina added, "Some of us really needed those tiles to come up with the formula in the first place."

Now, it was time for a break.

Math activity: Comparing Penny Jars, What to look for in a straight line

For the Math activity, participants were given four Penny Jar situations and were asked to make graphs of particular pairs. The purpose was to start thinking about what makes the graphs of two lines parallel, what makes the lines get closer as the x-values increase, and what makes them get farther apart. I wanted to give them a chance to think about these ideas before reading the cases in Chapter 4.

Small groups

As I visited with different groups, I recognized that there were still some conventions that needed to be cleared up. For example, Lamis did not realize you were "allowed to" plot a point on the y-axis, the point for which the value of x is 0.

In another group, the question was whether there is a Day 0 at all. I had thought we had cleared this up with Ivan's question in Session 2 but apparently not. Dina quite strongly wanted to hold onto having Day 1 correspond to the number of pennies you start with. Then, on Day 2, you add a round. I told her you could think about it that way, but actually, for these problems, it would be helpful to think about a start number at Day 0, and on Day 1, you add the first round. I pointed out that it was like Drew's problem: When you have 0 blue tiles, you have the 6 yellow tiles—just the two columns of 3. Dina said, "Oh! Right! I hadn't thought of that." That example really seemed to help her go with a Day 0 for the Penny Jars.

For the most part, participants moved through these problems with ease. Many of them made tables for each situation and created graphs from the tables. Periodically, I would hear, "Oh, look at that!" or "That's interesting," as they noticed what the graphs looked like.

Whole group

I posted the graphs of situations *a* and *b*, which I had prepared before the session. Then, I asked, "What do you see in this graph?"

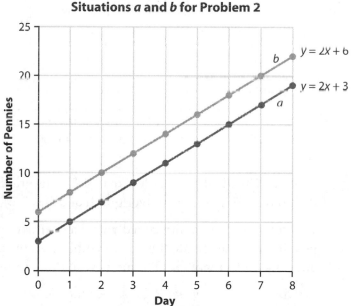

Situations *a* and *b* for Problem 2

Georgeann started us off. "It reminds me of my sister's and my ages. Every year, we each get another year older. She's always 3 years older than I am; we'll always be the same age apart; I'll never catch up."

This was interesting, that the idea of collecting pennies completely fell away. For Georgeann, the graph revealed a mathematical relationship, one that, in fact, was embedded in a very personal and important situation in her life—her own age relative to that of her sister. I wanted to use the word *rate* here, so I said, "This situation about pennies reminds Georgeann of her sister's and her ages. Because they get older at exactly the same rate, her sister will always stay exactly the same amount older." 330

Trudy said, "What doesn't work here is that the graph shows Georgeann beginning at 3 years old and her sister at 6, but you should really start when Georgeann was 0." 335

I listened to a few comments about this and then quickly sketched in another graph, this one with dates on the horizontal axis and a slope of 1. (After all, everybody ages at a rate of 1 year per year.)

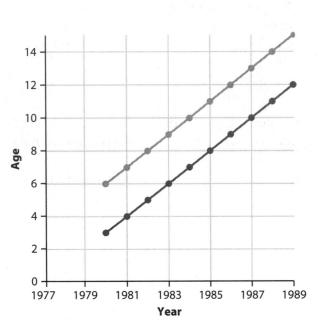

I asked Trudy if she would like to finish the graph, and she came and added the point (1977, 0) to the lower graph and (1977, 3) to the upper graph. 340

Even though I had prepared a graph of situations *b* and *c*, I decided not to post it but rather create the poster with the whole group. I asked, "What do *b* and *c* look like together? Tell me how to draw those graphs."

Dina said, "They have the same starting point and the top one is steeper than the bottom one." 345

I first sketched in the graph of *b*, since we had already done that. Then, pointing to the *y*-intercept, I said, "OK, so Dina says they have the same starting point, but the line is steeper. How steep is it? How do I draw the line?"

Meg said, "For the bottom one, you go up 2 each day. This time, you go up 3 each day." 350

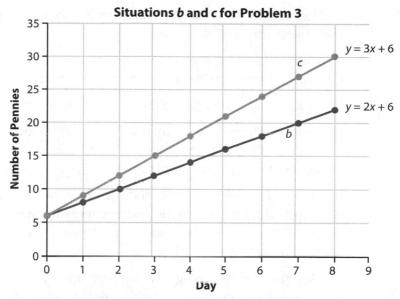

Situations _b_ and _c_ for Problem 3

I sketched the graph and illustrated what Meg said. "No matter what day I'm at, if I'm looking at the graph of _b_, when I go over 1 day, I go up 2 pennies, over 1 day, up 2 pennies. For the graph of _c_, when I go over 1 day, I go up 3 pennies, over 1 day, up 3 pennies. If I go over 2 days, I go up 3 pennies and then up another 3 pennies."

Lamis said, "The top line is going up faster because you put more pennies in the jar each day, even though they started with the same amount."

I asked, "If we're looking at graph _b_, what happens if I go over 2 days, how much do I go up?"

Flor said, "4 pennies."

I asked, "What if I go over 3 days?"

Ivan said, "You'd go up 6 pennies for line _b_ and 9 pennies for line _c_."

I posted the last pair of graphs and asked for descriptions of the situation.

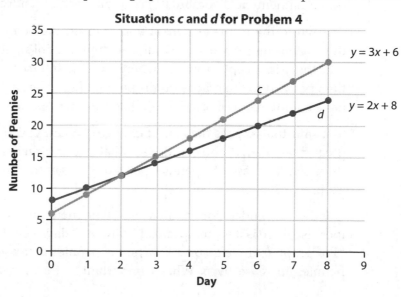

Situations _c_ and _d_ for Problem 4

Flor said, "One starts with more but its rate of change is less than the one that starts with less."

Sandy said, "One line is increasing faster than the other one. The line that starts lower is increasing faster. The line is steeper."

I asked, "So you're saying the greater the increase, the steeper the line?"

Sandy confirmed my point. "When you add more pennies each day, the line will be steeper than when you add fewer pennies each day. So, after a while, the two lines will intersect."

I pointed to the first graph and the graph of Georgeann's and her sister's ages, and said, "We started the discussion saying these two lines will not meet. What's in the situation that makes it so these two lines will never meet, but the ones in the last graph will?"

Meg said, "In the first graph, for both lines, you're putting the same number of pennies in the jar each day. In this last graph, they're different amounts. In the first, they increase at the same rate, but not in this one."

I commented, "I like hearing the word *rate*. It's useful to think about rate with these functions. Are you saying that, whenever two lines are increasing at the same rate, they will be parallel?"

Everyone nodded, so I said, "Tell me the difference between this graph of b and c and this graph of c and d.

Ivan said, "In b and c, they start in the same place, but c increases at a greater rate than b, so they'll keep getting farther apart. In c and d, since the one that starts lower increases at a greater rate, it will surpass the one that starts higher."

I nodded and paused for a moment. Then I told the group that they would be reading more about situations like these in the cases for the next session. However, before we ended the discussion, I wanted to make sure they had some mathematical vocabulary associated with the ideas at play.

I wrote the terms *y-intercept* and *slope* on the board, and mentioned that these terms might sound familiar from high-school algebra classes. I explained that the y-intercept identifies where the line intersects the vertical axis, and then pointed to the graphs on the board. "Line a has a y-intercept of 3; b and c have a y-intercept of 6; and line d has a y-intercept of 8."

I said that *slope* is the rate of change. "When you say that c increases at a greater rate than b, you can also say that c has a larger slope than b. In c, where there's an increase of 3 pennies per day, you say that the slope is 3. Line b has a slope of 2."

I then reminded participants what Flor and Ivan had said about how much increase there is if we jump ahead 2 days or 3 days, and I pointed to the graphs. "For graph b, if we go over 2 days, the pennies increase by 4; go over 3 days, pennies increase by 6. What's important is that if we look at the ratio of increase of pennies over number of days, we always get the same number—$\frac{4}{2} = 2$; $\frac{6}{3} = 2$—and that number is the slope." 405

I mentioned that in the next session, we'd have plenty of opportunity to use those terms.

Then I circled the point where lines c and d intersect. I asked, "What's happening here? What is this point?" 410

Flor said, "That's Day 2, and there are 12 pennies in the jar."

Lamis added, "Oh yeah! On that day, both jars have the same number of pennies. You can see that in the table, too!"

I nodded and said that these are all important things to look for—the slope, the y-intercept, and the point of intersection—in the next set of cases. 415

Planning for student-thinking assignment

For the last few minutes of class, I wanted participants to have a chance to brainstorm about the next student-thinking assignment. I also wanted to alert the group to an issue that I felt was important. I began by saying how much I enjoyed reading their first student-thinking pieces and that I always learn so much from reading them. I also said that when I write back about the ideas in 420 their papers, some of the ideas get crystallized for me, too.

I went on, "I want to alert you to something that has arisen in past classes of Patterns, Functions, and Change. This work with functions is really new to most of your students. If the only work they do in this area is your student thinking assignments, then you need to be sure you give them a task that makes sense 425 for them. If you choose to give your students a task from the cases, remember some of the students in the cases have had more opportunities to work on these ideas. If you choose a math activity from our class to complete with your own students, keep in mind we may have worked on this for several hours. We did a lot today on symbolic notation, but that isn't necessarily what we suggest for 430 all students as they begin to work with these ideas. The students we saw on the DVD were well into a unit on functions when the DVD was created."

With that caveat, I distributed the handout, "Planning for student-thinking assignment," and had the participants discuss their plans in approximate grade-level groups. 435

Homework and exit cards

For their exit cards, I asked participants to write directly on their homework in which they had worked out the formulas for the situations in the four cases of Chapter 3. They responded to, What did you figure out today? What questions do you still have? Then I looked over the homework and exit cards at the same time.

In the homework, most participants had found one version of the formula for each of the four cases. A few, like Yan, had found several expressions. For Case 11 in which students worked with tiles arranged in a square border, Yan had come up with three expressions, but for one of them the independent variable was defined differently than for the others. Her question, which she still held at the end of the session, was whether all three expressions are equivalent.

YAN: What I figured out was that there could be many notations that boil down to one simple notation. Drew's case was an example. I am wondering how, in Case 10, $4n - 4$, $4n + 4$, and $(n + 2)^2 - n^2$ could boil down to $4n + 4$ (I guess). But the n doesn't mean the same value in the first notation. Could it still boil down to one notation as the other might?

Otherwise, most of the questions people had in their homework were resolved during the session. Clearly, the session was very energizing and satisfying for almost everyone. Below is a sample of what they wrote after class:

JOY: The biggest idea that makes sense to me now comes from our discussion on $2n + 6$. It is interesting to me that several different representations come down to one and I understand all three that were shown. This goes along with my work on Question 3. After I read the case, I thought about an area problem, came up with a different equation, but then simplified it to my original equation. Now it makes sense—I can think about things differently, follow the steps, and end up in a different place, but it's still the same. Does that make sense?

In our small group, we also discussed Problem 1. I only saw it as rows across, plus 6 on the sides (3 + 3). Another member focused on the number of columns growing. It was interesting to see the same formula ($2n + 6$) from a different perspective.

BILL: Essentially I was able to look more closely at several different ways to view the same model and then connect those ways to each other, not only visually in the model but mathematically, as opposed to just looking at each model in one specific way. I suppose the one question that arises for me stems from the realization that there seems to be more than one way to look at EVERYTHING in a mathematical context. Is there any idea or problem in the math world where there is only one way to see it or solve it? Like is there some geometric proof that can only be proven in one way? This doesn't so much pertain to the class, just general curiosity.

GEORGEANN: I learned that y is what you're figuring out, x is what you know—and that this convention is related to the algebraic expression and the graph, too. Many of the ideas that I had trouble defining and labeling while doing my homework will now be much easier to express and to organize. The minor detail of figuring out what B really means (in my homework it meant the blue tiles—not the number of blue tiles) will be much less confusing. In fact, my homework is so messy because of the slipperiness of what really stood for what, that I really don't think you want to read it because you can't understand my ideas based on the symbols and letters I tried to express them with. But what I am still anxious about is really the articulation (or extrapolation) of a generalization. It feels like sometimes it's just this gestalt thing; sometimes I really see it but can't describe it in a way that holds it together. P.S. I had a great time, even with this lingering anxiety about what I don't grasp.

ROBIN: What I think I figured out: 1) there is a constant and a changing part to these functions; 2) there isn't a better way, just a simpler way; 3) identifying the change <u>and</u> representing it is helpful; 4) hang onto the table as a method for seeing this. Questions: 1) How can I more efficiently identify and represent the change and, therefore, the formula or rule? 2) What continues to be challenging or getting in the way of doing that? 3) What systems besides tables might there be for compiling and organizing information and making sense of it? 4) What happens when the action in the change doesn't directly translate into or look like the formula?

I was pleased to see how Celeste articulated what she was learning. Celeste is already familiar with much of the content that most participants in the seminar are coming to understand for the first time, and so it is especially important that she can also recognize the new insights she is gaining.

CELESTE: I felt that this activity really allowed me to explore deriving formulas from physical models. Working on these four problems pro vided the opportunity to examine the connections between the model, the T-chart, and the formula, which led to a greater understanding of the relationships between each of these tools. Although I generally find working with numbers to be easier than working with models, by strengthening my understanding of the connection between the formula and the model, I was able to use the model more effectively as a learning tool. I hope that I will be able to continue to develop these connections, as so many of my students work much better with models than with abstract numbers.

In contrast, I am quite concerned that Violet seems unable to use the seminar as an opportunity to gain new perspectives on familiar material—or to recognize that developing such new perspectives is, indeed, learning. Perhaps one of the issues at play here is that Violet has never taken a DMI seminar before. It might be that she has not before had the opportunity to realize that new insights into mathematics can come from examining student thinking or hearing the kind of questions naïve learners pose.

VIOLET: I didn't figure anything out. I was able to help people in my group. I think I'm getting better at knowing when to add information and when to question members of my group. I don't have any questions.

Violet's response is particularly disturbing in light of Sandy's comments, because they were in a group together.

> SANDY: As we engaged in a discussion about Drew's different ways of looking at the yellow and blue tiles, I found myself very confused. When I read the chapter after first engaging in the math, I was surprised to see the different solutions (expressions) that Drew came up with. I could not make sense of some of them (visually from the paper). When the opportunity was provided to have a further look at the different expressions, using the manipulatives was a way of entry for me. However, our group dynamic was frustrating. Trying to make sense while others were quickly explaining, reasoning, and expounding was challenging. I began tuning out explanations until I could make a little bit of sense. Then I was able to ask questions or request support to manage what I did and did not understand. After walking through the concrete model, writing symbols with explanations to help me to make sense of what we were doing provided the foundation I needed to follow the whole-group discussion. Although right now I don't have specific questions, I have learned how important it is to walk through slowly making sense of these ideas. It is challenging to think about these ideas, but at least I am thinking and enjoying the challenge.

Sandy did have a positive experience in class and knows what she needs to do to support her own learning. However, I am going to need to figure out how to address Violet.

Responding to the third homework

March 5

I wanted to use my response to clarify some mathematical issues for the whole class, and so I decided to write a letter to the whole group.

> *Dear PFC Class,*
>
> *As I read your exit cards from Session 3, I was again struck by the depth of your thinking and learning. I decided to write a group response to reflect back to you the ideas you were engaged with. I also thought it might be useful to you to have a written statement of some of those ideas.*
>
> *Many of you wrote about how useful it is, when studying the functions we have been working on, to look for what is changing and what stays constant. You also notice that, for the problems we have been working on, the change is happening at a constant rate. In fact, this is what characterizes linear functions. For all the different forms of representation we have been working with—tables, graphs, algebraic expressions—this is a powerful thing to look for. In each of those representations, where do you find the constant? In each, where do you find the rate?*

530

535

540

545

550

555

560

In the previous paragraph, I mentioned that we can look at the conventional representations—tables, graphs, and algebraic expressions—to find the two parts of the linear function. However, as many of you wrote, it is also powerful to look at the situation that embodies the function. By that I mean, when the problem is about arrangements of tiles, look at the tiles to find what is constant and what is changing. When the problem is about collecting marbles or pennies, or about crayfish racing to a finish line (as you will find in Chapter 4), there, too, it is useful to think in terms of the context to sort out the two components—the constant and the rate of change.

Many mentioned that finding the connections between the numbers in the table, the diagrams, and the formulas was a new experience. When we were K–12 students, it was all about numbers and formulas. The actual situations that were being represented were either very distant or nonexistent—until the dreaded application or word problems showed up. One hallmark of some of the change in math instruction is to make explicit the connections between the problem context, the numbers, the diagram, the graph, and the formula. They are all representations of the same phenomenon. This makes application not a separate activity but rather a part of understanding the mathematics. So throughout the seminar, you can look for opportunities to expand your own flexibility.

Several people wrote about how helpful it was to read descriptions of students' methods in the cases and to consider how other people in their group worked on a problem. A few mentioned that it was easier to look at someone else's method after they had settled one way for themselves first. Some also said that it was not until class when they had a chance to talk over what students were doing that their methods became clear. It can be easier to let in or hear other ideas when you have a solid way that works for you. What are the implications of that for the students we teach?

Some people wrote about how important it was to clarify the terminology, independent and dependent variables, and the significance of clearly stating what the variables stand for. For example, in the problem about a row of blue tiles surrounded by yellow tiles, the number of blue tiles is the independent variable (or input variable), the number of yellow tiles, the dependent variable (or output variable).

It is significant that we say "number of blue tiles" and not just "blue tiles." After all, it is how the quantities are related that we are concerned about here and not other characteristics. (For example, we are not concerned about the shade of the tiles or the texture. Nor are we concerned about other measurable attributes like the perimeter.)

Someone else mentioned a similar struggle when she worked on the formula for Henrietta's hens. She had written the formula $y = 2x - 1$ but then was confused because she had written "x = Henrietta." She began thinking x must *equal 1 because Henrietta is 1 hen. Finally, she realized y is the number of hens, but x is Henrietta's position.*

We also clarified that the convention is to use x to represent the independent variable and y to represent the dependent variable, though this is not a hard and fast rule. The formula for the problem about yellow and blue tiles is conventionally written $y = 2x + 6$, but it could also be written $y = 2b + 6$.

610

A different convention frequently used when the independent variable is discrete and only takes on whole numbers as its values, is to use n. The formula for the number of yellow tiles might be stated as $y = 2n + 6$. For the second problem about tiles organized into a square, we could write $t = 4n + 4$.

615

Many of you wrote about looking at the arrangements of tiles in a variety of ways to come up with different expressions for the rule. Some of you wrote about two different general strategies for the tile problems: 1) look for what is staying the same and what is changing, and 2) look at the area of the whole figure and subtract out what should not be included.

620

In class, we looked at the different expressions for the first problem that can be generated by decomposing the tiles in different ways and showed that they are all equivalent: For any value of x (or n, or whatever letter we have chosen), the same result is produced. All of the different expressions for the number of yellow tiles, depending on the number of blue tiles, were shown to be equivalent to $2x + 6$.

625

Some people also looked at different expressions that could be generated for the second problem, where tiles were arranged in a square.

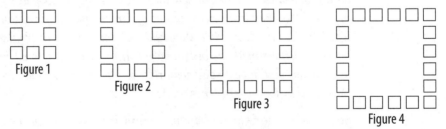

Figure 1   Figure 2   Figure 3   Figure 4

When n is defined as the figure number, many of you came up with two expressions, $4n + 4$ and $(n + 2)^2 - n^2$, for the number of tiles in the figure. These two expressions can also be shown to be equivalent: $(n + 2)^2 - n^2 = n^2 + 4n + 4 - n^2 = 4n + 4$.

630

However, one person asked about the expression $4n - 4$, which could also be used to describe the number of tiles in each figure. Here we come back to the issue of how the independent variable is defined. Whereas before we said n is the figure number, here the independent variable is the number of tiles on a side. Because we have a different way of defining the independent variable, we can assign a different letter to it, let's say k. We can say, if k is the number of tiles on a side, the number of tiles in a figure is $4k - 4$. (We subtract 4 because the corner tiles each appear in 2 sides and so were counted twice.)

635

We can also say that, for each figure, $k = n + 2$. If we want to show that the expression is equivalent, we need to show that each value of n produces the same result. If we replace k with $n + 2$, the expression now becomes $4(n + 2) - 4$.

$$4(n + 2) - 4 = 4n + 8 - 4 = 4n + 4$$

This issue arises with the Penny Jar scenario, too. That is, people are coming up with different tables, graphs, and algebraic formulas for the same Penny Jar situation, and this has to do with the different ways we can define the independent variable. Consider the situation of starting with 3 pennies in the jar and putting in 4 each round (1 round per day). Let p be the number of pennies in the jar and r be the number of times we have put 4 pennies in the jar. Then our rule is $p = 4r + 3$. However, if we say we perform one round each day, and we count the number of pennies at the beginning of each day, on Day 1, we have 3; on Day 2, we have 7, and our rule becomes $p = 4(d - 1) + 3$. Either way of defining the independent variable is correct. Because $r = d - 1$, the two formulas are equivalent.

If we can all see that both ways are correct, then it would be useful for us all to agree on how we will define the independent variable in each situation so that we are all talking the same language, so to speak. (However, some of you might still want to do the problems both ways to see what changes and what stays the same as you go from one way of defining the independent variable to the other.)

I also want to mention that several of you also wrote about how things are going in your group. Some of you wrote about needing to take control when the ways of interacting were not helping you think through the problem. Others said that, when the mathematics content is clear to you, you are working to understand how your behavior can support others' learning. If you feel you are in the latter category, I suggest you ask your group members what is helpful. If you are in the former, be sure to make your own learning a priority. If you need help, you can always call me over.

I'm grateful to be working with you.

Maxine

Detailed Agenda

Case discussion: Finding formulas

(75 minutes)

Small groups (mixed-grade level; 45 minutes)

Whole group (30 minutes)

The cases in Chapter 3 address these main questions:

■ How do students use their images of the tile arrangements to write arithmetic and algebraic expressions to express the patterns of growth?

■ What questions can teachers ask to call students' attention to these connections?

Organize participants into small groups and distribute the Focus Questions for Chapter 3. Inform them that they will have 45 minutes to work in their groups. Let them know they will have an opportunity to share their own work on these problems, but first you want them to discuss Nina's case.

In the cases of Chapter 3, participants have encountered students working to produce formulas by analyzing the arrangements of tiles. In the small- and whole-group discussions, ask questions focused on students' thinking as they make connections among the tables, the tile arrangements, and the arithmetic or algebraic expressions.

Focus Question 1 provides the opportunity for participants to discuss the various approaches Drew uses to decompose the tile arrangements and how each image Drew creates supports a particular way to write the algebraic expression. In their homework, some participants might have determined formulas based on the table of values without referencing the tile arrangements. Discussing Drew's thinking should help them make connections between the tile arrangements and the arithmetic or algebraic expressions.

For example, in Case 10, lines 37–44, Drew decomposes the tile arrangement for the 50th case into two vertical sections and three horizontal sections. This way of picturing the tile arrangements corresponds to expressing the number of yellow tiles in the 50th case as $(2 \times 50) + 6$.

$(2 \times 50) + 6$

3	50 yellow tiles	3
	50 blue tiles	
	50 yellow tiles	

For the 51st case, the two vertical sections remain the same; there are still 6 tiles. However, the 2 rows of yellow tiles are now 51 each. So the 51st case would be represented as $(2 \times 51) + 6$. Noting what changes and what remains the same as the tile pattern grows leads to the development of the expressions for the nth case: $2n + 6$. As the small groups work on Focus Question 1, ask questions to help them articulate the connections between the tile arrangements and the arithmetic and algebraic expressions in the case.

51st

$(2 \times 51) + 6$

What is *n*?

In writing an expression such as $2n + 6$ to represent the number of yellow tiles when there are n blue tiles, it is important to keep in mind that both n and $2n + 6$ are numbers and not the actual tiles themselves. The linear function $y = 2x + 6$ expresses a relationship between two quantities; in the tile situation x is the *number* of blue tiles and y or $2x + 6$ is the *number* of yellow tiles.

In response to Focus Question 2, participants will examine the different algebraic expressions that Drew creates to show how they are equivalent. One argument for their equivalence is the very fact that they represent the same situation. However, this question should also be used to support participants' ability to manipulate algebraic expressions. Some participants may recall some rules of algebra as they work on this task; others may not. Let the groups know they can skip this question for now if the ideas seem too distant. They will have an opportunity to work with this during the whole-group discussion.

Using Algebraic Notation to Express Multiplication

In Case 10, Drew writes a variety of expressions to express the number of yellow tiles when the number of blue tiles is n. For instance, he writes $(n + 2) \times 2 + 2$ and $(n + 2) \times 3 - n$. While neither of these expressions is incorrect, they do not reflect the standard conventions that are used to express multiplication.

Typically, multiplication is noted by simply juxtaposing the two terms to be multiplied—using no sign at all. It is also standard practice to write numerical values first and variables second. These conventions are adopted to avoid confusion. It is awkward to use x to represent multiplication when x is also used as a variable.

Using conventional notation, $(n + 2) \times 2 + 2$ would be rewritten as $2(n + 2) + 2$ and $(n + 2) \times 3 - n$ would be rewritten as $3(n + 2) - n$.

Focus Question 3 invites participants to share and revise the work they did on the four mathematics problems for homework. Because they have already worked extensively on the first problem, most of this time should be devoted to the remaining three problems. As you interact with the small groups, remind them of the methods Drew used to articulate the connections between the algebraic expressions he wrote and his images of the tile arrangements. Suggest they work at articulating similar connections as they discuss Focus Questions 3 and 4. In addition, if group members have written different expressions for the same problem, suggest they work to prove that the expressions are equivalent. See "Maxine's Journal" for Session 3 (pp. 90–94) for more information.

Focus Question 4 brings participants back to the cases to discuss student thinking in Case 11 in which students are able to determine a formula on the basis of the table of values but are in the process of making connections among the table, the formula, and the tile arrangements.

Showing Two Algebraic Expressions Are Equivalent

Drew generates a variety of different ways to express the nth case. Consider these two: $(n + 2) \times 2 + 2$, $2n + 6$. Since they are derived from the same situation and table, they must be equivalent; that is, they represent the same value when n takes on values in the domain.

For instance, when $n = 4$, each expression produces 14, the output that corresponds to the input 4.

$$(n + 2) \times 2 + 2: (4 + 2) \times 2 + 2 = (6) \times 2 + 2 = 12 + 2 = 14$$
$$2n + 6: 2(4) + 6 = 8 + 6 = 14$$

However, showing expressions are equivalent means explaining that they will produce the same value for every possible choice of n. One way to prove they are equivalent is to show by means of algebraic rules that each can be transformed into the other.

Consider this series of steps and the algebraic justifications for each.

$(n + 2) \times 2 + 2 = (2n + 4) + 2$	Distributive Property
$(2n + 4) + 2 = 2n + (4 + 2)$	Associative Property
$2n + (4 + 2) = 2n + 6$	Addition

It is also possible to model these transformations and these properties by examining the model representing the situation.

$(n + 2) \times 2 + 2$ is one way to label the parts of the diagram that correspond to the yellow tiles.

$(n + 2)$ is the top row. There are n yellow tiles in the rectangle and one tile added to each end.

$(n + 2) \times 2$ indicates that the total number of yellow tiles in the top and bottom row is double the number of the yellow tiles in the top row. This set of tiles can also be described as 2 rectangles with n yellow tiles and 4 individual tiles, one at each end of the rectangle or $2n + 4$. Therefore, $(n + 2) \times 2 = (2n + 4)$. This corresponds to the step above calling upon the Distributive Property.

$(2n + 4) + 2$ indicates the total number of yellow tiles is equal to the number of yellow tiles in the top and bottom row plus the 2 tiles in the middle row. This set of tiles can also be described as 2 rectangles each with n yellow tiles and an additional 6 yellow tiles, or $2n + 6$. This corresponds to the steps above calling upon the Associative Property and addition.

The whole group discussion should include

- Showing how different algebraic expressions are equivalent
- Making connections between algebraic expressions and the tile situations

Base the whole-group discussion on Focus Question 2 by inviting participants to show how the various expressions from Case 10 are equivalent. Begin by considering $(n + 2) \times 2 + 2$ and $2n + 6$. Ask questions such as "What does n represent in the situation?" "What is $(n + 2)$?" "Why is that multiplied by 2?" to verify how each component of an algebraic expression is connected to the situation.

In addition, ask questions so participants understand that n is the number of blue tiles and that $2n + 6$ is the corresponding number of yellow tiles. Ask participants to explain what the equation $(n + 2) \times 2 + 2 = 2n + 6$ means in the situation. Then as each step in the process of solving the equation is offered, continue to ask questions so that the connections between the algebraic steps and the tile situation are made visible.

Suggest that participants now consider how $(n + 2) \times 3 - n$ and $2n + 6$ are equivalent. If you have time, give participants a few minutes to talk in small groups. "Use methods similar to what we did in the whole group—matching the algebraic expression with the tile situation as you go through each step." Once participants have had a few minutes to think, work through this equation as a whole group.

DVD: Finding formulas for Penny Jars   (15 minutes)

Whole group

Tell the group they will be viewing a DVD segment of a fourth-grade class working with a Penny Jar situation, starting with 3 and adding 4 each round. The segment provides images of students connecting their arithmetic expressions for the 10th round with the Penny Jar situation. Ask the participants to take notes during the clip so they will be able to discuss the students' thinking. In particular, suggest participants pay attention to how students call upon the representation of the pennies in the jar in their explanations and discuss this aspect of students' thinking. You might also ask for comments about the teacher's interaction with students to highlight the role the teacher's questions played in the discussion.

Break
(15 minutes)

Math activity: Comparing Penny Jars, What to look for in a straight line
(45 minutes)

Small groups (grade band; 25 minutes)

Whole group (20 minutes)

The purpose of the Math activity is to analyze pairs of linear functions by comparing their graphs. Participants will get more out of the cases in Chapter 4 if they have some experience thinking about how pairs of linear functions are related to each other. This work also provides the opportunity for participants to continue to make connections among the graphs, the tables, the formulas, and the situations.

The following Facilitator Note compares the functions in Problem 1 of "Math activity: Comparing Penny Jars."

Graphing Linear Functions Without Plotting Points

It is possible to sketch graphs of linear functions by examining the y-intercepts and the slopes. Consider these four linear functions:
A. $y = 2x + 3$ **B.** $y = 2x + 6$ **C.** $y = 3x + 6$ **D.** $y = 2x + 8$.

Because A and B have the same slope (2), they will be parallel lines. A has a y-intercept of 3 and B has a y-intercept of 6, and so they will cross the y-axis at (0, 3) and (0, 6), respectively. Given this information, the graph of these two lines looks like this:

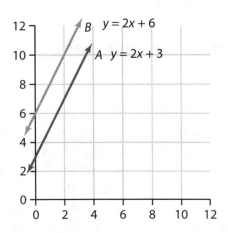

Finding Formulas

Because *B* and *C* have different slopes, they will not be parallel lines; the line for *C* will be steeper (slope of 3) than the line for *B* (slope of 2). Both of the functions have the same *y*-intercept 6, and therefore, both will contain the point (0, 6). Given this information, the graph of these two lines looks like this:

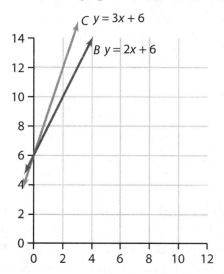

However, what happens if we compare *C* and *D*? They have different slopes and different *y*-intercepts.

Because they have different slopes, they are not parallel. In fact, they intersect at the point (2, 12).

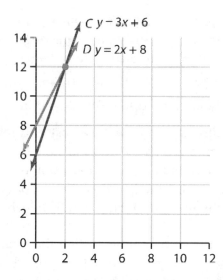

Now compare *A* and *C*. At first it may seem these lines, which are not parallel, do not intersect. However, if we extend our graph to include all four quadrants of the coordinate plane, we see that the lines intersect in the second quadrant.

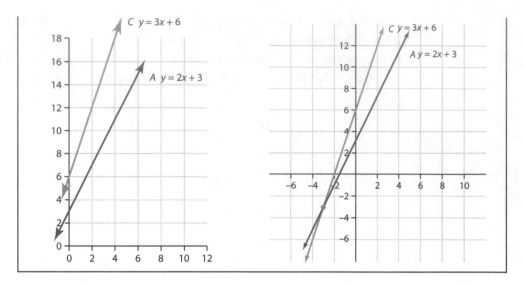

Organize participants in small groups and distribute "Math activity: Comparing Penny Jars." Let the groups know they will have 25 minutes to work on this activity. The main focus of this work will be on the graphs in Problems 2, 3, and 4. After small groups have worked on these three graphs, suggest they turn to Question 5 and list some observations. Use these problems as a vehicle to introduce the terms *slope* and *intercept* by connecting these terms to the language participants might use. For instance, if participants indicate one line is steeper than another, paraphrase their observation using the term *slope*; if participants talk about the different starting values, introduce the term *y-intercept*.

If groups have time to pursue Exercises 6, 7, and 8, remind participants to try to sketch the graphs without making a table for these problems. You might also ask if they can predict the formula by comparing these situations to those previously given.

The whole-group discussion should include

■ A discussion of the three posters (Problems 2, 3, and 4), each with a pair of graphs
■ A discussion based on participants' observations about the graphs addressing the question, "How does this aspect you noted in the graph show up in the tables or in the algebraic expressions?"

Begin the discussion by posting the three pairs of graphs. Have participants compare their graphs with those posted and discuss any differences. Then ask participants to share their observations. For each observation, have participants explain the observation and what it means in the context of the Penny Jar situation. Remind the group that they have looked at several ways to represent Penny Jar situations: tables, algebraic expressions, and graphs. Ask how this observation can be seen in the other representations. For instance, if participants observe that the two lines in Problem 2 are parallel, ask how they can see that feature represented in the tables (the number of pennies increases by 2 in both tables), the expressions (both functions include $2n$ as a term, and the slope is 2 for both functions), and the situations (both involve adding 2 pennies each round). See "Maxine's Journal" (pp. 96–101) for an example of such a discussion.

Write the observations and the comments about other representations on the poster for each pair of graphs. The most important features to capture in this discussion are connections between

- The steepness of the graphs (the slopes) and the constant rate of increase in the tables (the amount added each round in the Penny Jar situation)
- The starting amount and the intersection of the graph with the y-axis (the y-intercept)
- The intersection point of the graphs and table entries that share values for the same day

Planning for student-thinking assignment   (20 minutes)

Small groups

Remind participants that at the end of Session 1, they had an assignment to examine the thinking of their students. Distribute the "Fourth Homework" sheet and have participants read the description of the student-thinking assignment. Tell them that they will have time in this session to work in a small group to plan what questions they might ask and what they might expect their students to learn by working on those questions. Distribute the handout "Planning for student-thinking assignment" and suggest that they use this guide during their planning. Let them know that they will be in these same small groups next session to share their student-thinking assignment.

Optional reading of sections of Chapter 8

If you have decided to suggest participants read portions of Chapter 8 throughout the seminar rather than all at once, assign Chapter 8, Sections 1 and 2 at this point. You should alert participants that Chapter 8 will include references to cases they have not yet read and that there will not be time allotted at the next session for discussion of Chapter 8.

Exit cards   (10 minutes)

Individual

Let the group know that for their exit-card activity they are to write a reflection on the work they did on the four homework problems. Remind them that you will be writing a response to their homework, the additional work they did in class on the homework problems, and their reflective writing. Let them know that it is likely their ideas about these problems have changed and you want to give them a chance to express their current thinking. You may say something like, "Look over the work you did on the four homework problems and consider the work you did during this session. Then write a response to these two exit-card questions and attach it to your homework."

- What mathematics have you figured out?
- What questions are you still working on?

Before the next session...

In preparation for the next session, read participants' papers describing their mathematics work on the four problems and their reflective writing summarizing their current thinking on these problems. You might write a single response that incorporates comments from the whole set of papers or you may choose to write to individuals, commenting on their particular work. For more information, see the section in "Maxine's Journal" on responding to the third homework. Make copies of both the papers and your response for your files before returning the work.

DVD Summary

Session 3: Finding Formulas

Fourth-grade class with teacher Nancy (8 minutes)

In this segment, fourth-grade students are discussing a Penny Jar situation: Start with 3 and add 4 each round. The teacher has an image of the penny jar on the overhead. The 3 pennies that are present at the start are drawn on the bottom of the jar and then a line is drawn. The pennies that are added are arranged in rows of 4. Students talk about the connections among multiplication, arrays, and adding rounds of pennies to the penny jar. The teacher asks if they can imagine 10 rows of pennies. Students respond that there would be 40 pennies added and the total number of pennies would be 43.

Discussion Break

The second part of the segment includes students describing their methods for finding the number of pennies in any round. Dmitri explains that the formula for a penny jar with 4 to start and adding 9 each round is "the round number multiplied by 9 plus 4." Brooke offers a similar formula expressed in general terms, "Multiply the number of rounds by the number you add each time, and then you add the start number." Nina works to express the formula with symbols. The teacher continues to focus the conversation on how to use symbols, and Han summarizes the discussion with a statement that the formula for Dmitri's context is "r times 9 plus 4."

Poster: Comparing Penny Jars

Prepare a poster with graphs for Problems 2, 3, and 4 from "Math activity: Comparing Penny Jars." The graphs drawn here are meant to identify the *y*-intercept and to suggest how steep the lines are relative to one another.

Problem 2

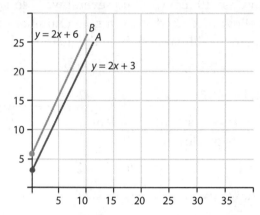

Problem 3

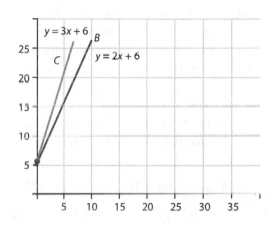

Problem 4

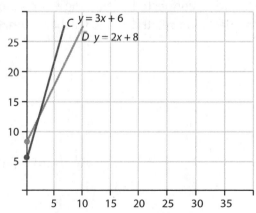

Focus Questions: Chapter 3

1. In Case 10, Drew offers several ways to approach finding the number of yellow tiles needed for a given number of blue tiles. Explain each of his methods, illustrating how the method corresponds to the situation.

   a. lines 25–27   b. lines 28–29   c. lines 31–34

   d. lines 37–40   e. lines 42–44   f. lines 46–49

2. Drew offers three different algebraic expressions for the same arrangements of tiles:

   $2n + 6$ $(n + 2) \times 2 + 2$ $(n + 2) \times 3 - n$

   Show how these are equivalent.

3. Revisit your solutions to the four homework problems in light of the explanations your group created for Drew's methods. Articulate the connections between the expressions you wrote and the arrangements of tiles. If members of your group had different ways to represent the nth case, work together to show how they are equivalent.

4. Consider Case 11.

   a. What is the concern the teacher, Nancy, raises in lines 139–143? How does she address the concern in lines 144–149 and what is her students' response?

   b. Explain the issue that the teacher, Nancy, raises in lines 163–167.

   c. In lines 167–175, Kevin offers an algebraic expression. How is Kevin's thinking connected to the original mathematics problem? How is Kevin's explanation related to the teacher's concerns?

Math activity: Comparing Penny Jars

In this activity, you will make graphs with pairs of Penny Jar situations on the same set of axes.

1. Make a table and a formula for each of these four Penny Jar situations:

   a. Start with 3; add 2 each day.　　c. Start with 6; add 3 each day.
   b. Start with 6; add 2 each day.　　d. Start with 8; add 2 each day.

2. On the first set of axes, graph situation *a* and situation *b*.

3. On the second set of axes, graph situation *b* and situation *c*.

4. On the third set of axes, graph situation *c* and situation *d*.

5. What observations can you make about each graph? How can that observation be seen in the situation? In the formula? In the table?

For Exercises 6–8, try to draw the graphs without making a table of values but instead by comparing them to the graphs you have already made. In each case, explain how you know how the new graph will compare with those already plotted.

6. On the same set of axes you used for Exercise 2, situations *a* and *b*, sketch a graph for this Penny Jar situation: Start with 5; add 2 each day.

7. On the same set of axes you used for Exercise 3, situations *b* and *c*, sketch a graph for this Penny Jar situation: Start with 6; add 4 each day.

8. On the same set of axes you used for Exercise 4, situations *c* and *d*, sketch a graph for this Penny Jar situation: Start with 6; add 2 each day.

Fourth Homework

Reading assignment: Casebook, Chapter 4

Read Chapter 4 in the Casebook, "Comparing Linear Functions," including the introductory text and Cases 14–16.

Writing assignment: Examining student thinking

Pose a mathematics task to your students related to the work of this seminar. You might pose a question taken directly from one of the cases or the mathematics work. First consider why you want your students to work on this question. What mathematical ideas do you want them to explore? Then consider what questions you might ask as they are working in order to bring that mathematics to the fore. You can use the planning worksheet from the small-group discussion as a support.

After the session, think about what happened. What did you learn? What surprised you? Write up your questions, how your students responded, and what you make of their responses (your expectations, your surprises, and what you learned). Include specific examples of student work or dialogue. Examining the work of just a few students in depth is very helpful.

At our next session, you will have the opportunity to share this writing with the colleagues from your small-group planning session. Please bring four copies of your writing to share.

Planning for student-thinking assignment

> **Task you are going to pose**

> **Why you are posing it: What mathematics ideas do you want students to work on?**

> **What do you expect students might do? What are some ways they might work on this?**

> **Questions you might ask as the students are working:**

PATTERNS, FUNCTIONS, AND CHANGE

Comparing Linear Functions

Mathematical themes:

■ Making connections among situations involving constant change and various representations of the situation, such as graphs, formulas, tables, and unconventional representations created by students

■ Interpreting graphs of pairs of linear functions

■ Finding the intersection of two lines on a graph and interpreting what it means in terms of a story situation, the corresponding table, and algebraic equations

Session Agenda

Sharing student-thinking assignment	Small groups (same groupings as for previous session)	30 minutes
Math activity: Catching up or not?	Small groups Whole group	25 minutes 25 minutes
Break	Whole group	15 minutes
Case discussion: Looking at students' representations	Small groups Whole group	40 minutes 25 minutes
DVD: Does Gowen catch up?	Whole group	15 minutes
Homework and exit cards	Whole group	5 minutes

Background Preparation

Read

■ the Casebook, Chapter 4

■ "Maxine's Journal" for Session 4

■ the agenda for Session 4

■ the Casebook: Chapter 8, Sections 1–3

Work through

■ the Focus Questions for Session 4 (p. 160)

■ the Math activity: Catching up or not? (p. 161)

Preview

■ the DVD segment for Session 4

Materials

Duplicate

■ "Focus Questions: Chapter 4" (p. 160)

■ "Math activity: Catching up or not?" (p. 161)

■ Resource materials from NCTM's *Navigating Through Algebra*, a lesson from each of the grade-band volumes (preK–2, 3–5, and 6–8). See p. 162

■ "Fifth Homework" (p. 163)

Obtain

■ DVD player

■ rulers

■ graph paper

■ index cards

Consider the following two functions:

$$y = 2x + 4$$
$$y = 2x + 10$$

Because the two functions have the same slope (2), they have the same rate of increase. When the x-values increase by 1 (e.g., from 2 to 3, from 4.5 to 5.5), the y-values increase by 2. When the x-values increase by 2, the y values increase by 4. When the x-values increase by $\frac{1}{2}$, the y-values increase by 1.

Notice the graphs of these functions. The lines are parallel. In fact, the lines are 6 units apart on the y-axis, and for all values of x, the y-values remain 6 units apart.

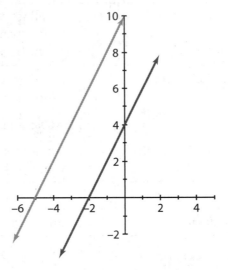

When two linear functions have graphs with different slopes, they intersect at some point.

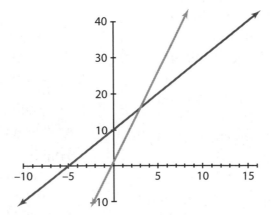

The Penny Jar context might help us think about what is happening with these functions:

Jill starts with 4 pennies, and she adds 2 each round. ($J = 2n + 4$)
Mike starts with 10 pennies and he adds 2 each round. ($M = 2n + 10$)

Mike starts with 6 more pennies than Jill. Because they both add 2 pennies each round, he will always have 6 more pennies than Jill. This situation corresponds to the first graph on the previous page and to the table below.

Number of Rounds	Number of Pennies for Jill	Number of Pennies for Mike
0	4	10
1	6	12
2	8	14
3	10	16
4	12	18

Claudette starts with 1 penny and adds 5 each round. ($C = 5n + 1$)

Claudette starts with 9 fewer pennies than Mike, and each round she adds 5 instead of 2. Therefore, each round, she gains 3 on Mike. After 1 round, she has 6 fewer; after 2 rounds, she has 3 fewer; and after 3 rounds, they have the same number of pennies in the jar. After Round 3, Claudette has more pennies than Mike. We can see this in the table below.

Number of Rounds	Number of Pennies for Claudette	Number of Pennies for Mike
0	1	10
1	6	12
2	11	14
3	16	16
4	21	18

We can also see this in the graph of $y = 2x + 10$ and $y = 5x + 1$ (the embedding functions). The lines intersect when $x = 3$; that is, when $x = 3$, the y-values are both equal to 16. So at Round 3, both Claudette and Mike have 16 pennies in the jar.

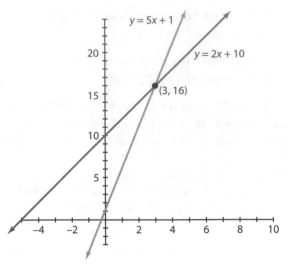

Heshim starts with 7 pennies and adds 5 each time. ($H = 5n + 7$)

Let's compare Heshim's jar with Jill's. Heshim starts with 3 more pennies than Jill. Each round, he adds 3 more pennies than Jill. That means he starts ahead and stays ahead; Jill never catches up.

Number of Rounds	Number of Pennies for Jill	Number of Pennies for Heshim
0	4	7
1	6	12
2	8	17
3	10	22
4	12	27

When we look at the graph of the embedding functions, $y = 2x + 4$ and $y = 5x + 7$, we see that they intersect at $x = ^-1$. However, because the domain of the Penny Jar functions is the set of whole numbers, it does not include $^-1$. That is, given its limited domain, it is possible to have Penny Jars that collect pennies at different rates but never have the same amount.

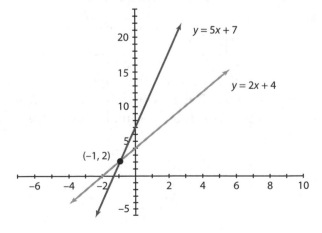

Comparing Linear Functions

There is one more situation to consider:

Elliot starts with 7 and adds 4 each time. ($E = 4n + 7$)

When we compare Elliot's jar with Mike's, we see that Elliot starts out with 3 fewer pennies than Mike. Because Elliot collects 4 pennies each round and Mike only 2, Elliot gains 2 pennies on Mike each round. So, after 1 round, Elliot is only 1 penny behind, and after 2 rounds, Elliot is 1 penny ahead. After that, Elliot always has more pennies than Mike. He jumped ahead without ever having the same number of pennies.

Number of Rounds	Number of Pennies for Elliot	Number of Pennies for Mike
0	7	10
1	11	12
2	15	14
3	19	16
4	23	18

If we look at a graph of the embedding functions, $y = 4x + 7$ and $y = 2x + 10$, we have another view of what is happening. The graphs intersect somewhere between $x = 1$ and $x = 2$. In fact, they intersect when $x = 1.5$ and $y = 13$. However, because 1.5 is not in the domain of the Penny Jar, neither Elliot nor Mike ever has exactly 13 pennies in his jar.

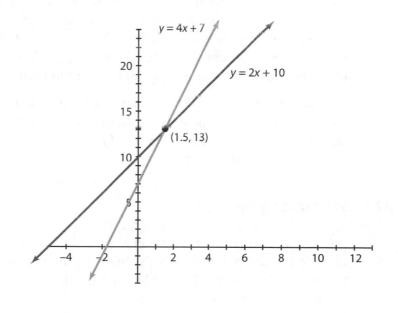

Maxine's Journal

March 17

For the first three sessions, we worked on different representations of functions—standard representations of tables, graphs, and algebraic expressions, as well as arrangements of tiles and cubes, pictures, and other informal representations—and learned how each revealed various characteristics of a function. In Session 4, we applied all of these types of representations to solve problems involving two linear functions. My sense was that, overall, participants found it immensely satisfying. 5

Sharing student-thinking assignment

At the start of the session, participants met to share student-thinking assignments. As I listened to their conversations, it sounded like many teachers discovered students making the same error—solving a linear problem by doubling. For example, Yan gave her students a problem about collecting bottles similar to the problem presented in Case 16. A student figured that, because Mario began with 10 bottles and brought in 5 each day for a total of 60 bottles on the 10th day, then on the 20th day he must have 120 bottles. Flor's students made a similar assumption: She had presented her students with the problem about the square arrangement of tiles from Case 11. After her students found that the 10th figure would be made up of 44 tiles, they assumed the 100th figure would have 10 times that number—440 tiles. I am sure there is much more to see in this set of assignments, but I informed participants that this is a common error and they will be reading about it further in Chapter 5. 10 15 20

When I stopped by Elinor's table, she told me that when she does the student-thinking assignments for this seminar, she feels like she can identify with her students. "I don't feel like I'm very far ahead of the children. I'm figuring out the ideas right along with them."

Math activity: Catching up or not?

The problems on the activity sheet all have to do with the situation in Case 15 about a fantasy planet on which children receive daily allowances of Magic Marbles for a month. Children begin the month with different amounts and accumulate marbles at different rates. 25

I began by pointing out that in the last few sessions, we have been working on different representations of functions. "In particular, we have been examining tables, graphs, and algebraic expressions to see how these show different 30 aspects of a function situation. In the math activity today, you'll be comparing two situations—like those you read about in the cases—and you'll be using various representations of functions to explore what's going on." I pointed to the instructions on the Math activity sheet. "It says that, when you make an observation based on one representation, identify how that observation can be seen in the other representations." Then the groups got to work.

Small groups

When I approached Sandy, Dina, and Meg, they already had tables, graphs, and algebraic expressions for the first problem (Franick begins with 30 marbles and gets 3 additional marbles each night; Bolar has no marbles at all at the beginning but gets 5 each night). Sandy was asking, "Can $5n$ be an expression? I don't like that. I don't like the way it looks. The other one is $3n + 30$. It looks better with $5n + 0$. Can you have just the $5n$? Don't you need an operation?"

I suggested that we look at $3n + 30$ and asked what each component of the expression represents. What is n, what is 3, what is 30? When I asked about $3n$, Sandy could say, "Oh, it's 3 times n."

I said, "Right. The operation of multiplication is there, even though you don't see the multiplication sign. When you write $3n$, it's implied that you multiply 3 times n. So what about $5n$?"

Sandy chuckled to herself. "That means 5 times n. You know, I knew that. It just looks funny; I have to get used to it."

I said, "$5n + 0$ is also correct. That's the same as $5n$. Remember last time we talked about the y-intercept? We can say that, when you write $5n + 0$, you're making the y-intercept explicit."

Then Dina spoke up. "When I look at the three representations, it's much clearer by looking at the table and graph that one is catching up to the other. I can't really see that just by looking at the formula."

Meg said, "In the expression though, you can see that there is a difference of 2 each time. Because one is $5n$ and the other is $3n$. Each day, Bolar is getting closer to Franick by 2 marbles. So it will take 15 days for Bolar to make up the 30 marbles."

I asked Meg, "What if Franick were getting 2 marbles each night instead of 3? How long would it take for Bolar to catch up?"

She said, "Bolar would be getting 3 closer each night. So, it would take 10 days to catch up."

I saw that Meg was able to think through the problem using the context and the algebraic expressions, though Sandy and Dina were not following this discussion. I suggested to Meg that she look at the graphs and tables with Sandy and Dina to identify those same ideas.

Flor and Mariam were saying that where the lines meet, the *y*-value has to be a multiple of 5. When Lamis asked why they thought that, they said, "Because all of Bolar's values are multiples of 5." Lamis pointed out that it might be the case that on one night, Bolar is behind, but the next night jumps ahead. "They don't necessarily have the same number one night." | 70

Lamis was right. She told me she realized that because she had worked out all the situations in Case 16, Collecting bottles. However, it does turn out that Franick and Bolar do have the same number of marbles on Day 15. | 75

I announced that when we start our whole-group discussion, we would discuss Problem 2 and then go back to Problem 1. I made sure everyone had time to get into the second problem before bringing the group together. | 80

Whole group

I began by pointing out that, when I looked around the room while they were working on the problems, I saw a lot of people making gestures with their hands. I thought it would be helpful to look at some of these gestures together and interpret what they mean. "Let's take a look at what people were showing as they moved their hands up and down." | 85

Nazir got us started by putting her two hands in front of her, one higher than the other, and then moving both hands up, but the lower one faster. I asked, "What is Nazir showing us there?"

Ariel said, "When she starts, one hand is above the other. That's like, Franick has 30 and Bolar has 0. But, as they start moving, the lower hand is moving faster than the upper hand, so it eventually catches up. While both hands are moving up, they move closer together, then they're together, and then they move farther apart." | 90

Other people added comments, essentially saying what Ariel said with other language. | 95

I then had them look at a different gesture. I put my hands in front of me, one hand above the other, and moved them both up, keeping the same distance apart. "What does that show?"

Georegeann laughed, "My sister's and my ages." She was referring to the discussion we had during the previous session. | 100

When I asked for another explanation, Bill said, "Two people start with different amounts but both get the same amount each night. So, they increase at the same rate, and the lower one never catches up."

Now I was ready to begin the discussion of Problem 2: Tovar begins with 20 marbles and receives 2 each night; Gowen does not have any marbles at the beginning but receives 3 each night. | 105

Comparing Linear Functions

I said, "OK, let's go back to Tovar and Gowen. Tovar starts ahead, but his rate of increase is lower, and so eventually Gowen will catch up and pass."

Sandy said, "What I'm seeing while you're doing that is a track. As we're coming around the track, one started ahead, but then they're catching up and one gets ahead. Tovar starts ahead, but his rate of increase is lower, so eventually Gowen will catch up and pass."

As Sandy spoke, she got up and showed the horses turning around a bend in the track. If she had been talking about a straight track with horses running at different rates, I would have felt more confident, but I suspected she was addressing a different issue. So I said, "Let's not think about the bend in the track right now. Let's just think about where the track is straight. One horse is behind but then makes a final push and starts to get closer to the horse in the lead. Racing horses and collecting marbles are very different situations, but if horses are running at a constant speed and marbles are collected at a constant rate, the underlying mathematics is the same."

I suggested we set up a table to help us understand the situation. Although in small groups participants created tables for every 5th night (as the Math activity said), we now created a table with increments of 1 night. Within a few minutes, we had this table on the board:

Number of Nights	Number of Marbles Tovar Has	Number of Marbles Gowen Has
0	20	0
1	22	3
2	24	6
3	26	9
4	28	12
5	30	15
6	32	18
7	34	21
8	36	24
9	38	27

At this point, Georgeann spoke up. "I'm trying to look at the different representations. How can I look at any other representation and find as much information as I can from the table?"

I asked, "So, what do you see in this table?"

Georgeann said, "I see that at the start, Tovar was at 20 and Gowen was at 0. Then Tovar goes up by 2 and Gowen goes up by 3."

I said, "Now let's look at the graph. Describe the graph and tell me what to draw."

Trudy said, "Put the night across the bottom, and the number of marbles on the side. The numbers get pretty high, so you can go up by some increment, not just 1."

I drew a pair of axes with the x-axis in increments of 5, the y-axis in increments of 10.

Yan said, "Tovar starts at 20 and Gowen starts at nothing," so I plotted the points (0, 20) and (0, 0). I mentioned that these points represented the y-intercepts.

I asked, "Where is Tovar on Day 10?"

Robin said, "At Day 10, he's at 20 plus 20," and so I plotted the point (10, 40).

Lamis asked, "So you just made this decision that you're not going to plot every point?"

I said, "Yes. Why do you think I can do that?"

Peggy said, "Because it doesn't matter. What matters is that each person's nightly amount is going to grow at a constant rate."

After a few more suggestions, the graph of Tovar's marbles looked like this:

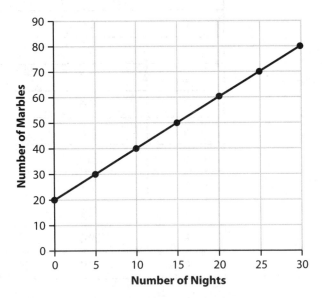

As different people commented on why it was not necessary to plot each point, I began to draw in points by each day instead of every 5 days. Lamis said, "Ohhhh. Right, the graph is the same straight line. It's just whether you show more points or not."

I then added the graph of Gowen's marbles and asked participants what they saw.

Comparing Linear Functions

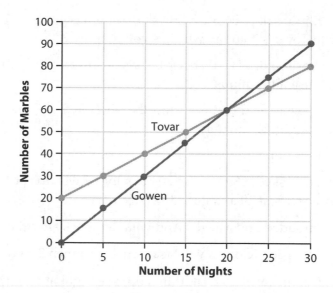

Georgeann said, "What I first look for is whether they're parallel or not. And, they're not."

I asked, "Why not?"

I heard different responses. "They're going in different directions." "They're going at different rates." "Gowen gets more marbles each night." | 160

I said, "The marbles are accumulating at different rates. In the last session, I brought up the word *slope*. We can say that Gowen's graph has a greater slope than Tovar's."

Dina said, "If the lines were parallel, there would always be a difference | 165 of 20, no matter what day. Here the difference between the lines is getting smaller."

I nodded and asked, "What else do you notice?"

Mariam said, "The rate of change is faster with the lower line."

I said, "Yes, and that shows up as the steeper line; it has the greater | 170 slope. In fact, the graph of Gowen's marbles starts out lower, but because the slope is greater, it reaches the graph of Tovar's marbles and after that is higher."

April said, "Because they're not parallel, they're changing at different rates, so the lines are getting closer and eventually cross." | 175

I asked, "How do these observations show up in the table?"

Flor said, "When they cross, you'd see in the table they have the same number of marbles on the same night."

Elinor said, "The distance between the 20 to 22 is 2, and the distance between 0 and 3 is 3, it keeps going up by 3." | 180

I asked, "What does that indicate?"

Elinor said, "Because Gowen's column is going up by 3, it's going up faster than Tovar's column, which is going up by 2."

April said, "The distance between Gowen and Tovar is getting closer by 1, because it's 3 minus 2." ₁₈₅

I pointed to the values across the table (on p. 131) and subtracted: "20 − 0 = 20; 22 − 3 = 19; 24 − 6 = 18 ..."

Lots of people were nodding as I did this.

Flor asked, "So it takes 20 days for Gowen to catch up because the difference starts at 20 and goes down by 1 each day?" ₁₉₀

I nodded and asked, "And what happens after the 20th day?"

Yan said, "Gowen will be ahead 1, and then 2, and then 3."

Georgeann said, "The difference keeps going down by 1 and eventually the difference will be 0. That's when the lines meet. What happens after that is the exact opposite. The difference will be 1, 2, 3, 4, but then Gowen will be ahead. ₁₉₅ And you see that on the graph because Gowen's line will be on top and will be moving away from Tovar's."

I requested that participants look at the table they created in small groups.

Number of Nights	Number of Marbles Tovar Has	Number of Marbles Gowen Has
0	20	0
5	30	15
10	40	30
15	50	45
20	60	60
25	70	75
30	80	90

Then I asked, "What happens when you look down the columns in this table?"

Elinor said, "Tovar goes up by 10 and Gowen goes up by 15." ₂₀₀

I asked, "How can we reconcile that? We didn't change the context, did we? All the data in this table still appears on the graph."

Lamis said, "But it's every 5th night. Not every night."

I asked, "So how do we get the rate per night by looking at this table?"

Meg said, "You have to divide by 5. For Tovar, when we see the column ₂₀₅ increases by 10, that's for 5 nights, so each night there was an increase of 2: 10 divided by 5."

I summarized by saying that, when determining the slope of a line, you can take any two points and divide the difference between y-values by the difference between x-values. We tried it with a few other examples. Gowen had 30 marbles on Day 10 and 60 marbles on Day 20. $\frac{60-30}{20-10} = \frac{30}{10} = 3$. Gowen had 90 marbles on Day 30 and 15 marbles on Day 5. $\frac{90-15}{30-5} = \frac{75}{25} = 3$.

I suggested that we now look at the formulas for Tovar's and Gowen's collections. I asked, "What expression shows how Tovar was collecting marbles?"

Within a few moments we had $2n + 20$ and $3n$ as representations of Tovar's and Gowen's collections, respectively. I continued by asking what each component of the expression represented. To make sure we were all clear about what's going on, I also asked what the expressions $3n$ and $2n + 20$ referred to, and participants explained that the expressions gave the number of marbles Gowen and Tovar have on the nth night.

April said, "Violet showed us how to figure it out with all this algebraic stuff. I wasn't really getting it, but now I'm starting to see it. To find out when Gowen catches up, we're trying to figure out when the number of marbles Tovar has is the same as the number of marbles Gowen has. That's $2n + 20 = 3n$."

April's comment directed the class in the direction that I wanted to head. So I wrote the equation on the board and discussed what it meant. I said, "We know that on most days the value of $2n + 20$ is not equal to $3n$. From what we saw in the graph and the table, on all the days before Day 20, Tovar has more marbles, and on all the days after Day 20, Gowen has more marbles. When we write this equation, it says there's a particular value of n that represents the day on which the two children have the same number of marbles. We already know that it happens on Day 20. However, we can solve this algebraic equation and see that we can get to 20 this way, too."

Together we worked through the steps of solving the equation.

$$2n + 20 = 3n$$
$$20 = 3n - 2n$$
$$20 = n$$

For this algebraic process I wanted to work through another example. So I suggested, "Let's go back to see how this works for Problem 1. That's where Franick starts with 30 marbles and gets 3 each night; Bolar starts with 0 and gets 5 each night."

Participants offered the expression for Franick's accumulation of marbles, $3n + 30$, and for Bolar, $5n$, and we quickly reviewed what the expressions meant. I then moved on to the next step: "So if we want to think about when Franick and Bolar have the same number of marbles, what do we do?"

Participants talked me through the steps of setting up the equation and then solving it:

$$5n = 3n + 30$$
$$2n = 30$$
$$n = 15$$

Having done that, I wanted to make sure these ideas were still connected back to the table and the graph. I said, "I'd like somebody to give a quick description of what the table and graph would look like."

Lamis said, "I'll do the table because that's real visual for me." She told me how to start the table.

Number of Days	Number of Marbles Franick Has	Number of Marbles Bolar Has
0	30	0
1	33	5
2	36	10
3	39	15
4	42	20
5	45	25
6	48	30
7	51	35
8	54	40
9	57	45

Then Lamis continued, "Whereas in the other one the difference changed by 1 each day, here the difference changes by 2 each day. Since they start 30 apart, the day on which the difference between them is 0 is Day 15. You'll see that if we continue the table to Day 15. I have to say, we already did that part. But to hold onto that equation, I don't know if it would mean anything to me if I hadn't done the table first and looked at those differences."

Lamis was making an important point that I wanted to emphasize. Particularly hoping these comments would register for Violet, I said, "The algebraic representation doesn't automatically come with meaning. Actually, neither did the table or the graph. The meaning gets developed as we work with the representations. As we work with the variety of representations and see how the same ideas show up in different forms, that is what helps us make sense."

Dina said, "Meg had a way of doing that equation without the equation. Sandy and I were thinking, why does that work? Now having that equation and working it out, I get the trick Meg was using."

Comparing Linear Functions

I said, "What Meg was doing might have felt like a trick to you, but it wasn't a trick to Meg. She was reasoning about the situation."

Georgeann said, "That's a question I have. I don't even want to do the equation. I want to look at the 30 and the $3n$ and the $5n$ and just know when they'll meet. Can you do that?"

Because the discussion was running long, I decided to explain Meg's method rather than having her explain it. I said, "Yes, here's what Meg was doing. She said the $5n$ and $3n$ tell her that Bolar is getting 2 more than Franick each night. That's the difference between the two rates. Franick starts out ahead, but each night Bolar gets closer by 2. Now, look at the difference between the starting amounts—that's 30. You can divide the difference between the starting amounts by the difference between the rates, and that tells you when the two children have the same number of marbles." I pointed to the equation, $2n = 30$. "Meg's reasoning was taking her right to this line."

I added one more thought. "We can say the same thing with the technical terms, too. To find the intersection, the point where the lines cross, you can divide the difference between the y-intercepts by the difference between the slopes." I knew that most people in the group already had their heads full, but I offered this last thought particularly for the middle-school teachers who were more familiar with the vocabulary.

Case discussion: Looking at students' representations

Because participants had already done so much work with Magic Marbles, I wanted them first to turn to Case 14, Crawling crayfish, to think through the same mathematical ideas embedded in a different context. I also wanted them to be able to find those ideas in the representations students devised as shown in lines 54–73.

Most groups spent quite a bit of time interpreting this representation.

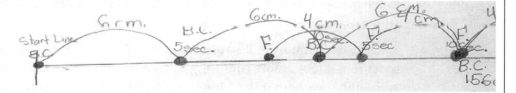

Celeste said, "The students are showing the values for both Big Claw and Flicker on the same line, but it looks like they are having difficulty coordinating the two over time."

Mariam added, "The jumps for Big Claw look to be about the same distance apart; same for Flicker. So I think they have a good understanding of a constant rate of change. I am not sure about what they are thinking with regard to time. Their line graph emphasizes distance. They are organizing their diagram and data around the distance of the race."

Lamis said, "That makes a lot of sense to me. The story is about a race. The first thing I think of is the racetrack. They are modeling the racetrack with Flicker getting a head start."

Putting herself in the heads of students, Lamis asked, "Why would students want to go to an x- and y-axis if they hadn't had much experience with this kind of representation? To us the x- and y-coordinate system is a great way to look at time and distance together, but it doesn't feel like it's modeling the situation in the same way that a track does."

Celeste said, "They are doing a good job of keeping track of the rate of change and showing that it remains constant over time. They are going to be able to use this to predict the future progress of the race, but I think they are going to have trouble with the time element. It's going to be difficult for them to compare the two ... to compare the distance each has traveled over time."

Now Flor jumped in: "I'm not so sure about that. Look at the diagram. At each dot they have recorded the time. Like Lamis was saying, they're seeing it as a racetrack and it feels like they're enacting the race just like they were watching a horse race or a car race. I think they do have a sense of the time. Look, after 10 seconds they show that Big Claw is at 12 centimeters and Flicker is at 18. They also show Big Claw at 18, but with 15 seconds marked for Big Claw. I think they have a real strong sense of the time and where each is. Perhaps we could ask them to explain what their diagram shows. I think this would reveal that they are not having trouble coordinating time."

Celeste responded, "Oh, yeah. Maybe they're not confused at all. It was just hard for me to read their representation."

I was interested in how this conversation developed. Celeste first found it difficult to interpret the students' representation, and so she attributed confusion to the students. However, as the group looked more closely at what the students had written, participants were able to see the method of keeping track of both distance and time for each crayfish. If Flor hadn't explained this to the group, I would have needed to draw participants' attention to how the students recorded time.

Celeste continued, "Because we didn't see the construction of this representation, it looks more confusing to us than it probably does to the students. Although, I wonder if they might be confused, too, if a couple of weeks later they come back to this diagram."

I stopped by another group, Violet, Bill, and Sandy, looking at the same representation. Violet was saying, "These children haven't a clue!" However, Bill and Sandy were looking more closely. Sandy suggested, "Let's see if we can recreate how the children might have drawn this. Like at the start, Big Claw is at 0 and Flicker is at 10. Now let's draw in what happens after the first 5-second period." I told Sandy that was a great idea; they'd get a lot of insight into students' representation by drawing it in for each 5-second period.

The next group I visited was looking at the second representation.

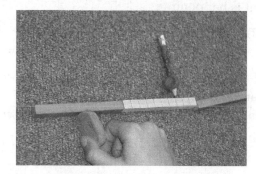

Robin said, "In the physical model, how students enact the model will give you a lot of indications as to whether they have a sense of the rate of change. But when they are done, there is no record of what was done."

Georgeann commented, "I would want to see students enact this. If they can articulate or demonstrate the rates of change consistently over time, then I would not be that concerned. It might be interesting to have them think about how they might record the data to share with someone else."

I mentioned to this group what Sandy, Bill, and Violet were doing and suggested that it might be interesting for them to do the same for this representation.

Some small groups examined the third representation carefully.

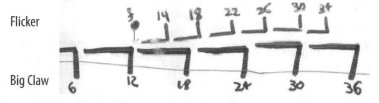

Ivan said, "They are tied when they get to 30 centimeters and then Big Claw pulls ahead."

Trudy asked, "Wait a minute. How do we know they're at 30 centimeters at the same time? If they drew it carefully enough, it would also look like they were at 18 at the same time."

Yan pointed out, "Flicker gets to 18 in 2 steps, but it takes Big Claw 3 steps to get there. That means they get there at different times. But they both get to 30 in 5 steps."

Trudy said, "I bet it's the same thing, that they drew in one step at a time for both crayfish—so they could keep track of when Big Claw caught up with Flicker, but it's harder for us to see."

Then the group looked more closely. Ivan said, "You cannot see a constant rate of change. Some of the lines are different lengths."

April added, "Look, Flicker is starting at the 12 centimeter mark. It should have been placed before the 12. Flicker starts at 10. I would want to ask a lot of questions before I would feel comfortable that the students have a sense of what is happening."

Trudy said, "Overall, I think this does show a good understanding. You can get an idea of constant rate of change and who wins."

I found these discussions of the representations quite interesting. I was aware of only a few groups getting into Focus Questions 2 and 3 during the time allotted. Even so, I felt the time was well spent.

Whole group

Before moving to the DVD, I decided to have a short whole-group discussion about what was the same and what was different among the contexts in the cases of Chapter 4. I pointed out that in one case, students were talking about two crayfish in a race; in the second, students were collecting marbles; and in the third, students were collecting bottles. "Within these contexts, what is the same, and what is different?"

The discussion produced two lists:

Similarities	**Differences**
■ Constant rates	■ Continuous vs. discrete data
■ Linear functions	
■ Comparing different rates	
■ Different starting points	
■ Increase over time (Are there situations involving decrease?)	
■ The lines intersect	
■ You can use the same method to find out where the lines intersect	

I then pointed out that all of the situations could be represented by a formula of the form $y = ax + b$. We considered different examples: In Case 16, when x is the number of days of bottle collection, the number of bottles Zelda collected is $2x + 30$. When x is the number of seconds into the crayfish race, Flicker's position in centimeters is $\frac{4}{5}x + 10$.

DVD: Does Gowen catch up?

The DVD segment shows a third-grade class discussing the same marbles situation as described in Problem 2 of the Math activity: Tovar began with 20 marbles and collected 2 each night, whereas Gowen started with 0 marbles and collected 3 each night. Students had first created a table with entries for every 5th night, and then they created a graph from the table. The DVD segment shows the class discussion of the graph.

Before showing the segment, I pointed to the graph of Tovar's and Gowen's marbles we had created earlier in the session. I said that, in the DVD, students are discussing this graph, but at the start, it's just with the discrete points, not joined by a line. During the course of the discussion, the lines are drawn in.

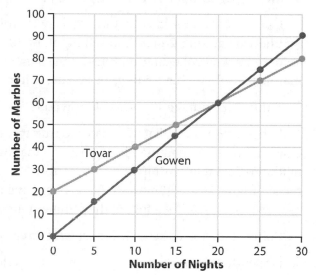

After viewing the segment, I asked, "What did you notice the children understood?" 415

Georgeann said, "They understood there was predictability beyond what they saw on the graph. They noticed the pattern of 20, 15, 10, ... that the numbers get closer by 5 each time, and the difference reaches 0, and then it goes up by 5s." 420

I checked to make sure participants understood why the numbers were getting closer by 5 each step. In fact, Gowen gets closer by 1 marble each night, but since the students graphed points at every 5th night, at each step (every 5th night) Gowen gets closer by 5.

Then I asked, "What else did you notice about the children's ideas on the DVD?" 425

Ariel said, "They knew the lines would never meet again. Once they went past the crossover point, they would never meet again but get farther and farther apart."

Peggy said, "They had the idea of constant slope. They were convinced that the lines wouldn't become curvy. They would stay straight, like an X." 430

I asked, "I'm wondering if this conversation was surprising to you."

Trudy said, "I was surprised when the boy said you could back up; if you went back, you could see it more like an X. I thought that was neat."

I asked, "Do you think that's what he was meaning, that you go to the left 435 of the y-axis? How did the teacher respond to that?"

Trudy said, "That they should stick to the story."

Celeste said, "I think what the boy was pointing out was that if you go up and to the right, the lines will get farther apart. And if you go down and to the left, the lines on that side of the X would get farther apart, too."

Meg said, "It would be like negative 1."

I said, "OK, let's look at this. At Day 0, Tovar has 20 marbles. We saw that he was getting 2 marbles each night, or 10 marbles every 5 nights. If we assume he was collecting marbles at the same rate before Day 0, how many marbles would he have 5 days before the original start?"

Trudy, "He'd have 10 less, so that would be 10 marbles."

I then suggested that we also look at what would be happening with Gowen, but explained that, in order to do that, we would need to remove the mathematical relationship out of its context. "Let's not bother trying to make sense of what it might mean to have a negative number of marbles. Let's just see what happens if we follow the number patterns before the original start."

Robin said, "So at Day ⁻5, Gowen will have ⁻15, whatever that means."

I extended the lines so the graph now looked like this:

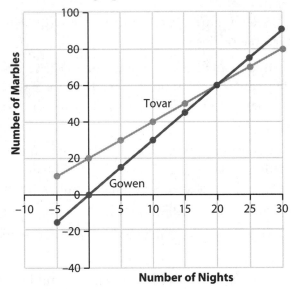

There was one other idea from the DVD I wanted to address, so I asked, "Did you notice the boy, Jacob, saying that as the days go on, Gowen's line is going to go straight up? Let's think about what that would mean."

Georgeann said, "I don't really think that's what he meant. Maybe he meant that it will always be increasing."

Because I really wanted to address a particular mathematical question rather than work to interpret what the student said, I redirected my question. "Let's set aside exactly what Jacob meant. I just want to use his words for a minute to get at this other question. Let's say the children in the story continued to accumulate marbles after Day 30, and so we extend these lines. What could it mean if the line does start going straight up?"

Comparing Linear Functions

I sketched in what the graph would look like.

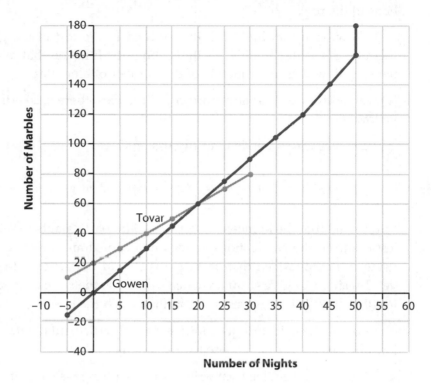

Georgeann said, "A line straight up would all be for one night. It would mean that a child has different numbers of marbles at the same time."

Dina said, "Time has stopped. If the line is going straight up, then nothing happens after that time."

Peggy added, "And he'd be getting different deposits at the same time."

I nodded and marked a couple of points, one above the other, on the graph.

Peggy continued, "That's right. It shows having different numbers of marbles on the same night."

I nodded again and said, "So we have a contradiction here, that we have two values for Day 50. That doesn't make sense. I want to point out a part of the definition of function that we haven't yet emphasized in this class. A function is a correspondence from one set to another—the input (or independent) variable and the output (or dependent) variable—and each value of the input variable has only one possible corresponding value of the output variable."

There was a pause to let the idea sink in. Then Bill spoke up. "OK, to take in this idea, I need to think about a bunch of contexts. So here, you can't have a child with different numbers of marbles at the same time. If I think about the crayfish race, the dependent variable is the position. The crayfish can't be at more than one position at the same time." Bill was now flipping through his Casebook to think about other functions. "If Henrietta sits in the middle of a line of hens, for whatever position she's in, there is only one number of hens in the row."

Following up on Bill's activity, I turned to the rest of the group to have them do the same thing. "Let's think about the function that relates the number of yellow tiles as a function of the number of blue tiles." | 490

Ivan spoke up, "For any number of blue tiles, there is a certain number of yellow tiles."

Time was up, so I ended our discussion there.

Exit cards

I explained that the homework would require participants to select one of the lessons from the Navigations Series I had copied and to write up a plan for using it. I emphasized that participants should not actually teach the lesson yet. I wanted to give them a chance to discuss their ideas about it with colleagues during the next session, and then teach the lesson after that. | 495

I posted the exit-card questions and told participants that, because it was late already, they could choose to answer one. | 500

- What are you getting from writing and discussing the work of your students?
- What questions are the seminar experiences bringing up for you? (These can be about math or learning or teaching or students.)

Consistent with the way this seminar has gone so far, it was a pleasure to read most of the exit cards. | 505

APRIL: I learn a lot from doing this math myself and then seeing what students do with it—how they are thinking, what connections they make, what mistakes they make. However, since it is all so new to me, it is sometimes hard for me to figure out what aspects of the math ideas the students are figuring out and where they might go next. For example, is the way the students are solving a problem showing they understand the functional relationship? Are they noticing patterns that are useful? | 510

I am learning to make sense of a lot of the algebra I did in school—did well—but never understood, really. I am learning some of this through the students' thinking and some through doing the math myself. | 515

YAN: For these assignments, I have chosen three students to work with. I am getting to know how these three students think. I am learning their strengths and weaknesses more than I did when they were members of the bigger group. They may represent the group and this gives me ideas regarding how to teach the group about what strategies may be helpful. | 520

One thing I learned tonight was the formula of difference of starting points divided by difference of rates equals the point of intersection.

Comparing Linear Functions

Then one teacher told me that helps solve those famous airplane problems. When do the planes meet?

DINA: Writing cases is always a good experience because it makes me listen and try to understand more deeply what the students are saying.

One question I keep thinking about though is why do I remember learning a symbol with a fancy *f* as a symbol for functions?

I read Dina's card before she left the room, and so I pulled her aside to show her the notation $f(x) = 2x + 6$. I explained to her that when you see $f(x)$, *f* isn't used as a variable the way *x* is here. The *f* just tells you that you are naming a function, and $f(x)$ tells you that the function *f* is defined in terms of the independent variable *x*. All of that was looking familiar to Dina, and so she felt satisfied.

It was fun to read Georgeann's exit card because she is so excited by what she is learning.

GEORGEANN: I am learning so much in the seminar—oh my, I feel like I want to talk the entire time because it's so full of stuff I get—or I have questions about that I can actually articulate! Completely surprising—and it would be entirely satisfying if I thought it wouldn't slip away ... but I cannot believe I'm having insights about these things. Thank you. Thank you. Thank you.

However, I was disappointed to read what Violet had written.

VIOLET: 1. There wasn't much discussion on my student case.
2. I'm learning more about how to slow down with my teaching. Unfortunately in my classroom, I need to cover too many topics to allow this kind of careful investigation of the math.

I am concerned that Violet is not figuring out how to learn in this seminar. She is not learning to attend to students' mathematical thinking, and she seems not to be figuring out how to go after deeper mathematical insight or what that might mean.

Responding to the fourth homework

March 19

I would like to share Violet's writing, mainly because my response to her homework addressed the concerns I have had about her for several sessions now.

Violet

Struggling Math Students

The mathematical idea in this lesson is an introduction to linear systems. We learned linear functions about two months ago. We left it to do some symbolic manipulation, and now we are revisiting linear relationships and comparing

525

530

535

540

545

550

555

linear functions. The purpose of this lesson is to revisit linear tables, graphs, and equations as a bridge to linear systems.

I have given a handout containing questions. Students answer the questions and then we have a whole-class discussion.

Problem scenario:

> *Barbara and Akia are racing.*
>
> *Barbara can run 2 meters per second.*
>
> *Akia can run 7 meters per second.*
>
> 1. *Make a table of values for time and distance for up to 15 seconds for each runner.*
> 2. *What do you notice about how the tables compare to each other? What is the same?*
> 3. *Because Barbara is so slow, the other runners have decided to give her a 20-meter head start. Barbara and Akia race. Make a table of time and distance for Barbara with her head start.*
> 4. *Compare Barbara's new table to Akia's table. What are the differences?*
> 5. *Can you tell from the table if Barbara catches up to Akia? How can you tell?*

Discussion:

In the discussion, I ask, "What is the same about the tables for Barbara and Akia?"

SUSAN:	*Each table goes up by the same number.*
TEACHER:	*Come up and show us what you mean.*

Susan comes to the overhead and draws a line connecting the distances in Barbara's table and says, "They go up by 2 each time."

GARY:	*They go up by a constant rate.*
BLANCH:	*They're going up evenly; they have a pattern.*
TEACHER:	*What is different about the tables?*
NICHOLAS:	*They go up by different meters per second.*
TEACHER:	*OK. So, now let's compare Barbara's new table with her head start to Akia's table. What are the differences?*
AMY:	*They end at different spots.*
TEACHER:	*What do you mean?*
AMY:	*At the bottom, Akia is farther than Barbara.*
NATHAN:	*Akia has the same meters as the old table, but Barbara has a head start and has different numbers.*

560

565

570

575

580

585

590

595

TEACHER:	*If you look at the tables, can you tell if Barbara can catch up to Akia?*

It's unanimous. She doesn't catch up.

TEACHER:	*How can you tell she doesn't catch up?*	600
MARYBETH:	*Look at the bottom. Akia is ahead.*	
TEACHER:	*OK. Now let's graph the information from the two tables on the same axes to get a different perspective on the information.... So now what do you think? Can Barbara catch up? What if the race was 24 meters? Who would win?*	605
NATHAN:	*(Quickly) Barbara. She only has to go 2 steps!*	
TEACHER:	*When does she get to 24 meters?*	
NATHAN:	*After 2 seconds.*	
TEACHER:	*How long does it take Akia to get to the 24-meter mark?*	
NATHAN:	*Over 3 seconds.*	610
TEACHER:	*What if the race was 28 meters long?*	
AMY:	*(Quickly) They would tie! That's where they meet!*	
TEACHER:	*What if the race was 50 meters long? Who would win?*	
BLANCH:	*Akia.*	
TEACHER:	*How can you tell?*	615
BLANCH:	*Because her line is steeper, and it only takes her 7 seconds to get there.*	
TEACHER:	*How long does it take Barbara to get to the 50-meter mark?*	
NICHOLAS:	*It takes her 14 seconds.*	
TEACHER:	*OK. Let's look back at our tables. Where do you see that Barbara and Akia meet?*	620
NATHAN:	*Right at the 4 and 28.*	
TEACHER:	*How do you know they meet there?*	
NATHAN:	*Because they both have 4 and 28.*	
TEACHER:	*So, what is the equation that represents Barbara's distance for any amount of time?*	625

I write "D =" on the overhead. Clevan, who has been reluctant to enter the conversation, pipes in, "20 + 2x."

TEACHER:	*How did he get that so quickly?*	
NICHOLAS:	*Because she has a 20-meter head start and she's running a rate of 2 meters each second.*	630

Nicholas is very proud of himself.

> TEACHER: *And, what is the equation that represents Akia's distance for any amount of time? D = ?*

Many of them shout out "7x."

> TEACHER: *So, if Barbara's equation is D = 20 + 2x and Akia's is D = 7x, how could we use the equations to find when they meet?*

Silence ... End of class.

Reactions:

I was very happy to see how quickly my students remembered a contextual constant rate of change and how that relates to the table. My experience with them is that they forget a good deal of the math they have learned, such as order of operations and operations with signed numbers. At first, I was surprised that they didn't notice the two runners meeting from the table. As soon as they saw the graph, they quickly changed their minds. On second thought, I shouldn't have been surprised because they consistently don't look closely at the numbers. They have learned to look for a constant rate of change and don't automatically know to interpret the information in other ways. The graph makes it easier for them to access the information. The thing that struck me the most is how quickly my students remembered this contextual type of math in stark contrast to symbol manipulation.

This assignment from Violet had much more detail than her first. It reads like she had taken my suggestion to tape record the discussion and use that to get a record of what students said. If I had not been so concerned about her general stance toward the seminar, I would have tried to write a response in which I dug more deeply into what the students were saying. In fact, that would be difficult to do. Although students do speak up in this episode, it is mainly offering correct answers to Violet's questions—either that or there is silence. Violet seems to think about her students' learning in terms of what they do and do not remember.

However, I have been concerned that at the end of each session, Violet indicates that she has not learned much. I am concerned that she has not been learning how to attend more deeply to students' ideas. It seems that she has not learned to learn from her seminar-mates' insights or questions, either. So this is what I wrote.

Dear Violet,

It seems this time you were able to capture some classroom dialogue for your student-thinking assignment. This is closer to what I expect from this kind of exercise. I wonder what strategy you used to record the conversation. I expect that if you were to keep at it, you would start hearing your students differently.

Comparing Linear Functions

Though from your exit card, where we asked what you learn from doing these assignments, it sounds like you didn't feel you learned very much. I wonder whether you can become more curious about how your students put ideas together. For example, you say that they remember math embedded in a context but don't remember symbol manipulation. Perhaps there are deeper questions to pursue there about what they do understand, what the context helps them do, and why they have a hard time making sense of the symbols.

You said that students didn't look closely at the tables when answering your question about whether Barbara caught up. But I wonder if that's the question you meant to ask. When they said Barbara never caught up, they were right. She started ahead, then Akia caught up, and Barbara was never ahead of Akia after that. Did you mean to ask if Akia caught up? If so, I suggest that you reread your assignment and see if you now come to a different conclusion about your students' understanding.

From your exit cards, it sounds like you don't feel you are learning any mathematics or anything about student learning. I would like to suggest that there is, in fact, quite a bit to learn, even if you have already had courses that covered the topics we are addressing. After all, the mathematical knowledge that supports effective teaching is far more extensive than the mathematics required to be a good student. For example, there is something to be learned about mathematics and about student thinking—by looking at alternative representations students devise. Although they look different from conventional representations and may be hard to read precisely because they don't use those conventions we're used to, they may be based in sound logic. It is a mathematical task of teaching to be able to look at a student's representation and figure out how it represents the phenomenon. Yes, the student may still need to learn the convention, but it's important to communicate to the student that his or her reasoning is sound. You do not want to communicate to students that they are confused when, in fact, their thinking is solid.

My own experience is that, when I listen to students who haven't yet put together the ideas I'm trying to teach, I learn a great deal of new mathematics. These students often highlight for me ideas that I had so taken for granted, that they were invisible to me. Trying to understand how they are thinking, viewing the mathematics from a new perspective, I make new connections. There are always new connections to be made.

There is something else I'd like you to pay attention to for the last four sessions of the seminar. I will point to one event from the seminar, though the issue is larger than that one event. In our last session, during whole-group discussion, one of your small-group mates mentioned that you had shown them a formula to use to answer the question (of when two children have the same number of marbles), but she didn't really understand what the formula meant until we worked out a set of ideas together. Her reference to understanding wasn't about symbol manipulation or if she knew what question the symbols answered. There was a different kind of internal experience she was after, which she called

675

680

685

690

695

700

705

710

715

"understanding." I'd like you to try to figure out what that kind of understanding is. It might be related to something you noticed about your students—their ability to think about the mathematics in its context.

I am not saying that you shouldn't have shown your seminar group the formula. That was fine. What I want you to work on is figuring out something about the experience of learning—what it means to have new insight, what it feels like inside oneself, and how it happens for other people. That means the focus comes off of your actions for a while. Rather than trying to figure out whether your questions help your group mates or not, try to figure out what other people are seeing and thinking.

You bring a lot of strength to your mathematics teaching. I am just trying to point out where you might draw your attention to become even stronger.

Maxine

720

725

Detailed Agenda

Sharing student-thinking assignment

(30 minutes)

Small groups

The first activity of this session provides the opportunity for participants to read and discuss what they wrote about the thinking of their students. In the previous session, participants met in small groups to plan for this assignment. Place them into the same small groups so they may share what happened. Remind them to read the set of papers before beginning any discussion. Their conversation should identify differences and similarities among the papers. Let them know they will have 30 minutes for this discussion.

The homework for next session will include participants examining NCTM materials designed to bring algebraic ideas to students of grades K–8. Participants will use the NCTM materials to prepare for the third student-thinking assignment, which is due at Session 6. As you listen to the small-group conversations, you might want to note comments participants make that you can refer to when setting up the homework assignment. For instance, some participants may say that it was difficult for them to find lessons in their existing curriculum that address these ideas; others may comment on their uncertainty about how to adapt the mathematics work they are doing in the seminar to make it appropriate for their grade level; others might express surprise at what their students are able to figure out.

Math activity: Catching up or not?

(50 minutes)

Small groups (grade-band groups; 25 minutes)
Whole group (25 minutes)

The Math activity is based on examining the situations in the Casebook and DVD as examples of linear functions, that is, functions with graphs that can be characterized by a y-intercept (in our examples, the starting number) and the slope (in our examples, the number added each time). There are three main purposes:

- The first is to make explicit the connections between the situation, the table, the formula, and the graph.
- The second is to use graphs to compare two linear functions. Are they represented by parallel or intersecting lines? If the lines are parallel, how can you see that in the tables? In the expression? In the situation? If the lines intersect, what does the point of intersection mean? How can the point of intersection be seen in the tables? In the expressions?

- The third is to examine a table in which the x-values do not increase by 1, but by 5. Ask questions to help participants see that the graph and the expression do not change and that the slope can be calculated by dividing the difference of successive y-values by the difference between successive x-values.

Organize participants into small groups and distribute "Math activity: Catching up or not?" Let the participants know they will have 25 minutes to work with their small groups on this activity. After 15 minutes have passed, announce that the whole-group discussion will focus on Questions 1 and 2 to ensure that all groups have the opportunity to think about those two questions.

As you listen to the discussions of the small groups, take note of the variety of methods participants use to work on Question 2 so you will be able to include the full range of methods in the whole-group discussion. Participants are likely to notice the point of intersection by looking at the tables or the graphs. Some participants might reason out the situation; for instance, for Question 1: "Bolar gets 2 more marbles than Franick each night. He starts out with 30 fewer marbles than Franick. It will take 15 days to make up this difference." Other participants might approach the problem algebraically by setting the two expressions equal to each other and solving the resulting equation. Ask questions so that participants can compare these approaches and see how they are the same and how they are different.

Also ask questions to ensure that participants recognize what in their work indicates *when* the number of marbles is the same and what in their work indicates *how many* marbles children would have at that point. If participants have answered the questions by reasoning from the context, ask how they can approach the same problem by examining the tables or the graphs or the algebraic expressions.

In addition, some small groups may need support in creating and interpreting the tables for Question 2. You might suggest they first find values for Days 1–10 and then record only the 5th and 10th day as a way to begin work on Question 2. Ask questions about how the information in this table is the same or different than tables used previously in the seminar in which the x-values increased by 1.

The whole-group discussion should involve making connections among the various methods your participants used to solve either Question 1 or 2. Choose a problem that all groups have worked on and one in which you know participants will present a variety of approaches (reasoning from the context, examining the graphs, looking at the table, and solving equations). Invite participants to ask each other questions about their methods. When observations are made about one of the representations, ask how that same aspect can be seen in the other representation. (See "Maxine's Journal," pp. 128–137.)

Set aside the last 10 minutes of the discussion to discuss the table that is used in Question 2. Consider questions such as "What does the change in successive y-values indicate in the table?" or "How does the table help you determine the steepness of the line on the graph?" or "What is the effect on the graph of using a table with increments other than 1?"

Let participants know that they will continue to think about these connections as they work on the Focus Questions and view the children on the DVD.

Break

(15 minutes)

Case discussion: Looking at students' representations

(65 minutes)

Small groups (mixed-grade band; 40 minutes)

Whole group (25 minutes)

The cases in Chapter 4 present three different contexts in which intersecting linear functions are significant. Case 14 describes a race between two crayfish, each moving at a constant rate of speed. Cases 15 and 16 are about collecting marbles or bottles at constant but different rates. As participants work on these cases, they will continue to develop their own mathematical ideas in addition to examining the thinking of students in the cases. An important focus is the representations students use. In Case 14, students create a variety of representations to act out the race; and in Case 15, the main representation is a table. In working on these two cases, participants will not only analyze what each of these representations offers, they will also examine graphs for these situations. In Case 16, students offer various ways to make a graphical representation of the data. In discussing this case, participants will work to examine how students were thinking and also to compare the students' representations with more conventional graphs.

Organize participants into groups of three or four and distribute the Focus Questions for Chapter 4. Inform them they will have 40 minutes to work in small groups. You can also suggest that, because they have done substantial work with the marbles scenario, they focus on questions about the case of the crayfish race and student graphs in the bottles case.

Focus Question 1 is based on the different ways students represent the crayfish race and how each method can be used to determine which crayfish finished first. Ask questions to focus participants on examining how the components of the situation are seen in each representation. For instance, "How does this representation show the constant speed? How does this representation show the head start? How does this representation show which crayfish wins?"

Focus Question 2 involves participants in creating a graph of each of the crayfish races based on the table presented by one student. As participants examine their graphs, ask questions to focus them on determining how the components of the situation are seen in the graph. For instance, "How does this graph show the constant speed? How does the graph show the head start? How does this graph show which crayfish wins?"

Focus Question 3 provides the opportunity to examine the thinking of students as they work to create graphical representations. Ask questions to keep the focus on what each representation does and does not capture about the situation. You might want to suggest that participants make their own graphs of the bottle situations in order to compare their own thinking with student work in the case.

In working on Focus Question 4 participants analyze how these different contexts can support work on the same mathematical ideas.

When there are 5 minutes remaining, inform the group that the whole-group discussion will involve Focus Questions 1 and 4. Suggest they talk in small groups about these questions in order to have something to offer the conversation.

The whole-group discussion should include two components:

- Examining the different representations in Focus Question 1
- Articulating the mathematical ideas in the cases in response to Focus Question 4

Begin the whole-group discussion by asking participants to explain how each of the representations in Case 14 can be used to illustrate the race situation and how each representation shows constant rate of change. If participants created their own representations or extended those offered by students, have the whole group explore those as well. Ask questions to examine how each representation shows time and distance. Avoid questions about which representation is better; keep the focus on the mathematics that is highlighted by each representation.

Acknowledge that graphs are another form of representation and post one or two participants' graphs of the crayfish race from Case 14. Once graphs are displayed, ask questions to focus on how the graphs show constant rate of change, the head start, and the winner of the race.

Finally turn to Focus Question 4. Solicit what is the same about the cases in the chapter by asking what mathematical ideas are explored in each context (constant rate of change, different starting values, point of intersection) and how those are each seen in the various representations.

Use this discussion to introduce the notation $y = ax + b$, if you have not already done so. Once the notation is posted and explained, have participants explain how they would adapt the notation to fit various Penny Jar, Magic Marbles, or collecting bottles situations. Depending on the background of your group, you may also want to use these examples to explain the difference between parameters and variables.

What Is the Difference Between *a* and *x*?

The slope-intercept form of a linear function is $y = ax + b$ (or, at times, $y = mx + b$). Even though a, b, x, and y may seem to be of the same character (after all, they are all letters of the alphabet), they are actually used in this formula in different ways. The letters a and b are being used as *parameters*; the letters x and y are *variables*.

The values of a parameter are defined by the specifics in a given situation. For example, the Penny Jar with start number of 3 and amount added of 2 determines the values for the parameters a and b, $a = 2$ and $b = 3$, and these define a particular linear function, $y = 2x + 3$. Once values for a and b are determined from the given situation, the values of a and b do not change for that function.

In contrast, the x- and y-values of the linear function are not limited to one specific value. Rather, the linear function $y = 2x + 3$ expresses a correspondence between all the values x can take on (the domain) and the resulting y-values that are generated by the formula (the range). For instance if $x = 3$, then $y = 9$; if $x = 12$, then $y = 27$; if $x = 0$, then $y = 3$. Because x and y vary, that is take on different values within the function, they are called variables.

It is a convention that letters near the beginning of the alphabet are typically used as parameters (a, b, and c), while letters near the end are used for variables (x, y, and z).

DVD: Does Gowen catch up? (15 minutes)

Whole group

The DVD segment is of a third-grade class working with the same situation as described in Problem 2 of the Math activity comparing Tovar, who starts with 20 marbles and receives 2 each night, and Gowen, who starts with 0 marbles and receives 3 each night. Let participants know the tables the students complete have entries with increments of 5, like the tables they completed for the Math activity. *Note*: The graphs are hard to see on the DVD. Before showing the segment, quickly sketch the graph on the board.

Instruct the group to pay close attention to the comments students make. Suggest they might want to take notes and should focus their attention on these questions: What ideas about graphing does each student understand? What ideas is each student confused about? Provide time for participants to discuss these questions.

Then use the student comments from the DVD about the line going straight up to discuss the definition of function. Ask what it would mean to have points that lie on a vertical line on a graph representing number of marbles and number of days. Participants might suggest the impossibility of this happening: "It would mean at the end of a given day you would have different numbers of marbles at the same time." Connect such comments with the definition of a function; a function is a correspondence from one set to another such that for each *x*-value there is one, and only one, *y*-value. In terms of the marbles scenario, on any given day there is exactly one quantity of marbles. In terms of a Penny Jar, after a specific number of rounds, there is one, and only one, quantity of pennies in the jar. You can let participants know there will be additional opportunities to consider this definition in other contexts as the seminar continues.

Interpretting a Graph That Goes "Straight Up"

A function is a correspondence from one set, the domain, to another set, the range. For each element in the domain; there is *exactly one* value in the range. Jacob's comment in the DVD provides an opportunity to consider what the latter part of this definition means.

In the DVD, Jacob suggests that if the graph of Gowen's marbles were to continue beyond 30 days, it would eventually go straight up. His classmates object to this idea, pointing out that if the slope of the line changes, that would mean that Gowen no longer collects 3 marbles each night as the story states.

The participants in Maxine's seminar do consider the question, what would it mean for the graph to actually go straight up? Georgeann points out, "It would mean that a child has different numbers of marbles at the same time." And Dina adds, "If the line is going straight up, then nothing happens after that time." (See lines 466–469.)

After 50 days, if the line were to go straight up, it would include the points (50, 150), (50, 151), (50, 152), (50, 153) ... As Georgeann and Dina point out, this makes no sense in the context of the story. Any graph that includes a portion of a vertical line cannot be the graph of a function.

Moving outside the context of Gowen's marbles, consider the vertical line for $x = 50$. It would take on many *y*-values; in fact, it would take on all the numbers on the number line: (50, 0), (50, ⁻5), (50, 100.2), (50, 250) would all fall on that line. However, the definition of function states that there is exactly one value in the range that corresponds to each element in the domain (and here we have infinitely many), so the vertical line does not graph a function.

See "Maxine's Journal," lines 481–493, for an example of a discussion in which Maxine's participants consider other contexts to get more of a feel for this aspect of the definition of function.

Homework and exit cards (5 minutes)

Whole group

Distribute the "Fifth Homework" and the lessons from the National Council of Teachers of Mathematics (NCTM) *Navigating Through Algebra* to each participant. Explain that the next student-thinking assignment, due at Session 6, will be based on a lesson from the NCTM materials *Navigating Through Algebra.* Have participants read over the assignment and ask if there are any questions. Let them know they will use this homework as an opportunity to think deeply about the possibilities for a lesson with their students and to find connections to the work they have already done with their students. Let them know they should write their responses to the planning questions and bring those, along with the NCTM materials, to the next session. In Session 5, they will be partnered with another participant and have time to read and provide feedback for each other. After that discussion, they will work with their students on the lesson they developed and then write about the outcomes of that lesson for Session 6.

Note: If part of the plan for your seminar is to support teachers in using a locally chosen standards-based curriculum, you might want to replace the NCTM materials with references to lessons in your curriculum. You will need to choose these lessons carefully so that your participants can use them to engage their students with the ideas explored in this seminar.

Solicit exit-card responses to the following questions:

- What are you getting from writing and discussing the work of your students?
- What questions are the seminar experiences bringing up for you? (These can be about mathematics or learning or teaching or students.)

Before the next session...

In preparation for the next session, read participants' papers describing the thinking of their students. Write a response to each participant. For more information, see the section in "Maxine's Journal" on responding to the fourth homework. Make copies of both the papers and your response for your files before returning the work.

Session 4: Comparing Linear Functions

Third-grade class with teacher Deborah (8 minutes)

This clip shows a class discussion that took place after students worked on a Marbles problem in which they compared Tovar, who starts with 20 marbles and receives 2 each night, and Gowen, who starts with 0 and receives 3 each night. The table they created shows values for the start and then for 5 days, 10 days, 15 days ... up to 30 days. The horizontal axis of the graph also marks every 5 days through 30 days.

Students are seated in a whole group, looking at an easel paper with a graph representing the number of marbles for Tovar and Gowen. The number of marbles for each is represented by a set of points; each set of points falls along a line. The lines are not drawn when the DVD begins.

The teacher, Deborah, begins the discussion by asking what would happen if this continued beyond 30 days. One student, Amanda, indicates that after they cross over, they will continue to get farther apart.

The teacher asks how far apart they are at certain days, and the class talks about the difference between the number of marbles Tovar and Gowen have from the beginning to where they meet and beyond. They make an argument based on the pattern: At the start, they are 20 apart, then 15 apart, then 10 apart, then 5 apart, then 0. After they meet, they are 5 apart, then 10 apart, then 15 apart the other way.

The teacher asks them to explain why and one student says, "Because they can't get smaller and cross over again."

Tom adds, "It will look sort of like an 'X,' because when they cross over, it will keep getting farther apart again, and it will end up being like ..."

One student suggests it would look more like an "X" if they knew more about what happened at the beginning. The teacher indicates we do not know about that but suggests that they do know that the increase keeps happening at this same rate, and she summarizes saying, "Gowen is going to pull ahead, really, a lot more marbles than Tovar." Several students agree.

At this point, the class decides to add several more points to the graph to see if the difference between the lines continues to increase. Then Tom makes an observation.

Tom indicates that he could tell from the beginning that Gowen would pass Tovar because the line for Gowen was so much steeper. "You can tell even if you cut off everything but like the first three from Gowen, that he was going to end up passing Tovar because he was so much steeper." After asking for someone to paraphrase, the teacher asks Tom to repeat his idea.

The teacher connects Gowen's first few points and asks the class to consider what Tom is saying about looking at only that piece of the graph and knowing Gowen would get more.

One student, Jacob, makes the comment that as the days go on, Gowen is going to go straight up.

The teacher responds: "Let's think about that, because that is a really important question."

The teacher asks him to clarify what he means, and he indicates that after a long time, Gowen will go straight up. The teacher asks other students what they think about that.

One student indicates she disagrees because a line going straight up would mean getting a different number of marbles all in one day. The teacher repeats this and other students agree that a line straight up does not match the idea of getting the same number of marbles each day.

Focus Questions: Chapter 4

1. In Case 14, lines 54–89, students offer three different representations:

   - Explain how each representation connects to the problem.
   - How does each representation show time? Distance?
   - Could each be used to solve the problem? Explain why or why not.
   - How are the representations alike? How are they different?

2. In Case 14 of line 79, Tyson's table is displayed. Use one set of axes to make a graph for Big Claw and Flicker. What observations can you make from the graph? What are the connections between what you see on the graph and what Tyson and Carl, on lines 80–87, see on the table? What connections do you see between the graph and students' comments based on the table in the remaining portion of the case?

3. In Case 16, students are developing graphical representations for their data on the collecting bottles problems.

   - Examine what each representation captures about the situation and what each representation does not capture. Consider each of the graphs in the case; these occur at lines 292, 297, 312, and 321.
   - What connections do you see between each of these student-created graphs and the conventional graphical representation? (You may want to construct graphs to represent the bottle collection problem in order to respond to this question.)

4. The three cases in Chapter 4 are situated in two different contexts; one is about motion, and the others are about collecting marbles or bottles. How are the mathematical ideas explored in the cases the same, and how are they different? Be explicit about articulating the mathematical ideas as you compare the cases.

Math activity: Catching up or not?

Use tables, expressions, and graphs to work on these problems. When you make an observation based on one representation, identify how that observation can be seen in the other representations.

1. Consider Franick and Bolar as described in Case 15:

   ■ Franick begins with 30 marbles and gets 3 additional marbles each night.

   ■ Bolar has no marbles at all at the beginning but gets 5 each night.

   Will Franick and Bolar ever have the same number of marbles? When or why not?

   Create a table with entries for at least the first 5 days that show the number of marbles each child has. Write an expression for the number of marbles each child has as a function of the number of nights that have passed. Make one set of axes and show graphs for both Franick and Bolar. What observations can you make from the graph? From the table? From the expressions?

2. In the DVD for this session, you will see students discuss this marble situation:

   ■ Tovar begins with 20 marbles and receives 2 each night.

   ■ Gowen does not have any marbles at the beginning but receives 3 each night.

   Will Tovar and Gowen ever have the same amount of marbles? When or why not?

   Make a table with entries for 5, 10, 15, 20, 25, and 30 nights in the left column. Compare the number of marbles for Tovar and Gowen. Is there a time when they will have the same number? Is there a time when Gowen will have more? How do you know? Make one set of axes and show graphs for both Tovar and Gowen. What observations can you make from the graph? How can you see this observation in the table? In the expressions? What is the impact on the graph of having the table entries increase by 5? What is the impact on the expression?

3. Compare the number of marbles for Gowen and Franick. Will Franick and Gowen ever have the same number of marbles? If so, when will they have the same number of marbles? If not, why is it not possible for them to have the same number of marbles? Make one set of axes and show graphs for both Franick and Gowen. What observations can you make from the graph? From the table? From the expressions?

Lessons from the NCTM Navigating Through Algebra Series

Duplicate a lesson from this list for *each* participant in your seminar according to grade level.

Prekindergarten to Grade 2:

"How Does It Grow?" pp. 24–26 and p. 79 of *Navigating Through Algebra in Prekindergarten to Grade 2* published by NCTM, 2001.

Grades 3 to 5:

"Watch Them Grow," pp. 12–14 of *Navigating Through Algebra in Grades 3 to 5* published by NCTM, 2001.

Grades 6 to 8:

"Building with Toothpicks," pp. 13–17 and Student Sheet p. 75 of *Navigating Through Algebra in Grades 6 to 8* published by NCTM, 2001.

Fifth Homework

Reading assignment: Casebook, Chapter 5

Read Chapter 5 in the Casebook, "Does Doubling Work?" including the introductory text and Cases 17–22.

Writing assignment: Planning for the next student-thinking assignment

Carefully examine the lesson from the NCTM publication series *Navigating Through Algebra* for the grade level you teach. Try the mathematics yourself. What mathematics ideas can the lesson highlight? Do not complete the lesson with students yet. You will have an opportunity to work on this lesson with your students and write about it for Session 6.

For Session 5, write about how you will use this material to bring out the ideas you are interested in exploring with your students by responding to the following planning questions:

1. What mathematical ideas do you want your students to work on during this lesson?

2. What do they already know that they might use to do this work?

3. What range of strategies or approaches do you expect to see in your class?

4. What questions might you ask as students are working to bring out the mathematics ideas?

5. What will be the main focus of the whole-group discussion?

Bring 3 copies of this planning work and the curriculum materials to Session 5 so you will be able to discuss your ideas with others.

Does Doubling Work?

Mathematical themes:
- Discriminating between linear functions with zero and non-zero intercepts
- Examining situations involving non-constant rate of change, that is, non-linear functions
- Graphing nonlinear functions

Session Agenda

Match participants to navigation lesson		
Case discussion: Does doubling work?	Whole group	15 minutes
	Small groups	25 minutes
	Whole group	25 minutes
DVD: A non-proportional linear relationship	Whole group	20 minutes
Break	Whole group	15 minutes
Math activity: Growing patterns	Small groups	15 minutes
	Whole group	10 minutes
	Small groups	25 minutes
Planning for student-thinking assignment	Pairs	25 minutes
Exit cards	Individual	5 minutes

Background Preparation

Read
- the Casebook, Chapter 5
- "Maxine's Journal" for Session 5

Work through
- the Focus Questions for Session 5 (p. 196)
- the Math activity: Growing patterns (p. 197–198)

Preview
- the DVD segment for Session 5

Materials

Duplicate
- "Focus Questions: Chapter 5" (p. 196)
- "Math activity: Growing Patterns" (pp. 197–198)
- "Sixth Homework" (p. 199)

Prepare
- Poster: Two tables

Obtain
- rulers
- calculators
- graph paper
- index cards

Two Types of Linear Functions

Consider this table from the marbles situation in Case 15:

Number of Nights	Number of Marbles Gowen Has	Number of Marbles Tovar Has
0	0	20
5	15	30
10	30	40
15	45	50
20	60	60
25	75	70

Gowen's situation represents a special type of linear function, one that is an example of a direct proportion. *Direct proportion* involves situations in which two values vary, but the ratio between the values stays the same. The ratio between the number of marbles in Gowen's possession and the number of days he has been collecting them—15 to 5, 30 to 10, 45 to 15—is always equal to 3. This is not the case for Tovar—the ratio of 30 to 5 is 6, 40 to 10 is 4 ...

Consider the graphs of these two functions:

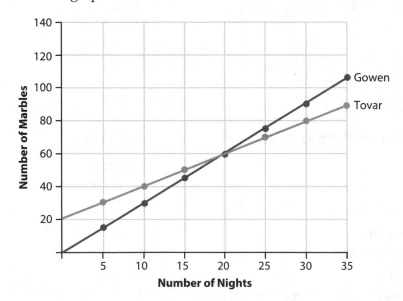

Notice that the line representing Gowen's situation has y-intercept 0; that is, it goes through the origin, $(0, 0)$, the point where the two axes intersect. The line representing Tovar has a y-intercept of 20. The graph of quantities that are in direct proportion always lie on a straight line that passes through the origin.

Does Doubling Work?

The formulas relating the number of days and the number of marbles for Gowen and Tovar are $y = 3x$ and $y = 2x + 20$, respectively. For a situation to be an example of direct proportion, the y-intercept or b-value of the function must be 0, as is the case with Gowen. Thus, the formula for a direct proportion is of the form $y = ax$.

For this situation, Gowen begins with 0 marbles; Tovar begins with 20. Because 0 times any number is 0, for a situation to be an example of direct proportion, there must be a 0 starting amount.

Other examples of direct proportion from the seminar include Lunch money models (Case 6), Big Claw's progress (Case 14), Cookies and candies (Case 17), and Penny Jar situations with 0 as a start.

Maxine's Journal

March 31

Through their student-thinking assignments, participants had already come across the common error of treating all linear functions as though the two quantities were directly proportional, though they had not necessarily articulated the issue. That is the work of Session 5: to clarify what direct proportions are and to identify how they differ from linear functions.   05

Toward the end of Session 5, we began our study of nonlinear functions. I also left some time at the end for participants to share their analyses of the lessons from the Navigations Series they were planning to teach.

I was a bit nervous about sharing my response to Violet's writing with her. At break, she asked if we could talk on the phone before the next session.   10

Case discussion: Does doubling work?

To start out, I wanted to make sure everyone understood the question we were addressing, so I put the following table on the board—a linear function with a non-zero intercept:

0	2
1	7
2	12
3	17
4	22
5	27
6	32

I said, "Here's a table. Let's say it's a Penny Jar context. What can you tell me about it?"   15

Ivan said, "It starts with 2 pennies, and you add 5 each round."

Dina said, "The graph would be a straight line."

I asked, "What would be the slope of that line?"

A few people answered, "5."

I asked, "What would be the y-intercept of the line?"   20

Again, a few people answered, "2."

"OK," I said. "Now I want you to come up with two different ways to find the number of pennies in the jar after 12 rounds."

As participants worked on this problem, I saw that several were coming up against the error that is so frequently made. To find the number of pennies after 12 rounds, they doubled the number of pennies after 6 rounds, for an answer of 64. However, once they used a different approach to solve the problem—for example, applying the rule $5n + 2$, where $n = 12$—they got an answer of 62. Because a couple of people were not quite sure which answer to believe, I suggested they fill out the table to see if that gave them more confidence.

Then I created a table for the Building Buildings context, in which each floor of a building has 3 rooms.

0	0
1	3
2	6
3	9
4	12
5	15
6	18

I described the context and asked how many total rooms would be in a building with 12 floors. Again, people were to find two ways to solve the problem. This time, doubling 18 gave the same value as all the other methods.

I said, "This is what we're investigating in the first part of our session today, through the cases and DVD. In some situations, if we have the value that corresponds to 6, we can double it to find the value that corresponds to 12. When we double the independent variable, we get the corresponding dependent value by doubling. And when it works, it's important for students to see that as a strategy. But sometimes, like in the Penny Jar context we just looked at, it doesn't work. And so we, and the students, need to understand what's going on there, too."

Small groups

Participants then moved to the cases, which they discussed in small groups.

Sandy, Lamis, and Flor were looking at Case 18, Cookies and candies, in which each cookie has 3 mints on it. Lamis was asking, "When they knew that 5 cookies have 15 candies, why do they think 10 cookies will have 18?"

Flor said, "It seems like they're just looking at the sequence of numbers in one column of the table. They're not thinking about how the number of mints relates to the number of cookies."

Sandy said, "Then the teacher emphasizes *five* cookies and *ten* cookies, so Charlotte realizes that there's a jump. Since she doubled the number of cookies, she has to double the number of mints."

Lamis added, "If you just look at a part of the chart, you can miss what's really going on. When Charlotte thought about the cookies, it helped her keep sight of what's going on. The other students seemed to be following a pattern without connecting back to the situation."

Sandy then took a moment to reflect on her own process. "I used to always start with tables, but now I always try to start with the model or situation because it helps me keep track of what is happening. It's not easy to see the patterns and the reasons for the patterns if you're just looking at the table. Before I took these seminars, I couldn't see anything in the models, but now I can. When I was in school, I would never have said, 'In the first 5 floors there are 15 rooms, and so on 10 floors you have 15 rooms and another 15 rooms, and so that's 30 rooms.' I would simply have thought 15 + 15 = 30. It was just numbers, and then we were somehow expected to connect things in story problems later."

Nazir, Elinor, and April were working on Case 21, with the square arrangement of tiles.

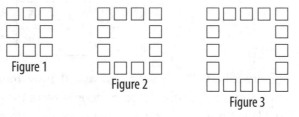

Figure 1

Figure 2

Figure 3

April commented, "It's interesting that kids decided to double at different times, but it never worked. Kevin tried to double to get from 10 to 20. Benito got the right answer for 20 but tried to double to get from 25 to 50."

I asked, "So, why doesn't it work to double? What's going on?"

April said, "I think it has to do with those 4 corner tiles. They're what makes this problem tricky. I bet it would help if we color coded the figures like we did before." She then proceeded to create tile arrangements for Figures 5 and 10, placing blue tiles at the corners and yellow tiles along the sides.

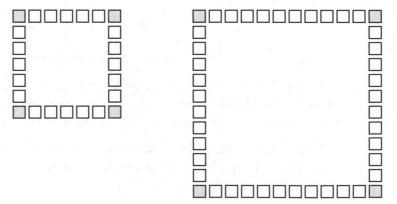

Does Doubling Work?

When I asked Elinor about April's arrangement, she said, "The number of yellow tiles along a side is the same as the figure number, and there are 4 sides. Then the 4 corners give the rule $4n + 4$." As Elinor talked, April and Nazir nodded.

I asked, "So, what doubles when you go from Figure 5 to Figure 10?"

At first they were not sure why I asked that question, but then Nazir spoke up: "You end up with twice as many yellow tiles!"

April added, "Yeah. If you double everything in Figure 5, you end up with twice as many yellow tiles *and* twice as many blue tiles. But you don't need the extra blue tiles. That's why, if you double the whole thing, you have to subtract 4 at the end."

Nazir had a different way to think about it. "If you just double the yellow tiles and add on the four blue at the end, you don't have to subtract."

Whole group

When I called the whole group together, the two tables I presented at the beginning of the session were still on the board. Now I said, "I'd like two more examples of tables, one for which doubling works, one where it doesn't. Let's start with one that does."

Trudy said, "I can give you a table, but I've now learned that it works a lot better for me if I first have a context. So I'm going to say we're making cookies and each cookie uses 5 mints."

As I started to create the table, I asked, "Does it make sense to talk about 0 cookies?"

Flor said, "Sure it does. When you have 0 cookies, you have 0 mints."

0	0
1	5
2	10
3	15
4	20
5	15
6	30

I asked, "Looking at this table, if you double the number of cookies, do you also double the number of mints? What happens if you go from 2 to 4 cookies?"

Everyone seemed to be clear that this was a context in which doubling worked. I asked, "What happens if you triple the number of cookies? Do you also triple the number of mints?"

Dina said, "Well, if you look at the table, when you go from 2 to 6 cookies, you go from 10 to 30 mints."

Trudy added, "But you can think about the context without going to the table. If each cookie has 5 mints, of course when you multiply the number of cookies by anything, you also multiply the number of mints by the same amount."

I then asked for a table in which doubling does not work. Georgeann said, "In the cases, we went back to the square arrangement of tiles. But, I want to think about Drew's function, with the blue tiles in the middle and the yellow tiles surrounding them."

While participants flipped back through their notebooks, I drew a picture on the board.

We generated the table, starting at 1, but I left a space at the top to think about what corresponds to a 0 value for x. When I asked about that, Robin said, "Oh, yeah. When the arrangement collapses so there aren't any blue tiles, there are still the 6 at the end. So, we can put (0, 6) in the table."

0	6
1	8
2	10
3	12
4	14
5	16
6	18

Now we had the following four tables on the board. I explained that in the category of functions for which the doubling strategy worked, the quantities are "directly proportional," so we might as well start using that term as we dig in further.

Not a Direct Proportion	
0	2
1	7
2	12
3	17
4	22
5	27
6	32

Direct Proportion	
0	0
1	3
2	6
3	9
4	12
5	15
6	18

Direct Proportion	
0	0
1	5
2	10
3	15
4	20
5	25
6	30

Not a Direct Proportion	
0	6
1	8
2	10
3	12
4	14
5	16
6	18

I reminded everyone that all four tables represented linear relationships and asked them to explain how they knew. They talked about the constant rate of change of the dependent variable. And then I asked, "So, when you look at the tables, can you see what characterizes a direct proportion?"

Meg said, "You can multiply across by the same number."

We looked at the tables to check out what Meg was saying. For the direct proportions, in one table, if you multiply the x-value by 3, you get the y-value; in the other, if you multiply the x-value by 5, you get the y-value. However, for the other two functions, you couldn't simply multiply by a constant number.

I pointed out that Meg's observation was an important one. I also mentioned that in our examples, the multiplier is a whole number, but that does not have to be the case. For example, you could multiply by 0.5 and it would still be a direct proportion. I added the following table to our collection.

Direct Proportion	
0	0
1	0.5
2	1
3	1.5
4	2
5	2.5
6	3

I suggested that we think about the graphs of these functions. I drew two sets of axes and, taking directions from the group, I drew the direct proportions on one graph and the other functions on the other. I asked, "What do you notice?"

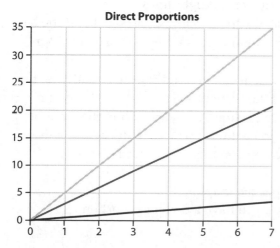

Direct Proportions

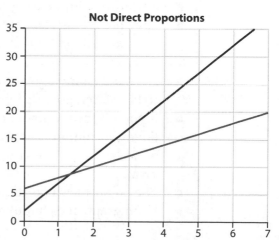

Not Direct Proportions

Dina said, "They're all straight lines."

Bill commented, "One of them is almost horizontal."

I said, "Right. That's the graph of $y = 0.5x$. The slope is smaller than the rest of the functions." Then I paused. "Is there anything that distinguishes the direct proportions from the other linear functions?"

Ivan said, "They all go through (0, 0)."

I said, "Right. The y-intercept is 0."

Then I suggested we check to see how this appears when we write out the algebraic expression for the formulas. We soon had the following formulas:

Direct proportions: $y = 3x$, $y = 5x$, $y = 0.5x$.

Not direct proportions: $y = 5x + 2$, $y = 2x + 6$.

Flor smiled as she said, "You have a direct proportion if you don't add anything on."

I nodded. "Whichever representation you're using, you can tell if it's a direct proportion. In the table, you can multiply the x-value by a constant to get the y-value. You can see that same constant in the algebraic expression. Also, because 0 multiplied by any number is 0, you know that (0, 0) will be a point in the table. So, when you look at the graph, you see that the direct proportions are straight lines that go through the point (0, 0)."

Trudy added, "In a direct proportion, the start number is always 0."

I agreed. "If you have a Penny Jar context and you start with 0 pennies in the penny jar, you'll have a direct proportion."

Now I wanted to take a few minutes to summarize what we had been learning about linear functions. I said, "Over the last three sessions, we've been focused on exploring the characteristics of linear functions. Let's step back and make a list of what we have found."

Within a short time, our list looked like this:

- Linear functions have graphs that are straight lines.
- They have constant rate of change. In a table you can see that if the left column goes up by 1, the right column goes up by a constant amount each time.

- If the left column goes up by a constant amount (not necessarily 1), the right column goes up by a constant amount.
- If you divide the amount the left column goes up by into the amount the right column goes up by, you get the slope. (Divide the difference between the y-values by the corresponding difference between the x-values.)

- The larger the slope, the steeper the graph.
- If the graph goes through (0,0), you have a direct proportion.

Does Doubling Work?

- The formula has an amount that you multiply and an amount that you add. For example, $p = 5d + 4$; 5 is the amount you multiply and 4 is the amount you add. In this example, 5 is the slope and 4 is the y-intercept.
- If the graph goes through (0, 0), then the amount you add in the formula is 0. For example, $y = 3x$.

DVD: A non-proportional linear relationship

Before turning on the DVD, I described the problem the fourth-grade class is working on: a Penny Jar context where you start with 4 pennies in the jar and add 5 each round. I put up the table the class has produced, showing the values up to 7 rounds.

0	4
1	9
2	14
3	19
4	24
5	29
6	34
7	39

The teacher in the DVD then asks the class to find the number of pennies in the penny jar after 14 rounds. I wanted participants to find the answer before listening to what the fourth graders have to say. Within a few moments, they determined that the rule is $p = 5r + 4$, where r is the number of rounds and p is the number of pennies. When $r = 14$, $p = 74$.

Then I started the DVD. In the first segment, a student, Jocelyn, says that she would "double the 7th multiple and then add 4." I stopped the DVD and asked about what Jocelyn said.

Georgeann said, "We don't really know what she means by '7th multiple.'"

I acknowledged that we do not know and suggested we consider the different possibilities and figure out the result for each.

Bill said, "If she really means the 7th value, then she would double 39 to get 78 and add 4 for 82."

I said, "Right. Jocelyn might be thinking there are 82 pennies after 14 rounds. What else might she mean?"

Celeste suggested, "She might mean the 7th multiple of 5, and then she'd be right. Take 35 × 2 and then add 4 and you get 74."

I summarized, "We have two interpretations of what Jocelyn might mean. With one interpretation, she doubles 7 × 5, then adds 4, and gets the correct answer of 74. With the other, she doubles 39 and adds 4, and gets the incorrect answer of 82."

We then looked at the next DVD segment of another student, Shannon, sharing her ideas. 210

Ariel said, "Shannon was right at first, too. She said you could take 4 from 39 and add the result to 39. But, then she got confused and subtracted 5 instead of 4. She said 39 + 34 instead of 39 + 35, so she was 1 off."

I wanted to make sure everyone understood what Shannon had done, so I said, "Let's take what Shannon said first—that you subtract 4 from 39 and add the result to 39. Do you get the right answer that way?" 215

Trudy said, "Well, 39 − 4 = 35 and 35 + 39 = 74. So, it gives the right answer."

I asked, "Do you think it's just a coincidence? Or will that strategy always give you the right answer?" 220

Bill said, "It has to work. If you subtract the start number, you get how many pennies you add in 7 rounds. That's going to be the same whether it's the first 7 rounds or the second 7 rounds. So, after the first 7 rounds, we know there are 39 pennies in the jar. Add in 35 for the next 7 rounds, and you get the number of pennies after 14 rounds." 225

I then showed the third segment, which again shows the student, Jocelyn, as she calculates 10 × 5 plus 4 × 5, giving 70, and then adds 4 to get 74.

Bill wondered why Jocelyn was working with the 10th and the 4th multiples. Dina pointed out that Jocelyn was now working with the rule—$5n + 4$. Dina said, "She's explaining how she multiplied 5 × 14." 230

In the last segment, the teacher explains why her interpretation of what Jocelyn did originally was incorrect—when she adds 39 + 39, she includes the start number twice. At that point Dina burst out, "Oh, I get it! That's what's going on!"

Ariel added, "Actually, if Jocelyn meant 39 + 39 + 4, she was including the start number three times, once for each of the 39s and another 4." 235

At this point in the discussion, I decided to call a break.

Math activity: Growing patterns

When we returned from the break, I told the group we had two big things to accomplish before the end of the session. "We want to move into the mathematics you'll be reading about in the cases, and I also want to give you time to meet with colleagues to prepare for your student-thinking assignment. So, as always, we need to be efficient with time." 240

I continued, "We've spent the last several sessions examining linear functions. Now we're going to start looking at nonlinear functions. We've studied growing patterns before, like Drew's blue and yellow tiles. We're going to study some more growing patterns to explore these new kinds of relationships. For each of the patterns on your Math activity sheet, you should focus on connecting your tables to the models and then to the graphs. But before you graph the function, I want you to record your prediction of what the graph will look like."

Small groups

The first problem involved growing squares:

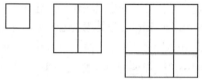

The second involved growing rectangles:

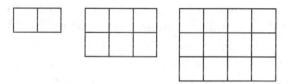

Most people recognized that the algebraic expression for the first problem was x^2, but they were quite intrigued by what else there was to find in the problem. Robin and Celeste told me they knew the graph would be a curve, but now they wanted to explain why. Celeste said, "The square is growing in two directions, and so each time you go from one step to the next, you need to increase the number of tiles you add on. If you have a 3×3 square and you increase only one dimension, it would become a longer and longer rectangle; with a width of 3, you increase by 3 each time. The change is constant. But if you start with the same square and increase in two directions, you add 3 tiles on 1 side, 3 on another, and the corner piece. The next time, you add 4 tiles on 1 side, 4 on another, and the corner piece. So each time, what you add on increases by 2."

Dina, Peggy, and Nazir pointed out to me that this is a function that includes the point (0, 0), and the graph goes through the origin. Dina asked, "So is it a direct proportion?"

I asked them to check out whether a doubling strategy works. Peggy said, "When x is 3, y is 9; when x is 6, y is 36. Nope. It doesn't work."

I suggested they also look at the table and see if they can look across and multiply by a constant to get the y value. Peggy said, "Nope, that doesn't work either. You multiply by 1 and then 2 and then 3 and then 4."

Then I summarized, "To have a direct proportion, it has to be a straight line that goes through (0, 0). In this case, you have a graph going through (0, 0), but it's not a straight line."

When I got to Ivan, Mariam, and Elinor, they had been working on the same idea. Now Ivan showed me how, when they go from a side of n to a side of $(n + 1)$, you need to add on n tiles at the side, n tiles below, and 1 at the corner. I showed him that one way to think about what he just showed me is to say $(n + 1)^2 = n^2 + 2n + 1$. We talked about it for a few minutes, pointing to what the different parts of the expression refer to, and he said he could see it. However, as I was working with him, I realized that he did not have memories of that equation from his algebra class, and so he seemed to be wondering why I was showing it to him.

On the other hand, some groups were thrilled to see equivalent expressions in the models. Bill, Sandy, and Flor worked on the second problem and showed me their two expressions. Sandy said, "Bill says it's $n(n + 1)$ because it's a rectangle and one side is one tile longer than the other. Flor said it's $n^2 + n$ because you've got a square and then you add on one extra column of tiles. This is so neat!"

Although a few groups were working on algebraic formulas, most were not. In fact, I encouraged some groups to explore the tables and graphs more deeply and set aside the formulas for later. I didn't want them to get so preoccupied with finding formulas that they missed out on identifying more accessible characteristics of these functions.

Whole group

With just a few minutes left before we had to move on to the next activity, I put up a table for Problem 1, the Growing Squares, and asked participants what they saw. Mariam said, "It increases by 3, then 5, then 7, then 9. The increase keeps going up by 2."

Figure	Number of Squares	
1	1	
		3
2	4	
		5
3	9	
		7
4	16	
		9
5	25	
		11
6	36	
		13
7	49	

I asked Ivan to come to the board to draw the squares to show us where those differences appear. He pointed out, "You add on a copy of two sides

Does Doubling Work?

275

280

285

290

295

300

each time, and since each side increases by 1, the amount you add on increases by 2."

When I asked what the graph of the function would look like, almost all the participants made a "swoosh" movement with their hand. I pointed out that nobody indicated a straight line.

Dina said, "The rate of change isn't constant. The rate has to be constant to make a straight line."

I also pointed out that everyone indicated the graph would bend upward, and I drew a quick sketch. Why was that?

Bill said, "Each time you go over one, you go up more than you did the last time. That makes the graph bend upward."

I told the class we would continue working with these problems in the next session. "I'd like you to work on the rest of the problems for homework, so when you come in next time, you'll be ready to share your thoughts about them."

Planning for the student-thinking assignment

I was committed to reserving time for groups to discuss the lessons from the Navigations series they had chosen so that they could think more deeply about their mathematical purpose for the lesson and adaptations they might make to achieve that goal. I wanted to make sure they could see that different teachers might have identified different mathematical goals for the same lesson, and so they might choose different strategies for setting it up and interacting with their students. I also hoped that, through these discussions, they would be able to articulate more clearly their mathematical agenda.

While groups were at work, I wrote up the exit-card questions and handed out the homework assignment.

Exit cards

I posed the following questions:

- What mathematics became clear for you in this session? How did that happen?
- What mathematical idea are you still puzzled about or trying to figure out?

I first wanted to see what Violet wrote. Did my response help her to shift her stance during the session?

> VIOLET: I love learning about direct proportions as linear functions with zero y-intercepts. I also enjoyed noticing the change in ratios of quadratic relationships.

I also enjoyed watching the variety of ways students/teachers discover the math.

At the end of this session, Violet could identify some important ideas that were new to her. Are we just now approaching territory that is less familiar? Was it the case that she was learning something in each of the previous sessions, as well, and just did not know how to answer my questions? Perhaps that does not matter. However, from now on, if she is able to name what she is learning, that might help her dig more deeply—and her comments can better guide me in my questions and challenges to her.

However, now I am concerned about Elinor.

ELINOR: Tonight I'm in the dark wrapped in a blanket of fog. I have two questions that have been grounding me. What stays the same? and What changes? These questions didn't help me tonight. I think it's because the change is happening inconsistently. I haven't figured out if anything stays the same. Maxine gave me a new question that I'll hang on to. How does the change vary?

Student thinking—I feel very close to the students I'm working with for this seminar. I guess I'm trying to wrap my head around their entry points.

Two sessions ago, Robin identified what she needed to pay attention to in order to write rules for a function: What is changing and by how much, and what is staying the same? (In formal terms, these are the slope and y-intercept.) Many of the participants, like Elinor, took on those ideas, which felt very solid to them. As long as we were in the world of linear functions, those are exactly what they need to pay attention to. However, now that we are leaving the linear world, they need to learn to pay attention to other aspects of functions. I will need to watch out for Elinor.

A sample of exit cards from other participants paints a picture of where most of the group is.

MEG: I am learning to explore different ways of looking at a mathematical problem: a) make a table (*T*-chart), b) figure out a pattern that the table follows, c) make a graph. Compare everything and look for patterns. This came about from working in small groups first, then seeing it all together in the large group and hearing from the other small groups as to what they discovered.

JOY: Today's work was interesting to me. Understanding the difference between linear and nonlinear graphs. Linear graphs are straight lines that increase at a constant rate [+2 more: (1, 1); (2, 3); (3, 5); (4, 7)]. Lines that end up curved are going up at a varying rate (it could go up +2, but it's in addition to what's already used [(1, 1); (2, 4) +3;

Does Doubling Work?

(3, 9) +5; (4, 16) +7]. It's still hard to explain, but it makes sense. The second example will be a curved line, going up at a different rate each time.

The "direct proportion" idea also became clearer today.

FLOR: I think I am getting clearer and clearer about direct propor- tions. I find that where I once relied upon the charts to think about the patterns, the graphs are beginning to make more and more sense. Right now, I feel that a lot of ideas that were puzzling me have now become clear. I'm sure that will change quickly. As always, illuminating!

Responding to the exit cards

April 2

The group didn't turn in written homework for this session, and so my writing to them was based on the exit cards.

Dear PFC Class,

I want to use this writing to summarize some of the issues that we worked on in Session 5. There were two main mathematical topics: 1) the relationship between direct proportions and linear functions and 2) beginning an exploration of nonlinear functions.

Many of you wrote about feeling much clearer about what is happening with direct proportions. When two quantities are directly proportional, they form a linear function, but linearity does not necessarily imply proportionality. We identified several traits of a linear function that must be present if the quantities are proportional:

- *The graph of the line goes through (0, 0).*
- *The y-intercept is 0. That is, the value of y that corresponds to x = 0 is 0.*
- *The rule is of the form $y = ax$, where a is any number (e.g., $y = 3x$ or $y = \frac{1}{4}x$ or $y = 7x$).*
- *If one of the quantities is multiplied by a fixed amount, then the other quantity is multiplied by the same amount. (If you double one quantity, you double the other.)*
- *The ratio between the quantities is constant.*

If any one of those is true, they are all true, and you have a direct proportion.

However, remember, we are talking only about linear functions here. As we began our work in nonlinear functions, some people noticed that in the first problem, the graph goes through the point (0, 0). However, in this problem, where the formula is $y = x^2$, the doubling rule does not work and the ratio between quantities is not constant.

Now that we have spent several sessions examining linear functions, all of you felt you were on solid ground. You know that the key to linear functions is to find the constant rate of change (the slope) and the value when x = 0 (the y-intercept). You were learning to find those parts in various representations: tables, graphs, algebraic rules, as well as thinking about the context itself. With that knowledge, you are now able to solve problems that involve two linear functions.

As we now move into the territory of nonlinear functions, things get a bit more complicated. The big change is that the dependent variable does not change at a constant rate anymore. From the exit cards, it seems that this is making some of you feel a little shaky. If that is the case, you should recognize that after a while, you will find some reliable patterns in this new arena, too.

At the end of Session 5, we talked about the first problem of the Math activity. The formula for the Growing Squares is $y = x^2$, and the table looks like this:

1	1
2	4
3	9
4	16
5	25

Some of you commented on how the increase of the dependent variable was changing—it first increased by 3, then 5, then 7, then 9—but you also noticed that those increases form a pattern.

That is a key to working with the functions that are explored in Chapter 6: If the function does not change at a constant rate, it still might change in predictable ways. A question to ask is, How does the change vary? That is what you will be looking for.

Maxine

Discussion with Violet

April 4

Violet called this afternoon to talk about my response to her second student-thinking assignment. I am so grateful that she initiated this telephone conversation and grateful for her willingness to consider what I was trying to communicate. She began the conversation by saying, "You know, when I read what you wrote, I felt like I was on the other side of an interaction I sometimes have with my own students. When they tell me they didn't learn anything from working on a problem, I want to say to them, 'That's because you didn't look deeply enough!' You're telling me I need to look more deeply."

Does Doubling Work?

Violet named exactly what I thought the problem was, and so I wanted to make sure she understood my concern for her and her learning. I said, "I think you're in a difficult position in this class. First, almost everyone else in the class has been in a DMI seminar before or some other class that was very similar. The others in the class already know how to read cases and analyze student thinking and they also know how to extend a math problem to move into questions that are new to them. The thing is, much of this math content is familiar to you but is new to almost all the other participants. When they are extending the problems for themselves, they aren't necessarily bringing you into new mathematical territory. So it's much harder for you to learn from them in this kind of seminar."

We talked some more about the content of what I had written. Mainly we discussed what April might have meant in Session 4 when she had followed Violet's explanation in the small group about how to use algebra to find the point of intersection of two lines, but said she did not understand it. What is the difference between following the steps of an explanation and this feeling of understanding that April might be after?

At the end of our conversation, Violet said this helped her a lot and she would refocus her attention for the rest of the seminar.

Detailed Agenda

The first hour of this session is devoted to examining the difference between linear functions with zero and non-zero intercepts, that is, those that represent a direct proportion and those that do not. This is significant because many students (and adults) approach the task of predicting the 10th or 16th value for a given relationship by doubling the 5th or 8th value. It is important to know when this is a useful strategy and when it leads to incorrect conclusions.

The ideas discussed here are based on the work participants have done in the past two sessions, and participants should be able to finalize their ideas in the suggested time frame. It is important not to extend the time for this component beyond one hour because the mathematical ideas participants will work on in the remaining part of the session are apt to be new, and they will need a significant amount of time for that work.

Case discussion: Does doubling work? (65 minutes)

Whole group (15 minutes)

Small groups (25 minutes)

Whole group (25 minutes)

The cases in Chapter 5 provide the context for discriminating between situations that are represented by linear functions with zero and non-zero intercepts. When the relationship between quantities can be expressed as a linear function with a zero intercept, the two quantities are in direct proportion. For example, in the Building Buildings situation (DVD from Session 1 and Case 17 in Chapter 5) in which each floor has the same number of rooms, the relationship between the total number of rooms in the building and the number of floors is a direct proportion. In this situation, if one quantity is doubled, tripled, or multiplied by any number, the other quantity is also doubled, tripled, or multiplied by that number. On the other hand, many of the linear functions we have worked with, like those based on Drew's tile arrangements or Henrietta's roost in Chapter 3, have non-zero intercepts and the quantities do not have such a direct multiplicative relationship.

Initiate a whole-group discussion before the small-group work to provide an example of each kind of situation. You can also use this as an opportunity to work on helping participants make connections between tables and situations.

Begin by posting the following table:

0	2
1	7
2	12
3	17
4	22
5	27
6	32

Solicit ideas about what situation this table could represent. Ask participants to find the 12th entry for this table in at least two ways. Use participant methods to highlight the fact that the 12th entry is not double the 6th entry.

Then post this table:

0	0
1	3
2	6
3	9
4	12
5	15
6	18

Ask participants to describe a situation that matches the data in the table. Again, they should find the 12th entry for the table in at least two ways. Use participant responses to highlight that in this example, the 12th entry is double that of the 6th entry.

Contrast these two situations and let participants know that in the seminar they have worked with both kinds of situations. Solicit participant responses to these questions: "What is it about a situation that relates it to this second type of example? How can you tell by looking at the table?" These questions will not be solved now. Rather, they set up the focus of the case discussion. See "Maxine's Journal" (pp. 168–169) for a description of participants' responses to this introductory activity.

Organize the participants into groups of three or four and distribute the Focus Questions for Chapter 5. Inform the group they will have 25 minutes to work as a small group.

Within small groups, ask questions to help participants make connections among the situations in the cases, the property of "doubling," and various representations such as tables, graphs, and formulas. Questions you might ask include: "How is the building situation in Case 17 similar to the cookies and candies in Case 18? How are they different? How are the situations in those two cases different from the situation in Cases 19 and 20? How can you tell a situation represents a direct proportion from looking at the graph? The table? The formula?"

Focus Question 1 invites participants to analyze the thinking of students as they use a doubling strategy appropriately. They are also asked to make a graph and formula for the situation in the case. Focus Questions 2 and 3 address a third-grade class (Case 19) and a fifth-grade class (Case 20) working on the Growing Worms problem in which doubling will not work. In discussing these cases, participants will explore how students make connections among given situations, the physical models that represent them, and the data they collect in tables. As they work with Focus Question 4, participants will make a graph and formula for the Growing Worms problem presented in Cases 19 and 20. Focus Question 5 involves participants comparing and contrasting the graphs from Focus Questions 1 and 4. Focus Question 6 invites participants to compare the different ways the third graders and the fifth graders express the general formula for the Growing Worms situation.

The whole-group discussion should include the following points:

- The significance of the distinction between linear functions with zero and non-zero y-intercepts
- The connection between linear functions with zero y-intercepts and direct proportion
- A summary of linear functions

Begin the whole-group discussion by asking participants to identify two more tables that can be posted. One table should represent a situation in which "doubling" works, such as those presented in Cases 17 and 18. One table should represent a situation in which "doubling" does not work, such as the tables for contexts presented in Cases 19–22.

Once the tables are posted, ask what observations participants can make about the tables for which doubling does work. Comments should include these two ideas:

- The tables (perhaps after being extended) include (0, 0) as an entry.
- Each entry in the second column is equal to the corresponding entry in the first column multiplied by some constant number.

Use this conversation to introduce the term *direct proportion*. Ask questions to highlight how the other two tables do not represent a direct proportion.

Turn to Focus Question 5 to bring graphs into the conversation. Post one set of graphs. Ask questions to help participants make connections between the observations based on the tables and the graphs. This discussion should establish that linear graphs that contain the origin (0, 0) represent situations that are direct proportions, and it is these kinds of situations in which doubling works. (See the whole-group discussion described in "Maxine's Journal," pp. 171–175.)

Let participants know they will have an opportunity to address Focus Question 6 later in this session.

Use the last 10 minutes of this whole-group discussion to summarize ideas about linear functions by stating, "We have spent the past three sessions focused on linear functions. Let's collect some ideas about them. Think about all of the representations we have been looking at, the situation, the table, the graph and the formula. What is it in the *situation* that indicates it is linear? What does a *table* for a linear function look like? What characterizes *graphs* of linear functions? What kinds of *formulas* do they have?" Collect participant comments on a poster titled, "What we know about linear functions," and post it.

The poster should include comments such as:

- The *situations* describe constant rate of change, that is, something that changes by the same amount for a given change in the input (or independent variable). Examples include the building scenario when each floor has the same number of rooms, the Penny Jar with fixed number of pennies added each round, and the tile arrangements described in the Session 2 homework.
- When the *table* entries for the input increase by a given amount, the table entries for the output change by the same amount. Examples:

Input	Output
1	4
2	7
3	10
4	13

Input	Output
0	6
5	26
10	46
15	66

- The *graphs* are straight lines. The line may go through (0, 0) or it may have a non-zero intercept.
- The *formulas* involve multiplying by a constant and adding a constant. Zero may be the amount added or multiplied. Examples: $y = 3x + 5$, $y = \frac{1}{2}x$, or $y = 5$.

DVD: A non-proportional linear relationship

(20 minutes)

Whole group

Let participants know they will be observing a fourth-grade class working on the Penny Jar situation: start with 4 and add 5 each time. Tell the group you will play a part of the DVD and then pause it for a discussion. The focus of the discussion will be on the mathematical thinking the students offer. Suggest they take notes so they will be able to contribute to the discussion. Some facilitators may prefer to post the discussion questions for all to see; others might state the questions orally at the appropriate pauses in the DVD.

Let participants know that in the first segment, one student, Jocelyn, offers an idea, but there are different ways to interpret her meaning. Show the first segment and ask, "What are two ways to interpret what Jocelyn means?"

Once participants have had an opportunity to express their ideas, mention that, although we really do not know what Jocelyn had in mind, the teacher and her classmates seem to interpret it one way.

Then show the second segment which shows a student, Shannon, sharing her ideas. Ask, "What is Shannon's reasoning?"

After a brief conversation, show the third segment and ask, "How do Jocelyn's comments add to the conversation?"

If participants do not notice, point out that Jocelyn may now be applying the formula for the situation: $5n + 4$, where $n = 14$.

Finally, ask, "How does the teacher connect the different ideas as she summarizes the discussion?" Some participants may believe that the teacher never did understand what Jocelyn said initially. On the other hand, some participants may find that the teacher's summary clarifies why doubling the value after 7 rounds does not give the value after 14 rounds.

Break

(15 minutes)

Looking at Nonlinear Graphs

The functions in the Growing Patterns assignment are examples of two types of nonlinear functions, *quadratic* (Growing Squares, Growing Rectangles, and Staircase Towers) and *exponential* (Allowance).

The rate of change for these types of functions is not constant, as it is for a linear function. Consequently, the graphs for these functions are not straight lines; rather they curve.

Consider this table and graph for the Growing Squares problem:

Does Doubling Work?

Side Length	Area
1	1
2	4
3	9
4	16

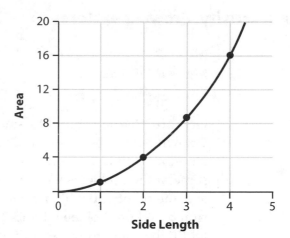

As the inputs change by 1, the corresponding change in output is 3, then 5, then 7, and so on. That is, as the inputs change by 1, the corresponding change in output increases by 2. This is an example of non-constant, although predictable, rate of change. A consequence of this non-constant rate of change is that the graph will curve.

Consider this table and graph for the Allowance problem:

Day	Number of Pennies
1	2
2	4
3	8
4	16

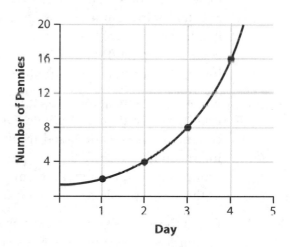

As the inputs change by 1, the corresponding change in output is 2, then 4, then 8, and so on. This is another example of non-constant, although predictable, change. Here, as the inputs change by 1, the corresponding change in the output doubles. Again, a consequence of this non-constant change is that the graph will curve.

In this session, which introduces these types of nonlinear functions, participants should examine tables and graphs to note the non-constant rate of change in the table and the curved nature of the graphs. Quadratic and exponential functions are a focus of Session 6. The note in the introduction to that session includes additional information about these types of functions.

Math activity: Growing patterns

(50 minutes)

Small groups (grade-band groups; 15 minutes)

Whole group (10 minutes)

Small groups (grade-band groups; 25 minutes)

Organize participants into small groups and distribute "Math activity: Growing patterns." Let participants know they will have a significant amount of time to work on these problems with their groups and that some of the problems will be discussed in the next session. Announce that at some point you will interrupt their work to have a whole-group discussion based on Problems 1 and 2 and that after the discussion there will be additional time to work in small groups. You should also let participants know that the focus of the first five questions is on making tables and graphs, not formulas. In Problem 6, they will have the opportunity to work on formulas.

As participants work on the tables and graphs, listen for comments that identify the difference between these functions and the linear functions previously examined in the seminar. Ask questions to elicit comments that contrast these tables with those of a linear situation. A key observation is that the situations and tables involve non-constant rates of change. For instance, changing the height by 1 in Problem 1 produces differing amounts of changes in the area; changing height from 2 to 3 produces a change of 5 in the area $(9 - 4)$; changing the height from 4 to 5 produces a change in area of 9 $(25 - 16)$.

Encourage participants to express their predictions about the shape of the graphs before they plot points. Once they have made graphs, ask how the comments they made based on the table can be seen in the graph. As you interact with the small groups, pay attention to their progress. Once all of the groups have worked on Problems 1 and 2, initiate a whole-group discussion of those two problems.

Focus the whole-group discussion on the question, "How are the tables and graphs for these two situations different from those of linear functions?" While some groups may have started working on other problems, have them set that work aside to have a whole-group discussion about the first two problems and tell them they will have more time to work on the remaining problems after the discussion. In fact, let them know you expect the ideas in this discussion to be useful to them when they return to the rest of the questions.

Begin the discussion by asking about the predictions they made for the graphs of the two tables in Problems 1 and 2. Ask how they could tell the graphs were not going to be linear. The discussion should establish the idea that for these two functions, the rate of change is not steady but, in fact, increases. This makes the graphs curve. Have participants draw both

Does Doubling Work?

graphs and then make connections between the shape of the graphs and the comments they made about the non-constant change. Ask how the tables reflect non-constant change.

Invite participants to return to the small-group work, keeping in mind what they have noticed about these graphs by saying, "As you work on the remaining situations, compare the tables you generate to the ones just discussed. How are they the same and how are they different? What does that indicate about the graphs?"

While participants will encounter a variety of mathematical ideas as they work on the remaining problems, ask questions to be sure every group's work includes a focus on predicting and discussing the shape of the graph. In each case, the graphs are not linear. The situation in Problem 3 is an example of an exponential function; the situations for Problems 4 and 5 are quadratic (as are the situations for Problems 1 and 2). When you work with the small groups, ask what they predict for the graphs on the basis of the table values to help them articulate why these are not linear.

Problem 6 invites participants to write formulas for the quadratic functions generated by the Growing Squares, Growing Rectangles, and Staircase Tower problems. As participants work on these problems, ask questions to help them make connections between their diagrams, their tables, the situations, and the graphs.

Developing a formula for the Growing Rectangle problem might include expressing the area of the rectangle as the product of its dimensions:

Height	Number of Tiles (Area)	Calculation
1	2	1 x 2
2	6	2 x 3
3	12	3 x 4
4	20	4 x 5

This leads to the algebraic expression $x(x + 1)$ for the number of tiles needed for the xth case. If participants use this approach, ask how they can connect that expression with the tile arrangements. "Can you see x groups of $(x + 1)$ or $(x + 1)$ groups of x in the diagram or with the tiles? You might want to begin with some of the numerical examples. How can you see 2 groups of 3 or 3 groups of 2 here?"

Other participants might notice the relationship between this table and the Growing Squares situation:

Height	Number of Tiles	Calculation
1	2	1 + 1
2	6	4 + 2
3	12	9 + 3
4	20	16 + 4

This would lead to $x^2 + x$ as the algebraic expression for the area of a rectangle with a height x. Ask participants to draw a diagram or build with tiles to represent this way of expressing the relationship, for instance:

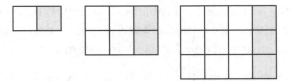

Each complete rectangle is created from a square with dimensions x by x and a smaller rectangle with dimensions x by 1. Adding the areas of these together yields $x^2 + x$ as the area of the entire figure, the largest rectangle.

When both expressions ($x^2 + x$) and $x(x + 1)$ are developed for the same situation, ask how they can show the expressions to be equivalent. When diagrams or tile models are proposed, ask questions so that components of the expressions are linked to the models.

Continue to ask similar questions as participants work on developing formulas for the Growing Squares and Staircase Towers situations. For an example of such work, see "Maxine's Journal" for Session 5 (pp. 176–181) and Session 6 (pp. 208–213).

Note: Participants are not asked to write a formula for the Allowance situation. If some groups are interested in doing this, one way to support their thinking is to suggest they express each entry in the table as a product of 2s.

Day	Number of Pennies	Number of Pennies
1	2	2
2	4	2 x 2
3	8	2 x 2 x 2
...	...	...
n	2^n	2 x 2 x 2 x 2... n times

Does Doubling Work?

If they are not familiar with notation for exponents, show this to them after they have created the table. For example, $2 \times 2 \times 2 = 2^3$.

When time is up for this small-group work, let participants know there will be a discussion in the next session based on these graphs, and tell them to work on any questions they have not yet explored in preparation for Session 6. You can also let them know the cases in Chapter 6 will illustrate students working on similar mathematics.

Planning for student-thinking assignment   (25 minutes)

Pairs (with the same lesson choice)

This activity is designed to provide support for participants as they plan work for their own class based on one of the lessons in the National Council for Teachers of Mathematics (NCTM) series, *Navigating Through Algebra*. Participants have prepared for this activity by choosing a lesson and writing a response to a set of planning questions. This time is set aside for pairs of participants to read and examine each other's planning work and to collaborate in the development of a lesson that they will present to their students and write about for the next session.

Before turning to the small-group planning work, spend 5 minutes discussing Focus Question 6. "In Cases 18 and 19, we saw students of different grade levels working on the same mathematics problem. What did you notice about that?" After soliciting a few comments, suggest they keep these ideas in mind as they consider how to adapt their given lesson to make it appropriate for their students.

Group participants in pairs (or threes, if necessary) according to the lesson they have planned. Tell them to read over each other's responses to the planning questions before beginning any conversation about the lesson. They should first share their ideas about the ways they expect their students to work on the lesson; that is, what scenarios do they expect to see in their classroom? Also suggest that this is an opportunity to work on developing questions they might ask their students both in small and whole group. Pairs should also talk about the focus of the whole-group discussion in the lesson with questions such as, "What are the main ideas you want to have included in the whole-group discussion? What will you look for in the small-group work to help you with the whole-group discussion?"

Let the pairs know they will be grouped together in the next session so they will have the opportunity to share the outcomes of their lesson with these same colleagues.

Optional reading of sections of Chapter 8

If you have decided to suggest participants read portions of Chapter 8 throughout the seminar rather than all at once, assign Chapter 8, Section 3 at this point. You should alert participants to the fact that Chapter 8 will include references to cases they have not yet read and that there will not be time allotted at the next session for discussion of Chapter 8.

Exit cards
(5 minutes)

Individual

Because participants will not hand in a homework assignment at this session, the exit-card reflections will provide the opportunity for feedback. The fifth homework assignment that participants completed for this session will be collected along with the writing assignment that they will complete for Session 6.

Use the last 5 minutes of the session for participants to reflect on these questions and let them know you will be writing responses to them based on this reflection.

- What mathematics became clear for you in this session? How did that happen?
- What mathematical idea are you still puzzling about or trying to figure out?

Before the next session . . .

In preparation for the next session, read participants' remarks on the exit cards and write a response. You might write a single response that incorporates remarks from the whole set of cards, or you may choose to write to each individual, commenting on that person's particular thoughts. For more information, see the section in "Maxine's Journal" on responding to the exit-card comments. Make copies of both the exit cards and your responses for your files before returning the work.

DVD Summary

Session 5: Does Doubling Work?

Fourth grade with teacher Michelle (7 minutes)

The fourth-grade students are having a class discussion based on the Penny Jar situation—start with 4 and add 5 each round. On the board is a table with values for the first 7 rounds and a graph. The teacher asks about the 14th round.

Jocelyn says you can look at the 7th multiple and double that and add the starting number.

Discussion Break

Shannon explains that if you did that you would be doubling the start number. Shannon suggests that you would need to subtract 4 from 39 and add the result to 39. When she does the calculation, however, she loses track and is off by 1.

Discussion Break

Jocelyn offers a way to find the 14th round: "10 times 5 plus 4 times 5 is 70 plus 4 is 74."

Discussion Break

The teacher shows that 39 + 39 = 78 and points out that is not the right answer and again asks what it is you are doubling when you double 39. A student says if you do this, you are doubling the start number.

The teacher summarizes by making three statements:

- If you double, you are doing "start," "start."
- Shannon's method will work if you modify it. You can double the 7th case to get the 14th case if you remember you are counting the start number twice by subtracting one of the 4s.
- Another way to get the 14th case is to do (14 × 5) + 4.

PATTERNS, FUNCTIONS, AND CHANGE

Focus Questions: Chapter 5

1. In Case 17, Sam and Karen both used a doubling strategy to find the number of rooms in a building of 10 floors because they knew the number of rooms in a building of 5 floors. How did they explain why that works for this situation? What is your explanation for why that strategy works for this problem? What would a graph look like for this situation? In Case 18, what is the formula that expresses the relationship between number of cookies and number of mints? What would a graph look like for this situation? Will a doubling strategy work for this situation? Why or why not?

2. Trace the thinking of students in Case 19 by examining these three sections of the case: lines 187–211, lines 212–236, and lines 237–239. Explain both the thinking in each section and how students build on ideas as the case continues.

3. In Case 20, a fifth-grade class works on the same problem as the third graders did in Case 19. The fifth graders generated two different ways to picture the situation and to express the formula for any age worm. Explain both ways and the connections between them.

4. Make a graph and a formula for the Growing Worm problem in Cases 19 and 20. Make observations about the graph, and connect them to the situation.

5. How are the graphs you made for Focus Questions 1 and 4 the same, and how are they different?

6. Taken together Cases 19 and 20 illustrate how students of different grade levels can work on the same problem. What are the similarities and differences you see in the approaches and conclusions of the two groups of students?

Math activity: Growing patterns

1. **Growing Squares:** Extend this table for the number of tiles needed to make squares with side lengths 1, 2, 3, ... up to 10. Make observations about the values in the table. What would a graph for this situation look like? Will it be linear? How do you know? Make a graph to check your prediction.

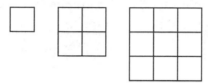

Side Length	Number of Tiles
1	1
2	4
3	9
4	?
5	?

2. **Growing Rectangles:** Instead of growing squares, suppose we are growing rectangles—specifically rectangles in which one side is 1 unit longer than the other. Continue the table up to rectangles with a height of 10. Make observations about the values in the table. What would a graph for this table look like? Will it be linear? How do you know? Make a graph to check your prediction.

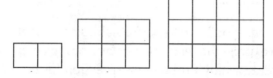

Height	Number of Tiles
1	2
2	6
3	12
4	?

3. **An Allowance Story:** I ask my Mom for an allowance. All I want, I say, is for you to give me an allowance for this month. Give me 2 pennies on the 1st day of the month, double that for the 2nd day, double that for the 3rd day, and so on. On the 1st day, I will get 2 cents; on the 2nd day, 4 cents; on the 3rd day, 8 cents etc. That is all I want.

Make a table to show how many pennies I will get each day for the first 10 days of the month. Make observations about the values in the table. What would a graph look like? Would it be linear? How do you know? Make the graph to check your prediction.

Staircase Towers: Previously we examined the relationship between the number of towers and the number of cubes in the tallest tower. Now consider the relationship between the number of towers and the number of cubes needed to build the *entire* staircase.

For the two staircases described below, make a table expressing the relationship between the total number of tiles and the number of towers. Make observations from the table. What would graphs look like? Would they be linear? How do you know? Make the graphs.

4. Staircase Towers: Jumps of 1   5. Staircase Towers: Jumps of 2

Number of Towers	Number of Tiles
1	1
2	3
3	6

Number of Towers	Number of Tiles
1	1
2	4
3	9

6. In these problems, you have looked at tables and graphs for the situations. Now, work to express the relationships by finding an expression for the 50th or 100th case and then by finding an expression for the nth case.

Sixth Homework

Reading assignment: Casebook, Chapter 6

Continue working on "Math activity: Growing patterns," which will help prepare you for the next set of cases. Read Chapter 6 in the Casebook, "Examining Non-Constant Rate of Change," including the introductory text and Cases 23–26.

Writing assignment: Examining student thinking

Pose the mathematics task you have chosen and modified from the NCTM resource. Write about what happened.

- What did you learn?
- How did your students respond?
- What do you make of their responses?
- What surprised you?

Include specific examples of student work or dialogue. Examining the work of just a few students in depth is very helpful.

At our next session, you will have the opportunity to share this writing with your partner(s) from the planning session. Please bring three copies of your writing to share.

PATTERNS, FUNCTIONS, AND CHANGE

Examining Non-Constant Rates of Change

Mathematical themes:
- Comparing graphs of nonlinear and linear functions
- Making connections between the shape of a graph and a situation describing change
- Writing formulas for quadratic and exponential situations

Session Agenda

Sharing student-thinking assignment	Small groups (same groups as last session)	20 minutes
Tables and graphs of nonlinear functions	Pairs Whole group	5 minutes 20 minutes
Case and math discussion: Quadratic and exponential functions	Small groups Whole group	30 minutes 25 minutes
Break		15 minutes
Poster discussion: What we know about functions with curved graphs	Whole group	15 minutes
Teachers' moves discussion	Individual/pairs Whole group	25 minutes 20 minutes
Exit cards	Individual	5 minutes

Background Preparation

Read
- the Casebook: Chapter 8, Section 4
- "Maxine's Journal" for Session 6
- the agenda for Session 6

Work through
- the Focus Questions for Session 6 (p. 233)
- Examining teachers' moves (p. 234)

Materials

Duplicate
- "Math activity and Focus Questions: Chapter 6" (p. 233)
- "Examining teachers' moves" (p. 234)
- "Seventh Homework" (p. 235)

Prepare
- Poster: Graphs from growing patterns (p. 232)

Obtain
- index cards
- poster created in Session 5: What we know about linear functions

Examining Change in Quadratic and Exponential Functions

Consider these tables representing three functions, A, B, and C.

Input A	Output A
1	3
2	7
3	11
4	15
5	19
6	23
...	...

Input B	Output B
1	2
2	8
3	18
4	32
5	50
6	72
...	...

Input C	Output C
1	4
2	16
3	64
4	256
5	1,024
6	4,096
...	...

Examine the way each function's output changes as the input changes by 1.

- For Function A: There is a constant change of 4.
- For Function B: The changes are 6, 10, 14, 18, 22 .... The changes are increasing; each change is 4 more than the previous one.
- For Function C: The changes are 12, 48, 192, 768, 3,072, ... The changes are increasing; each change is 4 times larger than the previous one.

These examples illustrate three types of functions that can be characterized by the rate of change. As we have already discussed, when the rate of change is constant, the function is linear. Function A is a linear function.

For Function B, the rate of change itself changes by a constant amount; in this case, as the input increases by 1, the changes in the output increase by 4. While the function values do not fit a linear model, the sequence of changes does; that is, in the sequence of changes, the difference between successive terms is constant. Function B is a quadratic function.

For Function C, as the inputs increase by 1, like Function B, the changes in the output increase: 12, 48, 192, 768, ... However, unlike Function B, the sequence of changes does not fit a linear model. For Function C, each change is 4 times the previous one (just like the output itself). Function C, for which the output is equal to a constant times the previous output—and consequently, the changes have this same property—is an exponential function.

Examining Non-Constant Rates of Change

Formulas and Graphs for Quadratic and Exponential Functions

The general form for a quadratic function is $y = ax^2 + bx + c$, where b and c can be any number on the number line; a can be any number except 0. Here are some examples of quadratic functions and their graphs:

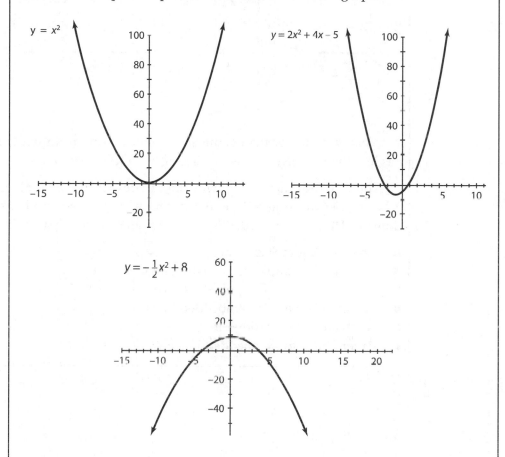

Graphs of quadratic functions are called parabolas. Unlike linear functions that either increase or decrease, quadratic graphs increase over some parts of the domain and decrease over other parts. The sign of a indicates whether the graph opens up or opens down. The value of a indicates how narrow or wide the parabola is. The value of c indicates the point where the graph intersects the y-axis. The values of b and c can be used to determine the location of the turning point, or vertex, of the graph.

A basic exponential function has this formula: $y = a^x$, where a must be a positive number. Note that in this case, the variable is the exponent. Here are some examples of exponential functions and their graphs:

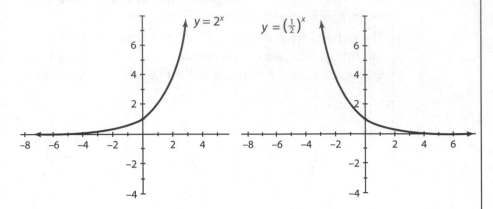

When a is greater than 1, the graph is increasing from left to right; when a is less than 1, the graph is decreasing from left to right.

Note that the functions for Growing Squares, Growing Rectangles, Staircase Towers, Allowance, and Paper Folding have only whole-number values in the domain. They are embedded in the continuous functions described here:

- Growing Squares is embedded in $y = x^2$.
- Growing Rectangles is embedded in $y = x^2 + x$.
- Staircase Towers 1 is embedded in $y = \frac{1}{2}x^2 + \frac{1}{2}x$.
- Staircase Towers 2 is embedded in $y = x^2$.
- Allowance is embedded in $y = 2^x$.
- Paper Folding is embedded in $y = 2^x$.

Examining Non-Constant Rates of Change

Maxine's Journal

April 14

In Session 5, we began looking at functions with non-constant rates of change. Today we would continue, giving particular attention to quadratic and exponential functions.

However, as participants entered the room, their heads were filled with the Navigations lesson they had just taught. Dina walked in and declared, "My lesson bombed! My students got so caught up in the calculations, they didn't have an opportunity to explore the ideas about functions." I found it interesting that she could be so clear about what had gone awry and also that she continued to smile. She shrugged and said, "The lesson did give them a good opportunity to work on calculations." With this, we began the session reflecting on the student-thinking assignments.

Sharing student-thinking assignment

To begin, participants met with a partner who had written about the same Navigations lesson. They read their colleague's assignment with interest and the discussions were very focused.

After 25 minutes discussing the work in pairs or threes, I brought the group together to ask what they got from this assignment. I said, "I gave you a lesson to use. You had an opportunity first to read the lesson and plan to teach it, then to meet with colleagues to discuss your plans, then to teach and write about the lesson, and then to meet with a colleague again to discuss what happened. What was that whole experience like for you?"

Everyone indicated this process was very useful. Robin said, "It was really great to meet with Dina and Trudy ahead of time because it helped me to clarify the purpose of the lesson. I had a different idea than Dina and Trudy because I wanted to give my students the challenge to organize the information. They wanted to give students tables to fill in, so it was already organized."

Trudy chuckled and said, "Yeah, some of us have more controlling personalities."

I pointed out that it is not a matter of personality and whether you are controlling or not. "You make different decisions about how to set things up, depending on your goal, the mathematical agenda for the lesson. If figuring out how to organize the information into a table is what you want students to work on, you'll set up the lesson like Robin did. But, Trudy, you wanted to give your students an opportunity to see how those functions behave, and you didn't want to commit time to their fumbling around with organization—and so you gave them tables to fill in."

Then April said, "I want to say what I learned from doing the same lesson as Joy and then reading her case. When I did the lesson, I only got so far and my students were confused and I didn't know how to go any further. We were looking at the table, and they expected to be able to double the value for 5 to get the value for 10, and I didn't know what questions to ask to get beyond that. When I read Joy's case, I saw exactly what I needed to do. Joy's students were at the same place, and she had them go back to the context. That made them see why doubling wouldn't work."

Ivan said, "I really appreciated first talking with a colleague about the purpose of the lesson. I was that much clearer about how to set up the lesson to get at what I thought were the important mathematical ideas. Then it was interesting to see how Nazir and I set up the lesson differently, even though we had talked last time and were in agreement. And then we had a chance to see how two different groups of students responded."

I thanked the group for using the opportunity to think together so fruitfully.

Tables and graphs of nonlinear functions

In the last session, participants began work on a Math activity to explore quadratic and exponential functions. For homework, they were asked to continue with that activity and to read a set of cases in which students were working with those types of functions. I wanted to use both the Math activity and the cases to clarify the characteristics of the functions. Both quadratic and exponential functions are nonlinear; their graphs are curved; the rate of change is not constant. A distinguishing feature of quadratic and exponential functions is the way the changes vary.

To begin, I wanted to have a short discussion about three of the problems participants worked on in Session 5. I hung the poster I had prepared showing the tables and graphs. I suggested participants spend a few minutes in their small groups to refresh their memory of these problems before we discuss them. I asked them to think about what is the same about the graphs and tables, what is different, and how the nonlinear nature of the graphs is related to the tables and the contexts.

I reminded the group that the functions for the contexts in the problems have whole-number domains so that graphs are the discrete points. However, I explained that I drew in the curves by connecting the points so we can better see what is going on. I also suggested that they not spend this time thinking about the formulas; we would get to those later. I wanted to make sure they first considered the connections between the tables and graphs.

Examining Non-Constant Rates of Change

Figure Number	Number of Tiles
1	2
2	6
3	12
4	20
5	30
6	42

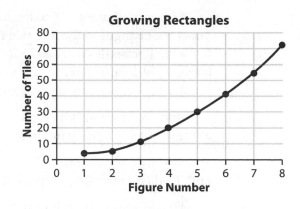

Figure Number	Number of Cubes
1	1
2	3
3	6
4	10
5	15
6	21

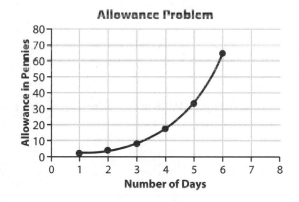

Number of Days	Allowance in Pennies
1	2
2	4
3	8
4	16
5	32
6	64

After giving them 5 minutes in small groups, I brought participants together for whole-group discussion. I asked that we first consider Growing Rectangles and Staircase Towers. Trudy started us off by saying, "The numbers grow in a particular way in the right column, but it's different from the left. It's predictable but not by the same amount at each step."

Robin added, "In Growing Rectangles, the increases go up by 2 each time. In Staircase Towers, the increases go up by 1 each time."

Georgeann asked, "Is it logical to say that the rate of change is twice as fast?"

Robin and Georgeann were pointing us right in the direction we needed to be headed, but I was concerned this last question could cause us to bypass some important points. I needed to be careful. I responded, "Robin has us looking at the changes in the first two functions. She pointed out that the *changes* in Growing Rectangles increase by 2 each time, and the *changes* in Staircase Towers increase by 1 each time. So, the rate of change of the *changes* in the first table is twice as fast as the rate of change of the *changes* in the second."

Elinor called out, "Oh—last time you told me to look at the changes of the changes. That's what you meant."

I said that we would get back to thinking about this some more. However, now I asked what the graphs of the two functions look like.

Mariam said that both of them curve gently upward, but the curve of the Staircase Tower's graph is much gentler.

Then Flor asked, "What's the slope?" and I realized that we needed to go back and look at lines. With Georgeann's question in mind, I created two tables, which I labeled Tables *A* and *B*. (I chose the output variables to match the differences found in Growing Rectangles and Staircase Towers.) I asked participants to help me graph the lines that correlated with these tables.

Table *A*			Table *B*	
x	*y*		*x*	*y*
1	4		1	2
2	6		2	3
3	8		3	4
4	10		4	5

Within a few minutes, we had the following graph.

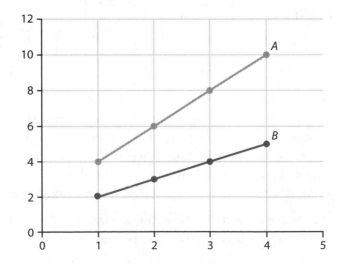

I said, "Let's go back and think about what *slope* means. If you pick any two points on the line, it's the amount you go up divided by the amount you go over." As I said this, I marked different places on the graph to show distance

Examining Non-Constant Rates of Change

over and distance up. "When you have a straight line, no matter what two points you pick, you'll always get the same value for the slope."

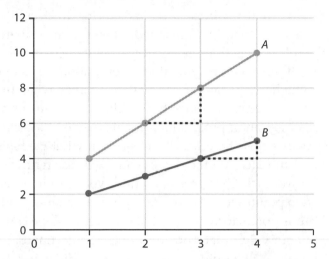

With a little more discussion, we determined the slope of line *A* is 2; the slope of line *B* is 1.

Now, I turned back to Georgeann's question. "You can think of slope as the rate of increase. And when you look at these two straight lines, the slope of the line for Table *A* is twice that for Table *B*. The rate of increase is twice as fast."

At this point, Georgeann made an excited discovery about how I had chosen the values for Tables *A* and *B*. She said, "Your tables and graphs represent the *increases* for Growing Rectangles and Staircase Towers."

I nodded and said, "The rate of increase of the increases in Growing Rectangles is twice as fast as the rate of increase of the increases in Staircase Towers."

Then I took us back to Flor's question. "Flor asked about the slope for Growing Rectangles and Staircase Towers."

We looked at the graphs of these two functions, picking different pairs of points to show that if we go over, say, 2 spaces, we go up more and more the farther out we go.

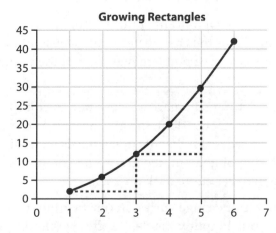

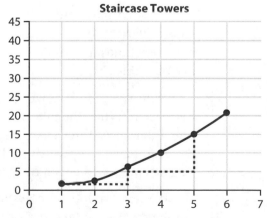

I explained, "When we have functions like this, the ratio is always changing. We do not have a constant slope; there is not a constant rate of change." 120

I stood there for a second, trying to decide if I should go further with
this idea than I had planned. Then I decided to go with it. "OK, I'm going to
explain something really quickly, but we're not going to spend a lot of time on
it. If this confuses you, don't worry about it. Here it goes: This question about
whether you can measure rate of change when the rate is changing bothered 125
mathematicians for centuries. Then they came up with the following idea: You
can get an approximation for the slope at a particular point by picking two
points close together. It's clear from what we have seen that, if you pick different places on the curve, you'll get different values for the slope. However,
if you pick a target point, and if you take these approximations by choosing 130
two points close to your target point, in a curve like this, the closer you bring
your points to your target, the values of slope converge to a single value. That
single value that your approximations converge on, that's the slope of the
curve at that point. And that's what differential calculus is about."

I do not know if it was useful for me to get into a short description of dif- 135
ferential calculus, but it did not take very much time. I summarized by saying,
"Basically, differential calculus takes on Flor's question, 'How can you think
about the slope of a curve?'"

Then I suggested we turn to the Allowance problem, the third table, and graph.

Nazir said, "The graph starts out slow and then goes up really fast. It 140
curves in really fast. Like a backward *c*, but it won't go back."

I asked, "What does it mean to go back?"

Trudy said, "If it goes back, it wouldn't be a function. You can't have two
points for the same *x*-value."

Yan said, "See, it might start out kind of slow, but after a while it shoots 145
up really fast."

I asked, "What can you say about the change?"

Lamis said, "It doubles. It doesn't go up at a constant rate."

I nodded and said, "This is a very significant thing to notice, how the
change varies. You notice that sometimes the change varies at a constant rate, 150
and sometimes it doesn't. For the Allowance problem, we see that the change
doubles at each step."

I then said, "Before we go on, let me summarize a few points from this
discussion. When the rate of change is not constant, the graph is not a straight
line. From these three examples, we see that if the rate of change is increasing, 155
the graph curves upward. As Trudy pointed out, the graph can continue getting steeper and steeper, but it will never curve back on itself.

"We can also look at how the rate of change varies. In our first two tables,
we see that as we take steps of 1 in the input variable, the changes in output

Examining Non-Constant Rates of Change

increase by a constant amount. In the first table, the change in the output increases by 2; in the second, the change increases by 1. This kind of change is a characteristic of a particular kind of function called *quadratic*."

I added two columns to the tables for Growing Rectangles, Staircase Towers, and Allowance Problem. As I did, I explained that the column of changes in the output column is called "First Difference," and the changes in that new column is called "Second Difference." I said, "In a quadratic function, the second difference is constant."

Growing Rectangles

Figure Number	Number of Cubes	First Difference	Second Difference
1	2		
		4	
2	6		2
		6	
3	12		2
		8	
4	20		2
		10	
5	30		

Staircase Towers

Figure Number	Number of Cubes	First Difference	Second Difference
1	1		
		2	
2	3		1
		3	
3	6		1
		4	
4	10		1
		5	
5	15		

Allowance Problem

Figure Number	Allowance in Pennies	First Difference	Second Difference
1	2		
		2	
2	4		2
		4	
3	8		4
		8	
4	16		8
		16	
5	32		

I continued, "The Allowance problem is an example of a different kind of function. Here we see that when we look at the second differences, this fourth column here, we do not have a constant. However, this column also has a special characteristic. The values double each step, just like the previous two columns. This is an example of an *exponential function*.

"The students in the cases of Chapter 6 were also working with quadratic and exponential functions. So, we're going to spend some time with those cases now to let some of these ideas sink in. You can also spend some time looking at the formulas that match these functions."

Case and math discussion: Quadratic and exponential functions

Small groups

When I began to visit smaller groups, Peggy told me she felt very much at sea. She was working with Dina and Lamis who usually worked very well with partners. Thinking that my comments to Elinor in the last class had helped her to focus, I explained to Peggy that we had spent several sessions looking at linear functions in which rate of change was constant. Now, we are moving into new territory, where the rate of change is not constant, but it does change in predictable ways. Since Dina and Lamis were discussing Case 23, Fastwalker, I thought this would be a good place for Peggy to enter—to think about a function where the change is increasing.

On my suggestion, Dina and Lamis reviewed what they had seen in the table of Fastwalker's height.

Fastwalker's Age (years)	Fastwalker's Height (cm)
0	1
1	2
2	4
3	7
4	11
5	16

Lamis said, "The table shows his height at birth and each year after that. But it's when you look at how much he grew each year that you really get the pattern."

Dina went on, "During his 1st year, he grew 1 centimeter. During the 2nd year, he grew 2 centimeters, and during the 3rd year, he grew 3 centimeters. Do you see that Peggy?"

Flor, Bill, and Ivan were also looking at Fastwalker's table but comparing it to Problem 3 from the Session 5 math activity. Flor said, "In both, the change increases by 1 each time. The changes are 1, 2, 3...."

Number of Steps	Number of Cubes
1	1
2	3
3	6
4	10
5	15

Ivan said, "It's weird, because Fastwalker starts at year 0, but our table for the staircase starts at 1."

Bill said, "But look. If you just compare the values at 1, 2, 3, 4, Fastwalker is always 1 more than the staircase."

I pointed out that this is a very helpful observation. They might compare the graphs to see what the difference is. And they might use what they know about the formula for the staircase function to figure out the formula for Fastwalker.

Most participants readily saw that the Paper-Folding case yielded the same table and graph as the Allowance problem. They took a few moments to review important characteristics. I heard Flor say, "The output values double each step. So does the change, and so does the change of the change."

When I came to Robin, Mariam, Elinor, and Sandy, they said they had trouble making the formulas for the problems from Session 5. "The first one, Growing Squares, is easy," Sandy said. "That's $y = x^2$. But after that, I couldn't find anything." I asked them to show me what they had done and realized they had been trying to devise the formula from the data in the table. I suggested we look back at the figure instead.

In fact, even though the table for Fastwalker looks simple, the formula is more difficult to find directly from the table. I wanted to make sure they had formulas for the growing patterns first, so they could derive Fastwalker's formula from those.

We began with Problem 2, Growing Rectangles, in which one side is always 1 unit longer than the other: $1 \times 2, 2 \times 3, 3 \times 4$, etc. We had tiles handy, and to make sure they knew what the pattern was, I had them build the first few figures.

I said, "One way to think about a formula for these figures is to compare them to some figures for which we know the formula. You know the formula for Problem 1 is $y = x^2$. How are the figures in Problem 2 different from those in Problem 1?"

When I said that, Elinor began rearranging the tiles by color so that they looked like this:

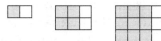

Elinor explained, "The blue tiles make up the square. That part we know is n^2. So, what's the yellow?"

Sandy said, "It's one more column with n tiles. So the rectangle is $n^2 + n$. OK. That wasn't so hard."

I looked at Mariam who had been quiet. She nodded and said she gets it. Then Robin brought us to Problem 4. She said that during the week she had asked someone to tell her the formula and learned that it is $\frac{n(n + 1)}{2}$, but she just doesn't see it.

Problem 4 was about Staircase Towers, stepping up 1 each time. I told them that we could do something similar, comparing these figures to another that we know. However, there is something a little tricky to help us see the relationship. I asked them to make two sets of figures, one all yellow and the other all blue. Once they were done, I aligned the figures to show how they can fit together.

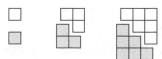

I asked, "If we push the figures all the way together, what kind of shape do you end up with?"

Robin said, "You've got rectangles," and Mariam added, "You've got the same rectangles as in Problem 2."

I nodded. "So, how can you use the formula you know from Problem 2 to get the formula for Problem 3?"

Robin said, "Well, it's going to be half. So that's $\frac{n^2 + n}{2}$." She then looked at the formula that someone had given her, first with a frown and then with a smile. "I see. That's the same as $\frac{n(n + 1)}{2}$."

Mariam was not so satisfied. "How do we know that trick of copying the figure, turning it upside down, and putting it together with the original? That would never have occurred to me."

I said that sometimes knowing mathematics involves experimenting with different ways of taking things apart and putting them back together. "If you work with problems like these, you develop a feel for strategies that often prove to be fruitful. You saw how the shapes of Problem 2 were related to those in Problem 1. Often when you're working on a problem, you should ask, how can I use something I know to figure out something I don't know? You might see if you can apply a similar strategy to Problem 5."

While I talked, Sandy was pointing to the posters at the front of the room. "Look at the tables for Growing Rectangles and Staircase Towers," she said. "All the values in the first table are double the values in the second! So of course you divide by 2 to get the formula."

Whole group

To start the whole-group discussion, I posted the table and graph for Fastwalker.

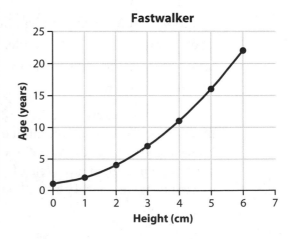

Age (years)	Height (cm)
0	1
1	2
2	4
3	7
4	11
5	16
6	22

I asked, "What do you notice about Fastwalker's table and graph?"

Examining Non-Constant Rates of Change

Ariel pointed to the poster from the first discussion and said, "It's like Growing Rectangles and Staircase Towers. If you look at the increases in output, they go up linearly."

Flor said, "Fastwalker is more like Staircase Towers. When you look at the increases in Staircase Towers, they go up by 1 each time, starting at 2: 2, 3, 4, 5, 6. In Fastwalker, the increases start at 1: 1, 2, 3, 4."

When I asked about the graph, Trudy said, "The Fastwalker graph is curving up gently, like the others."

Bill said, "In fact, the Fastwalker graph is the same as Staircase Towers except it's higher." He showed how he had drawn the two graphs on separate sheets of paper and when he put one over the other, he could align the Fastwalker graph so that it fell exactly on the Staircase Towers graph.

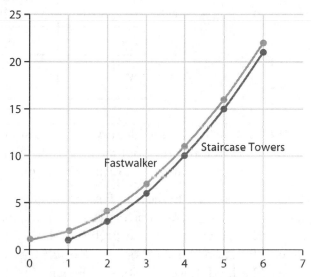

Yan said, "But what about the formula? I can't figure out the formula for Fastwalker and am feeling pretty frustrated."

I said we could come back to that and suggested we first work on the formulas for the other problems. Everyone said they had an easy time finding the formula for Growing Squares, $y = x^2$, and had eventually figured out the formula for Growing Rectangles: $y = x^2 + x$. Some had written the formula as $x(x + 1)$, and so we showed how the two expressions are equivalent.

Robin showed how the tile arrangements for Staircase Towers can be seen as half the arrangement for Growing Retangles, giving us the formula $y = \frac{x^2}{2} + \frac{x}{2}$, which can also be written as $y = \frac{x^2 + x}{2}$ or $y = \frac{x(x + 1)}{2}$. She also pointed out how you can see the halving relationship by comparing the tables.

Mariam then talked about the Staircase Towers with Jumps of 2, "At first we were really surprised that the table was exactly the same as Growing Squares. But, then we saw how each arrangement can be made into a square. So the formula for that one is also $y = x^2$.

265

270

275

280

285

When we came to the Allowance problem, Ivan said, "I get that you keep multiplying by 2 to get the next output. So when $x = 4$, $y = 2 \times 2 \times 2 \times 2$. What I don't see is how to write that as a formula."

I wrote out the formula for the Allowance problem: $y = 2^x$. Ivan was surprised to see that the variable could be an exponent.

I said, "We will get back to Fastwalker in a moment, but first I want us all to look at these formulas together."

I had made up a list in two columns, and now I wrote a heading on each column so the list looked like this:

Quadratic Functions	Exponential Functions
$y = x^2$	$y = 2^x$
$y = x^2 + x$	
$y = \frac{x^2}{2} + \frac{x}{2}$	

I asked participants to identify what is common among the quadratic functions. When they pointed out the x^2, I circled that part of each of the formulas. I acknowledged that this characterizes all quadratic functions.

Then I pointed to the x in the exponential function and said, "This is the part of the rule that characterizes an exponential function. The independent variable is an exponent. Our problems don't illustrate this, but we could also have a function like $y = 3^x$ or $y = 10^x$ or $y = (\frac{1}{2})^x$. These are all exponential functions." I added those functions to the list.

Then I suggested, "Let's go back to Fastwalker. What do we know about this function?"

Flor said, "It's a quadratic function, so it has to have x^2 in it."

I nodded. Then Bill said, "We compared Fastwalker to Staircase Towers. Look at the tables."

Ivan added, "It might be confusing at first, because Fastwalker begins with 0 and Staircase Towers begins with 1. But, if you ignore the first entry for Fastwalker, the rest are 1 more than Staircase Towers."

There were some murmurs in the room, and so I suggested everyone talk to a partner to discuss what Ivan was saying. Two minutes later, I called the group back together, and asked, "Does that help you figure out what the formula is?"

Yan said, "I get it. You take the Staircase formula and add 1. So it's $y = \frac{x^2}{2} + \frac{x}{2} + 1$."

Examining Non-Constant Rates of Change

I added that formula to the list of quadratic functions. Now the table looked like this:

Quadratic functions	Exponential functions
$y = x^2$	$y = 2^x$
$y = x^2 + x$	$y = 3^x$
$y = \dfrac{x^2}{2} + \dfrac{x}{2}$	$y = 10^x$
$y = \dfrac{x^2}{2} + \dfrac{x}{2} + 1$	$y = \left(\dfrac{1}{2}\right)^x$

There was still one more thing I wanted to show participants. I reminded them that the functions for Growing Rectangles, Staircase Towers, and Allowance all had whole-number domains. However, once we have these formulas, we can step out of the context and look at the functions with the domain of all the numbers on the number line. When we do that, the graph is not just the discrete points but also all the points on the curve between them. Not only that, but it also extends to the left of the vertical axis, where the domain takes on negative values. I suggested we look at some of the graphs to see what happens on the other side of the y-axis.

I said, "We will look at the simplest of the quadratic functions, $y = x^2$." I asked the group to make up a table that includes the values for x from $^-5$ to 5 and then to create a graph. Not everyone remembered the rules for operating with negative numbers, and we were not going to get into explorations of it here. This is, in fact, the content of another DMI module, *Reasoning Algebraically About Operations*. However, in small groups, those who did not remember that the product of two negative numbers is positive had a chance to be reminded.

As participants worked, I heard comments like, "Oh, cool," and "Wow." Then I drew the graph on the board.

Quadratic Function: $y = x^2$

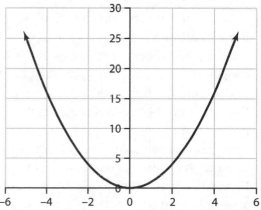

I said, "This is the basic shape of all quadratic functions. The graph might be more open, or squeezed together; it might move up or down, left or right; and it might be flipped over. The graph of any quadratic function is going to have this cup-like shape.

"However, the graph of an exponential function looks quite different. For $y = 2^x$, make up a table, and draw a graph for a domain that extends from ⁻5 to 5." ₃₄₅

Here, again, some participants needed help to find the value of 2^{-1}, 2^{-2}, etc. However, soon most groups had the graph of the exponential function, which I sketched on the board. ₃₅₀

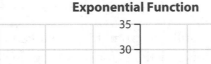

Exponential Function

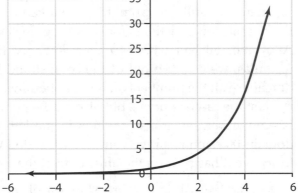

I acknowledged that, by this time, most participants' heads were swimming. I said, "I know we've covered lots of territory. We're going to take a break, and then take a moment to review what we've learned before looking at teachers' moves."

After break, I said, "So, let's take a minute to write out what we know about nonlinear functions; what do we know about functions with curved graphs?" I suggested that participants look around the room at the posters of tables, graphs, and formulas. ₃₅₅

The group generated the following list:

- The rate of change is not constant. ₃₆₀
- For a quadratic function, as the inputs increase by a constant amount, the difference between changes in the output (the second difference) is constant.
- For an exponential function, as the inputs increase by a constant amount, the difference between changes in the output (the second difference) is not constant. ₃₆₅
- The graph of rate of change of a quadratic function is a straight line.
- The graph of rate of change of an exponential function is a curve.
- For an exponential function, the variable is the exponent. There is a constant multiplier. ₃₇₀

Examining Non-Constant Rates of Change

- For a quadratic function, the variable is the base. There is always an exponent of 2.

I acknowledged that this was a lot to absorb, and I was sure many people were not feeling solid about everything on this list. I said, "What I do want to make sure everybody feels solid about is the first item on this list. In a non-linear function, the rate of change is not constant. Allow yourselves some time to let everything else sink in."

Case discussion: Teachers' moves

I told the group we would have another look at the cases, this time thinking about the moves the teacher made to support student learning. Participants returned to their small groups, and I asked them to concentrate on Case 23, Fastwalker, because that would be the focus of the whole-group discussion. If they had time, they could also look at the other cases.

Small groups

As I visited small groups, it seemed clear that although the case is short, there was plenty to examine. Everyone was looking very closely at how the teacher orchestrated the lesson.

Whole group

When I brought the whole group together, Georgeann said, "First, what's really important is that the teacher was thinking about what the students had done before, how this lesson built on those ideas and what was different."

Ivan said, "But she didn't tell them what's different."

I asked, "What's significant about that?"

Ivan said, "They get to discover it. Once they see what's different, they're really curious and want to think about it."

Robin said, "I'd like to know more about the table. I wish I could roll this episode back and hear more of the discussion about the numbers in the table. That's where our class is; we talk a lot about the table. I'm looking at lines 36 to 41. I'd like to hear the teacher asking questions like, 'What's the evidence?' 'Where do you see that?'"

I asked, "Why is that important?"

Robin said, "It might be that not everyone gets what other children are saying. Like the first child said, 'Each year Fastwalker grows more the age it is becoming.' We had to think a lot about what that might mean. If the student has to explain, and show it with numbers, then maybe more students in the class will be brought into the idea."

Elinor said, "I saw it more like brainstorming. Everyone's ideas can be heard, and you get a whole variety of ways of looking at it." 405

Ivan asked, "Isn't it a way for the teacher to gauge informally levels of understanding?"

I asked, "When you look at what the children say in lines 36 to 41, is there anything that can be interpreted as incorrect?"

Meg asked, "What did the child mean by 'switchable' in line 41?" 410

Trudy said, "I think the child meant that the rate of change is changing. Fastwalker grows at a changing rate."

Flor said, "I'm interested in the non-mathematical language students use to describe the graph. At line 61, someone says, 'It looks like a wave,' or back at line 51, 'half of a tree trunk.'" 415

April said, "There's something important about students being free to use vocabulary that's natural to them at the same time that they're learning specific technical vocabulary."

Georgeann said, "I feel so close to these kids. I'm learning about the relationship between the data in a table, and the graph, and the situation that's being represented. When I read this case and see the steps the teacher took the students through, I think it's brilliant. She goes through stages. She gave them a table that was different than all the other tables the class had seen so far. So first, she gave them a chance to study the table, and then they had a discussion about the phenomenon that is represented by the table. Then before they actually did the graph, she asked them what they thought the graph would look like. Then all the children had a chance to plot the graph and write about what it looked like. And then they had a discussion about what they saw in the graph. And the kids could do all this with whatever language is available to them." Georgeann concluded by saying, "This lesson was orchestrated very carefully." 420 425 430

Exit cards

I posted these questions for people to respond to:

■ What component of tonight's session was particularly useful or interesting to you? Why?
■ Is there anything else you want to tell me? 435

As I looked over the exit cards, I saw that each component of the session was important for participants.

LAMIS: Going over and sharing the episodes that we prepared during the last session, hearing the experiences of the others who did it in classrooms with students of different ages, provided different perspectives. I liked hearing the variety of questions the writer asked the students. 440

Doing the different kinds of graphs—taking time and comparing them was very useful to me. My group worked for me.

BILL: I really enjoyed our discussion on the different types of nonlinear functions. There were questions that I was exploring as I was noticing the varying rates of change in different graphs. I wish we had more time to explore these ideas even more in depth. I suppose it's because these are ideas I haven't explored since high school, and even then it was an entirely different exploration.

APRIL: I was very interested in this idea of the constant change of a rate of change. Last week, we had looked at this in a table, and I quickly lost track of what the numbers were standing for. If the values go 1, 4, 9, 16, and the differences are 3, 5, 7, and the differences of those are 2, "What is this 2?" I was able to make sense of the constant change of the rate of change today.

JOY: I found it helpful to re-examine the work we did last time, then compare it to the math in the cases. I've discovered that predicting what a graph will look like before making it has helped me understand the graph better. I can tell more about what it means or what it's describing. I think telling the story about the graph was easier because of predictions we have been making. It makes more sense now.

FLOR: I enjoyed the discussion of Fastwalker. It is always interesting to me to see how other teachers bring out the ideas for the students—the questioning, changing of agendas, ways of reaching the "main idea." It was also a great idea to look at the same case with different lenses.

Trudy and Robin both said they appreciated my showing them how to derive the formula for Staircase Towers numbers, and then they described the method.

Violet said that the second discussion of Case 23 was important because she could see that there are various ways to interpret a teacher's moves, depending on the teacher's goals.

I was happy to see that Elinor was feeling stronger again than she had at the end of the last session.

ELINOR: I found it helpful to return to the Math activity from Session 5. During Session 5, I just scratched the surface. Between sessions, I worked on it some more. It was helpful to continue the conversation with my group.

However, now I am worried about Peggy.

PEGGY: The pace is very fast for me, and it seems to have accelerated sharply. I was delighted with how previous classes made sense. I am worried that I will be lost in the remaining classes.

As I'm writing now, I remember that Peggy had left Session 5 early because of an appointment she could not reschedule. It seems to have been a real setback for her not to have started the work on nonlinear functions with the rest of the class. I will want to watch out for her in the last two sessions.

Responding to the sixth homework

April 16

Participants had said that it was very useful to share their assignments with others who had done the same activity. It was also interesting to me to read different teaching episodes based on the same lesson. The Navigations materials all resulted in productive lessons for students and significant learning opportunities for teachers.

Because of my concern about Elinor, I will include her assignment here.

ELINOR: Third Graders Growing Worms

Students will describe the pattern of the worm's growth and represent the pattern in a table. They will discuss the relationship between the age and the number of triangles needed to build the worm. They will apply their understanding of the relationship to make predictions about the number of triangles needed to build the worm without actually building the worm. They will develop numerical expressions that describe the relationship between the age of the worm and the number of triangles needed to build the worm.

My first surprise came as I introduced the activity. The words for my introduction were taken from the Navigating curriculum: "Our work today is to discover how many triangles will be needed to construct a worm that is 20 days old." I held in my palm the isosceles triangles for students to see and explained that they would be using the triangles to build the 1- and 2-day-old worms. "We'll be using these triangles to build the worms." We observed my drawings of a 1-day-old and a 2-day-old worm. Some immediate comments that burst out were, "Counting by 2," "She's adding one more," "The pattern is going 1 by 1," "Add a square for each one," "They put one more shape," "My pattern looks like a triangle looks up, down, and sideways." It took me by surprise that so many students saw the pattern as growing by 1 square rather than 2 triangles.

I asked, "What do they use to make the square shape?"

Manuel answered, "2 triangles."

I drew a table on the board that's in Figure 1.3 in the Navigating lesson and together we filled in the number of triangles for a 1- and 2-day-old worm. Then I asked the students to predict how many triangles we needed to construct a 3-day-old worm. Predictions were 3, 5, and 8 triangles.

Students then constructed the 3-day-old worm, and we compared the number of triangles in the constructed worm to the predictions. Manuel explained that his prediction of "3" was right because he had "3 shapes." He wasn't attending to the 2 triangles that made up the squares at all. Students who predicted 5 also attended to the 3 squares in the middle, and they counted the 2 triangles on either end. They were counting the number of shapes they

Examining Non-Constant Rates of Change

saw. We added information to the table, and I thought they all were convinced that 8 triangles were needed to construct the 3-day-old worm. Once again, we took the time to comment on patterns we saw emerging in the table. There was mention that "the triangles were going up by 2 every time the worm got older." I thought everyone was now focused on the triangles that were composing the worm's body.

I altered the directions from the Navigating lesson and allowed students to build the 4- and 5-day-old worms. I also encouraged them to predict the number of triangles needed before actually constructing the worms. The majority of students built the worm, counted the number of triangles, and then "predicted" the number of triangles needed. I wish I had insisted on this step and repeated the process of predicting before building with the whole class.

The majority of students constructed the worm and then counted the number of triangles used. Francis described to me how she would construct the 4-day-old worm.

"The 4th has 4 squares. Use 2 triangles to make a square. Use 1 more square or 2 more triangles to make it." She couldn't mentally calculate the number of triangles, nor did she seem to recognize the pattern that the total was increasing by 2, even though she said the worm grew by "1 more square or 2 triangles." Francis's comments made me wish I had repeated the process of predicting and then building with the whole class. In Francis's written work, she predicted the number of triangles in the 10-day-old worm by doubling the amount in the 5 day old worm.

Chang drew in all the triangles for 10-, 15-, and 20-day-old worms, and I assume he counted to complete his table. He described his rule as: "The rule is like if the age is 1 up, and the worm adds 2 triangles." As an example, he drew the 1- and 2-day-old worms and showed that they go from 4 to 6 triangles, and then he wrote "4 + 2 = 6."

Cynthia wrote, "I notice that you kept on adding 1 and when you put like 1, 2, 3, 4, it has really that number in the middle. If you started in 1 you kept on adding 1."

Terry wrote, "This is how I did the rule. I did 1 worm age is like 1 box and 2 worm is like 2 boxes. My rule is a box each."

Cynthia and Terry remained focused on the squares in the middle of the worm's body. Cynthia's rule refers to the age as equal to the number of squares. Neither student made a table to represent the age and the number of triangles.

This is the third time these students have helped me with my homework for the seminar. In the first session, they worked with Cube Train patterns. Manuel was unable to build the train with the repeating pattern. Today, he successfully drew illustrations of the 1- through 5-day-old worms and the 10-day-old worm.

Keith explained the rule as, "My rule is that every year older the worm is it will grow 2 more triangles." He didn't write an equation, but he did calculate the number of triangles for 10-, 15-, and 20-day-old worms without making a representation. Work of 4 out of the 19 students is similar to Keith's.

My biggest surprise came from Eliza. She wrote, "My rule is the first number and multiply it by 2 and then add 2 more." She hadn't said anything out loud during class. Keith, Chang, and James nodded in agreement and were very excited by Eliza's equation. Keith said, "I did that, too." We had to stop at this exciting point because time was up, and most students were fading out.

I think the majority of students are still in the construction and count phase. They are able to verbally describe the change in the number of triangles that takes place as the worm grows. The majority also represent the change in a table. Only a few students are able to apply the pattern that they describe to predict future change.

Although students in this class were not all "successful" with the lesson, it did sound to me like they were all working on important mathematics, and I wanted to highlight these ideas for Elinor. I also wanted to give Elinor a sense of success in terms of her understanding of functions and the ideas that can be brought to the elementary classroom.

Dear Elinor,

In your work with this third-grade class, I think you're learning about how students move into this new content area. It isn't necessarily appropriate to go right through the instructions that are given in the Navigating series. For some students, there is a constellation of new ideas embedded in the activity, and it is important to slow things down.

For the Growing Worms activity, it might be the case that many students needed to create worms and count triangles in order to see what was happening. If they perceive the worm as made up of squares, and if they aren't completely solid with the idea that two isosceles right triangles make up a square, they might need to do lots of building to solidify it. If they're still struggling with calculations, or aren't so sure about how doubling and counting 2s are related, there is another idea that needs to be worked out. Then there's the basic issue of what goes on with functions: keeping track of how two variables are related. So when Terry (or Cynthia or Manuel) say that each time you add a day, you also add 1 box, they are getting started with this idea of how two variables can be related. A next step for them would be to think in terms of triangles—each time you add a day, you add 2 triangles.

Eliza did make a clear statement of the formula, and I'm interested that Keith, Chang, and James were excited by her formula. It seems they recognize that she has articulated an idea that they were very close to; they must feel very satisfied to discover words that are so close to their idea.

Examining Non-Constant Rates of Change

It seems to me the students in your class have made good progress with this content. It's also important to see that, while delving into the content of functions, students also have opportunities to continue working on the content of number and operations (and in this example, a little bit of geometry).

It also seems to me that you have made important progress. You are beginning to understand the concept of functions and learning how it can become the content of elementary school.

Maxine

610

Detailed Agenda

Sharing student-thinking assignment

(20 minutes)

Small groups (same groups as last session)

The first activity of this session provides the opportunity for participants to read and discuss what they wrote describing the thinking of their students. In the last session, participants met with a partner or partners to plan for this assignment using a lesson from the NCTM *Navigating Through Algebra* series. Participants should meet with the same partners so they may share what they wrote. Remind them to read each other's papers before beginning any discussion.

You might want to suggest some questions to spur the discussion:

- What was difficult for you in teaching this lesson?
- What did your students do that surprised you?
- What mathematics came up in the whole-class discussion?
- If you were going to continue this lesson, what would you do next and why?

Let them know they will have 20 minutes for this conversation.

As you organize groups for the next activity, remind participants to turn in both their planning sheet (homework from Session 5) and their student-thinking assignment (the current homework) for your feedback.

Tables and graphs of nonlinear functions

(25 minutes)

Pairs (5 minutes)

Whole group (20 minutes)

Use the graphs from the Growing Patterns work to focus the discussion on three points:

- Curved graphs involve non-constant change.
- There are different kinds of curved graphs.
- The different kinds of non-constant change can be noted in both the table and the graph.

Display the poster with the tables and graphs for the Growing Rectangles, Allowance, and Staircase Towers with Jumps of 1 problems.

Tell participants to turn to someone next to them and to talk about these two questions for a few minutes:

Examining Non-Constant Rates of Change

- What is it about each situation or the table that results in the nonlinear graphs?
- How are the graphs similar, and how are they different from each other?

In the whole-group discussion, ask questions to make connections between the non-constant rate of change in these situations and how the graphs curve. You should also ask questions to highlight the way the Allowance graph and table is different from the other two graphs. Use the whole-group discussion as an opportunity to introduce the word *quadratic* to describe the graphs for Growing Rectangles and Staircase Towers and the word *exponential* to describe the graph for Allowance. See "Maxine's Journal," Session 6, pp. 206–211, for an example of the issues that may arise in this discussion.

Case and math discussion: Quadratic and exponential functions   (55 minutes)

Small groups (30 minutes)

Whole group (25 minutes)

The cases in Chapter 6 illustrate students of Grades 1–3 working with situations in which the rate of change is not constant. While the students' reasoning is based on tables, participants are asked to predict and draw graphs based on the cases. The situations in Cases 23, 25, and 26 will have quadratic graphs similar to Growing Squares. Case 24 involves an exponential function based on doubling just like the Allowance situation.

Organize the participants into groups of three or four and distribute the Focus Questions for Chapter 6. Inform the group they will have 30 minutes to work in small groups.

Focus Question 1, based on Case 23, provides an example of a quadratic function similar to one of the Staircase Towers. Participants are also asked to make a table and graph for the change in the growth, which will be a linear function.

Although the context is different, Focus Question 2 addresses the same exponential function as in the Allowance situation. Examining the graphs from these cases will provide the opportunity for participants to solidify the ideas from the earlier whole-group discussion based on Growing Patterns.

As they respond to Focus Question 3, participants will compare the formulas they created for the Growing Squares, Growing Rectangles, and Staircase Towers situations with each other. Focus Questions 4 and 5 continue to highlight quadratic relationships. In Focus Question 5, participants are invited to make two graphs. One represents the number of tiles needed to make a square and will be quadratic; the other represents the number of tiles added to build one square from the previous one and will be linear.

In discussing these questions, participants should first make connections to their mathematical thinking and then examine the way students encounter these ideas. As you interact with the small groups, ask questions about what they see in the cases that is similar to and different from their own ways of thinking about these situations. You should also continue to ask questions focused on the connections among the situation, the models, the tables, and the graphs. This is particularly useful when examining the versions of the formulas that participants have written.

The whole-group discussion should include two components: 1) a review of quadratic and exponential tables and graphs based on Fastwalker and the Paper Folding problems and 2) an examination of how thinking about a model is linked to the way the formula is written. Use the Growing Patterns problems for the second component of this discussion. Because you had a substantial whole-group discussion focused on the first component earlier in the session, devote most of the time to the second component.

Begin the discussion by posting a table and graph showing Fastwalker's height. Ask for observations based on the table or the graph. For each observation ask how that feature can be seen in the other representation. In particular, participants should notice that the differences between output values increase linearly, a characteristic of quadratic functions. This should establish the notion that the table illustrates non-constant change similar to that of the Growing Squares, Growing Rectangles, and Staircase Towers models. The resulting graph is curved upward. With the participants, generate a table and graph for the Paper Folding situation and ask how they are alike and different compared to the table and graph for Fastwalker. Then ask what the table that represents the *change* in the Paper Folding situation would look like. Ask questions to elicit how the changes in that situation are different from the kinds of changes in the quadratic situations. Ask how that is seen in the graphs. Summarize this discussion by pointing out that the Paper Folding situation, like the Allowance situation, has an exponential graph.

Turn to Focus Question 3 and invite participants to illustrate their methods for determining the formula for the Growing Rectangles problem. Ask questions to help participants identify the connections between the model and the expression; for instance, "How is $x(x + 1)$ seen in the model? In the table?" "How do you see $x^2 + x$ in the model? In the table?" (See the Session 5 Agenda for more information about this problem.) Then turn to the Staircase Towers Jumps of 1 situation for a similar discussion linking the table values and the models to the formula. See "Maxine's Journal" for Session 6, pp. 211–219 for an example of such a conversation.

Break   (15 minutes)

Examining Non-Constant Rates of Change

Poster discussion: What we know about functions with curved graphs

(15 minutes)

(Whole group)

Draw participants' attention to the poster the whole group made in the last session about linear functions and tell them to generate observations for a similar poster describing functions with curved graphs. Acknowledge that they had several sessions focused on linear functions and less time focused on nonlinear functions, so they should not expect the same level of familiarity with the nonlinear functions as they may feel with the linear functions. You should also assure them that noting the attributes of various nonlinear functions could also help them see more clearly the attributes of linear functions.

After giving participants a few minutes to think, solicit ideas about the situations, tables, graphs, and formulas for the quadratic functions.

Comments might include these points:

- The *situations* of quadratic functions describe a relationship with a non-constant change. Examples from our work are Growing Squares, Growing Rectangles, and Fastwalker.
- When the input values in the *table* increase by 1, the output values do not increase by a constant amount; rather they increase by differing, although predictable, amounts. In fact, the change in the output values is linear.

Input	Output	Change
1	1	
2	4	3
3	9	5
4	16	7

Input	Output	Change
0	1	
1	2	1
2	4	2
3	7	3

- The *graphs* are curves.
- The *formulas* involve a term containing x^2 such as $y = x^2$ or $y = x(x + 1)$.

Let participants know that even though they have worked with only one exponential function in two different contexts (Allowance and Paper Folding), you are interested in having them note how this function is different from the linear or the quadratic functions. Create a poster with their ideas.

Comments might include these points:

- The *situations* of exponential functions describe a relationship involving repeated multiplication. Examples from our work are the Allowance problem and Paper-Folding situations.
- When the input values in the *table* increase by 1, the output values are found by multiplying the previous output by a given number. The changes in the output values are also made by repeated multiplication.

Input	Output	Change
1	1	
2	2	1
3	4	2
4	8	4
5	16	8

Input	Output	Change
0	1	
1	3	2
2	9	6
3	27	18
4	81	54

- The *graphs* are curves but curve differently than the quadratics.
- The *formulas* involve a term containing a variable in the exponent such as $y = 2^x$.

Teachers' moves discussion
(45 minutes)

Individual/pairs (25 minutes)

Whole group (20 minutes)

This activity provides an opportunity for participants to focus on actions of teachers in the cases and to consider the impact of the teachers' actions on their students' thinking. You might want to clarify the term *teacher's moves*, so that it is clear this refers to mathematics tasks the teacher poses, questions she asks, classroom structures she sets up, as well as mathematical goals and pedagogical decisions.

Distribute "Examining teachers' moves" and ask participants to read over the assignment. Have participants work individually to locate examples of teacher moves they find interesting and complete the analysis of the examples. After 10 or 15 minutes of working individually, participants should share their examples with a partner.

As you work with participants, be sure to help them stay specific and focused on the situations in the cases. While this is a time to talk about what teachers might do or say, comments should still be grounded in the cases. For instance, one component involves participants making inferences about the agenda the teacher has for her students. When participants offer such inferences, ask what evidence in the case supports that inference.

As you interact with the pairs, take note of examples that you want to include in the whole-group discussion. Because all groups will have worked with Case 23, focus the whole-group discussion on examples from this case. As groups discuss the teacher's moves in whole group, ask questions so their description includes responses to the bulleted questions. You should also ask how these examples help them think about their own teaching decisions.

Examining Non-Constant Rates of Change

Exit cards

Individual

Use the last 5 minutes of the session for participants to reflect on these exit-card questions:

- What component of this session was particularly useful or interesting to you? Why?
- Is there anything else you want to tell the facilitator(s)?

Before the next session...

In preparation for the next session, read what participants wrote for homework for Session 5 (the planning sheet based on the NCTM materials) and Session 6 (the description of student thinking based on this lesson). Write a response to each participant. For more information, see the section in "Maxine's Journal" on responding to the sixth homework. Make copies of both the writing and your responses for your files before returning the work.

Poster: Graphs from growing patterns

This poster should display the graphs and tables for the Growing Rectangles, Allowance, and Staircase Towers problems (Questions 2, 3, and 4 from Session 5, "Math activity: Growing patterns"). You may post tables and graphs that participants have made or prepare a poster of these yourself.

Growing Rectangles

Side Length	Area
1	2
2	6
3	12
4	20
5	30
…	…

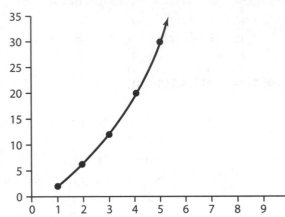

Allowance

Day	Pennies
1	2
2	4
3	8
4	16
5	32
…	…

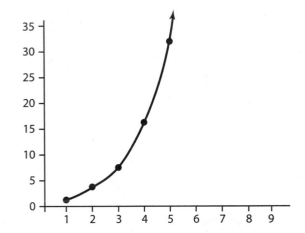

Staircase Towers Jumps of 1

Number of Towers	Number of Tiles
1	1
2	3
3	6
4	10
5	15
…	…

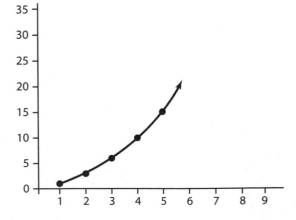

Math Activity and Focus Questions: Chapter 6

1. In Case 23 at line 27, a table is presented of Fastwalker's height over time. Would a graph of this table be linear? How can you tell? Look at the graph at line 52. Explain why the graph looks like it does. Which of the problems in the Growing Patterns assignment is this similar to? How is it similar and how is it different? What would a graph of Fastwalker's yearly growth look like?

2. Consider the Paper-Folding situation in Case 24. Extend the table beginning in line 102 so it has entries from 1–8. Would a graph of this table be linear? How can you tell? Make the graph and describe what you see. Explain why the graph looks like it does. Which of the problems in the Growing Patterns assignment is this similar to? How is it similar and how is it different?

3. Revisit Questions 1, 2, 4, and 5 from the Growing Patterns math activity. Compare the formulas you made with those made by others in your group.

4. In Case 25, consider lines 224–227. What is it that the students are noticing? How do their ideas connect with the work you did on Question 1 of Growing Patterns? Why does it make sense for the students to create a Growing Squares pattern if the problem is about the number of outfits you can make with a certain number of pants and shirts?

5. In Case 26, consider both Paul's comments on lines 295–300 and the table the teacher makes to record Paul's thinking. What would a graph for the "Number of Tiles" look like? Why? What would a graph of the "Number of Tiles Added" look like? Why? Make each graph and describe what you see. Explain why the graphs look like they do.

Examining teachers' moves

The teachers in these cases make a number of decisions and strategic moves to draw their students' attention to particular mathematical issues. Some of these decisions are seen in the questions they pose to the class; some are seen in the classroom activities they set up.

Go through the cases in this chapter—beginning with Case 23—to identify specific examples of these teaching decisions or moves.

For each example, identify the teacher's move. Where in the case does this occur? What has the teacher done?

Then address each of these questions in detail, giving specific evidence from the cases for your conclusions:

- What can you infer about the teacher's agenda for her students?
- How does the teacher's action connect with her assessment of their understanding?
- What do you think the teacher is trying to accomplish?
- What is the impact of the teacher's move on the students' thinking?

Seventh Homework

Reading assignment: Casebook, Chapter 7

Read Chapter 7 in the Casebook, "Functions Without Formulas," including the introductory text and Cases 27–29.

Writing assignment: Ideas about teaching and learning mathematics

For previous seminar assignments you have examined the mathematical thinking of your students or engaged with mathematics for yourself. At this point in the seminar, we are interested in how your ideas about teaching and learning mathematics have been influenced by the seminar experience. Please write about this.

Functions Without Formulas

Mathematical themes:

- Making connections between the shape of a graph and the story of a phenomenon

- Describing both quantity and change in quantity on a graph

Session Agenda

Math activity: Stories and graphs	Small groups Whole group	40 minutes 35 minutes
Break		15 minutes
DVD discussion	Whole group	10 minutes
Case discussion	Small groups Whole group	35 minutes 35 minutes
Homework and exit cards	Individuals	10 minutes

Background Preparation

Read
- the Casebook, Chapter 7
- "Maxine's Journal" for Session 7
- the agenda for Session 7
- the Casebook: Chapter 8, Sections 5 and 6

Work through
- the Math activity: Stories and graphs (pp. 267–268)
- the Focus Questions for Session 7 (p. 269)
- Read over "Categories of Functions" (If any of this information is new to you, consult with someone familiar with these terms.)

Preview
- the DVD for Session 7

Materials

Duplicate
- "Math activity: Stories and graphs" (pp. 267–268)
- "Focus Questions: Chapter 7" (p. 269)
- "Eighth Homework" (p. 270)
- "Categories of Functions" (pp. 271–273)

Obtain
- DVD player
- graph paper
- index cards

Introducing Hyperbolic and Sine Functions

The chart to be distributed at the end of this session lists general forms, tables, graphs, and a few applications for five types of functions. Three of these (linear, quadratic, and exponential) have been the focus of the past sessions. The other two (hyperbolic and sine) have been represented only by a single example.

Hyperbolic functions:

In the Session 2 "Math activity: Graphing functions," Problem 1 was about sharing the cost of a $36 gift.

Number of Contributors (x)	Cost Per Contributor (y)
1	36
2	18
3	12
4	9
5	7.2
6	6
…	…

The quantities x and y are indirectly proportional. That is, the product of x and y is constant. In this example, the product is 36, and one way to express the relationship between x and y is $xy = 36$. If one variable increases, the other must decrease in such a way as to keep the product constant. The sharing-the-cost-of-a-gift situation is embedded in the *hyperbolic* function $y = \frac{36}{x}$. Because neither x nor y can be 0, the graph does not touch the x- or the y-axis.

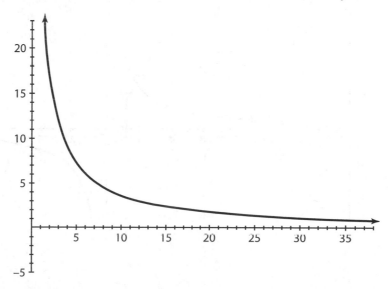

Consider some other situations in which variables are indirectly proportional:

- If you have to travel a certain distance, the faster the speed, the less time it takes. That is, time is a function of speed: $t = \frac{d}{s}$.
- If you have a particular task that needs to be done, the more people working on it, the less time it takes. The time it takes to complete the task is a function of the number of people working on it, and assuming everyone works at the same rate, the variables are indirectly proportional.
- If a child is sitting on a seesaw and an adult is at the other end to balance it, the adult (who presumably weighs more) must sit closer to the fulcrum. The heavier the adult, the closer to the fulcrum he or she must sit.

Any function of the form $y = \frac{a}{x}$ is an example of a hyperbolic function. Although the examples above all take on positive values, we can consider functions whose domain is all the numbers on the number line except 0.

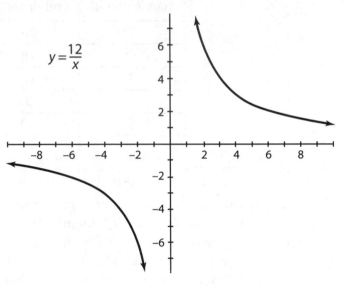

$y = \dfrac{12}{x}$

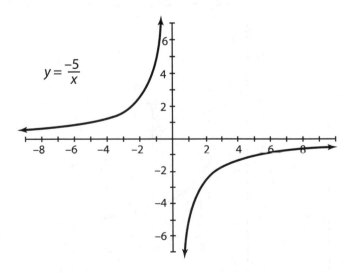

$y = \dfrac{-5}{x}$

Functions Without Formulas

An example of a periodic function: The class of sine functions

In this session, one of the qualitative graphing questions, "Stories and graphs, Part III. Question 1," is about a child riding on a Ferris wheel. The graph of the height of the child from the ground relative to time has a special character because, as long as the Ferris wheel rotates at a constant rate, the function repeats the same shape for each cycle of the ride. Such functions are called "periodic."

An important mathematical function that is useful in representing phenomena with this feature is the *sine* function. To define the function *sine of x*, consider a circle on the coordinate plane whose center is at the origin (0, 0) and whose radius is 1. Now, think of a dot that begins at the point (1, 0) and starts moving around the circle. If *x* is the distance the dot has traveled along the circle, *sine of x* (also written *sin x*) is the height of the dot.

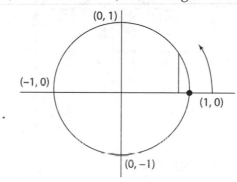

Note that the dot can travel all the way around the circle and then keep going. Each time the dot completes one rotation, the function repeats.

A general form for many of these graphs is given by $y = a \sin bx + c$.

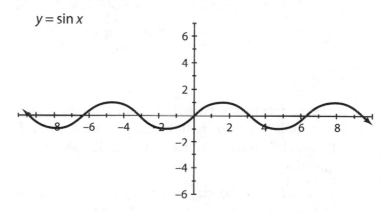

$y = 2 \sin x$

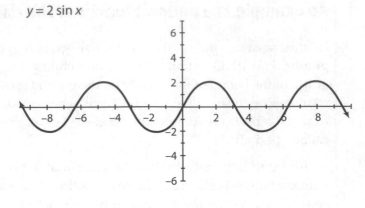

$y = (\sin x) + 4$

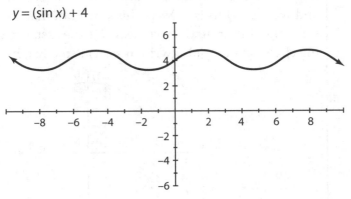

$y = \sin 2x$

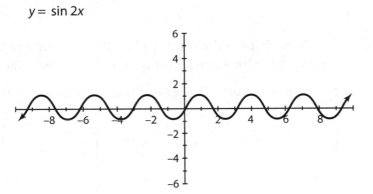

These graphs are *periodic* because a certain portion of the graph (called the "period") repeats itself throughout the domain. The frequency of a periodic graph is related to the length of the period and is determined by the value of b.

The height of the graph from peak to trough is called the amplitude and is determined by the value of a. The value of c determines where the graph crosses the y-axis. Values of $c > a$ result in graphs that do not take on any negative values. The terms *frequency* and *amplitude* are suggestive of sound. These terms were borrowed from that context to apply more generally to any phenomenon that travels in waves.

Functions Without Formulas

Maxine's Journal

April 28

At this point, we are close enough to the end of the seminar that we can look back and analyze the development of the ideas. As we started the seventh session, I wanted to present a quick overview.

I reminded the group of the work we had done in the second session, where we looked at a variety of situations, considered their tables and graphs, and talked about characteristics and categories.

"We noted that some graphs were straight lines and others curved. After that, we spent several sessions looking closely at situations in which graphs are straight lines. We saw that those situations involve a constant rate of change, and we examined how that appears in tables and formulas, as well as graphs. We learned how to compare two linear functions and then looked at situations for which the variables of a linear function are directly proportional.

"During Sessions 5 and 6, we studied functions that are governed by formulas but are not linear. Of those, we focused our discussion on two types—quadratic functions and exponential functions—but there are many, many types of nonlinear functions. In our work today, we'll come across a different one."

I continued, "In the cases you read for today, we saw examples of data-based functions that are not governed by formulas. What we find is that when we look at tables and graphs, we can apply some of the same principles to describe what is happening as when we studied formula-governed functions.

"Today we'll continue to look at those same characteristics. We'll start out considering a set of questions through our Math activity. Then we'll look at third- and fourth-grade classrooms on DVD, and we'll discuss those together with the cases you read from the Casebook."

Math activity: Stories and graphs

Small groups

Now we turned to the day's Math activity. I distributed the Math activity sheet in which participants make stories for graphs and graphs for stories, and participants got right to work. I noticed that some small groups chose to begin the task by spending the first several minutes working alone. Others jumped right into the group discussion.

One of the issues that came up several times involved participants interpreting a graph as a picture of the phenomenon. For example, Ivan and Nazir looked at the first problem about the book-carrier operated on a rope by pulley and thought that the horizontal graph (Graph 4) described books moving straight across, and the vertical graph (Graph 3) described books going straight up.

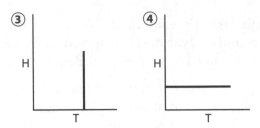

Their partners helped them go back to the context—all of the graphs were supposed to be about books moving straight up and down on the book-carrier—and assisted them in recognizing the graph as height of the books over time. The horizontal graph indicated no change in height over time, while the vertical graph presented an impossible situation. Joy explained, "The vertical graph would mean that the books are at different heights at the same instant. That can't happen!"

Most participants could see that Graph 1 shows books going up at a constant rate; in Graph 2, books start rising at a constant rate and then slow down; Graph 6 shows books increasing in speed, and Graph 5 shows the books moving faster and then slowing, faster, then slower.

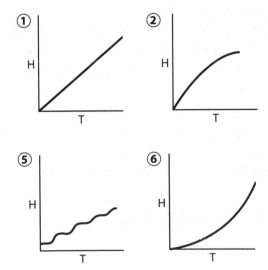

Some participants argued that the fifth graph is most realistic, because each time the operator pulls the rope, the book-carrier speeds up. Others said that the operator could learn the technique to move the books at a constant rate so that Graph 1 or 2 would be more realistic.

Then participants turned to the falling-keys problem: If keys are dropped from a rooftop, which of three graphs most realistically illustrates the height of the keys over time?

55

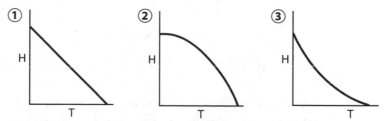

Many people first said they had to know more physics to answer this problem. However, after a few minutes, they began to realize they knew more than they thought. Peggy said, "When I dive off the high dive, I know I'm hitting the water faster than when I dive off the side of the pool." Ariel said, "I'd rather be hit by an acorn from a small tree than a tall one." Lamis added, 60 "If a glass drops 1 foot, it's less likely to break than if it drops 4 feet." They all concluded that as the keys fall, they fall at an increasing rate.

Even once that was determined, some participants still misread the graphs. April, Lamis, and Elinor dismissed Graph 2 because "the keys would fall straight down, and this shows them moving in an arc." They turned to Graph 65 3, marked off a scale and put in values to make sense of it. Eventually, they determined that this graph showed the keys slowing down. They turned to Graph 1, still dismissing Graph 2, but soon realized this showed the keys falling at a constant rate. Then Lamis said, "Wait a minute. These graphs don't show the path of the keys. The path is just straight down. We're looking to see 70 how the speed changes." This brought them back to Graph 2.

Lamis said, "Graph 2 starts out going slower, but then at the end, it decreases faster than Graph 1. You can tell that because of the change of steepness in the graph."

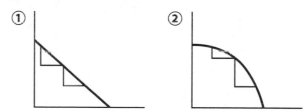

She drew in some lines to show the changing rates. "In Graph 1, I can see 75 that each time I go over a certain amount, I go down the same amount. But, if we look at Graph 2, we can go over that same amount in the beginning, and you can see it goes down just a little. Later on, you go over the same amount, and look at how much it drops. At that point, it's dropping a lot more than in Graph 1. So the second graph has to be the one." 80

Robin, Georgeann, and Meg looked at this picture to interpret the second graph.

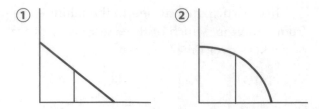

Robin explained, "You look at what's going on after half the time it takes for the keys to reach the ground. If the keys are falling at a constant rate, like in Graph 1, then they fall the same amount the first half and the second half. What you see in Graph 2 is that they fall more the second half than the first half. And, so it has to be Graph 2." 85

I acknowledged what Robin said and then gave a bit more information: "You're right, the keys don't drop at a constant rate. However (although we can't tell this from this sketchy graph), the speed increases at a constant rate. 90 That makes the function of height over time quadratic."

Whole group

In their small groups, all participants spent some time on the Ferris wheel problem: to graph the height of a child on a Ferris wheel over time. I decided to start the whole-group discussion by posting the four types of graphs they produced. 95

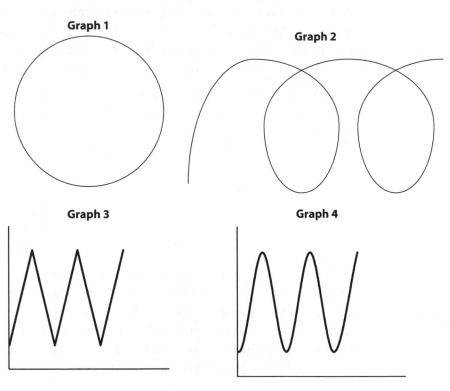

Graph 1

Graph 2

Graph 3

Graph 4

Nazir said, "The circle is the path that the child travels. That's not a graph of height."

I was pleased to hear Nazir say this, because this had been the source of her confusion on the book-carrier problem.

Meg said, "If time is the *x*-axis, the circle doesn't make any sense. It seems like time is traveling backward."

Trudy said, "That can't be a function. It says the child is at two different places at the same time." Trudy came and drew a vertical line through the circle. "See, at this particular time, it says the child is at two different heights." Then she turned to the second graph and added, "You've got the same problem here."

I checked in with Mariam and Sandy who had drawn these first two graphs. Mariam said she wanted to listen to the rest of the discussion to make more sense of it. Sandy said, "I get what Meg said. If you follow my graph, it shows time going backward, and that doesn't make any sense."

That left the other two graphs. I pointed to the rounded graph and asked that someone tell me what happens there.

Flor said, "When the Ferris wheel goes around, the child goes up and down, and you repeat that action over and over again."

I said, "Flor is pointing out an important feature of both graphs, that they show a certain shape repeating over and over. A function that has that feature is called a periodic function.

"Now I want you to tell me how these two graphs are different. What does the straight-line graph tell you and what does the curved graph tell you?"

Yan said, "The straight-line graph says the child's height is changing at a steady rate. The wavy lines say the height is not changing at a steady rate; it's gradually increasing or gradually decreasing."

I pointed near the bottom of the first dip on the curved graph. "What can you tell me happens right around here, as it going around this bend?"

Ariel said, "As the child approaches the bottom, it slows down and then, as it starts back up, it goes slowly at first and then speeds up. Then when it nears the top, it slows before it heads back down again."

I asked, "How is that different from the straight-line graph?"

Ariel said, "It goes down at a steady rate, hits the bottom, and instantly turns around and heads back up at a steady rate."

I nodded and gave these ideas a moment of "wait time" to let them sink in. Then I called on Georgeann who had been waiting to speak.

Georgeann said, "You need to figure in the time factor. The time intervals matter. Like, Tim and I drew graphs that looked really different even though we were graphing the same event."

At first I was not sure what Georgeann was saying; but as she spoke, I drew these two graphs.

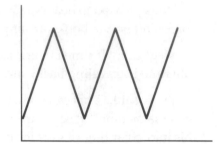

Georgeann said, "That's exactly what I mean. Those two graphs can be of the very same event."

Georgeann was raising a different issue, not one that would necessarily help us think about the Ferris wheel, but it was a worthwhile point to consider. I turned the question back to the group, "Georgeann claims that both graphs can be of the same phenomenon. How can that be?"

Nazir said, "One graph is more spread out. It could be the time from one peak to the next is the same on both."

Georgeann said, "I was bringing this up because people were saying that the steeper a line is, the greater the speed. But, as someone learning this stuff, I have to keep track of all of these things at the same time. Even if it's nearly vertical, it might be measured over a long period of time, and so it might mean that it's really more gradual."

I said, "Georgeann is making an important point. When we look at two different graphs, they might be drawn with different scales. So we can't make the comparison unless we know the scales."

Until now, the discussion had been without reference to any numbers. Now, I suggested, "Let's move out of the Ferris wheel context for a few minutes to think about this. Let's just say we have some object moving up and down, and say from the bottom to the top, it took 2.5 seconds to go 5 feet."

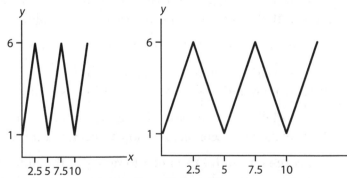

I continued, "The slope is the amount you go up divided by the amount you go over. So we have 5 ÷ 2.5, which equals 2. The slope of the upward portions of the line is 2 on either graph; it's 2 no matter what the scale is.

"I want to make sure you know that *slope* is a technical term. It's also a word in English that is related, but it isn't the same. *Slope* is a term that requires you to coordinate the two scales."

Elinor said, "But I don't know where the 2 is."

I said, "One way to think about it is the amount you go up when you go over 1 unit. We can think about it with some more familiar contexts, too. If you have a Penny Jar situation where you start with 7 and add 3 pennies each round, what's the slope?"

Elinor said, "OK, I get it. The slope is 3."

I turned back to the graph. "One other point to be made: When the object is going down, the slope is negative. You have $^-5 \div 2.5 = ^-2$.

"Now, I want you to think of a Penny Jar context that has a slope of $^-2$."

Robin said, "What if you take pennies out of the Penny Jar each round?"

I nodded and looked around to see others' reactions. They were nodding, so I left it at that.

Dina reminded us that we had not discussed which graph, the third or fourth, fits the Ferris wheel problem. I summarized where we had left off: "We had determined that Graph 3 shows the height going up at a steady rate and then suddenly going down at a steady rate. Graph 4 shows the child first moving up slowly and then more quickly and then more slowly again, until she starts to descend, first slowly, then more quickly, and then slowly. Which describes the child's height on the Ferris wheel?"

Bill said, "I think it has to be Graph 4." He came to the board to show us his thinking.

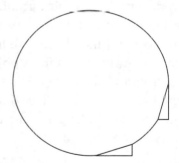

Bill continued, "When you're down at the bottom of the circle, if you travel a certain distance, you go up only a little bit. But as you come to the side, as you travel that same distance you're going up a lot. The height is changing more when you're at the sides than when you're at the top or the bottom."

There was a murmur throughout the room, so I asked people to talk about these issues in their small groups. After a few minutes, I brought them together in a whole group. At this point, several more people made arguments for why Graph 4 represents the height of a person on the Ferris wheel. Nobody argued against it.

I pointed to Graph 4 and said, "I want to take a moment to talk about this function. First, I'd like to hear you describe it. What are the characteristics of this graph?" Participants offered the following points:

- It goes up and down.
- It repeats.
- It's always curving.
- The rate of change is smaller at the top and bottom than in the middle.
- It's symmetrical. The top part is the same shape as the bottom.

I said that these are all important observations. Then I said, "This particular function has a name: *sine*. It is based on the vertical component of circular motion." I asked if anyone had ever heard of a sine function before. Some participants recalled learning about it in a trigonometry class.

I said, "Sine functions have particularly important applications for sound and light and anything that travels in waves."

Then it was time for break.

DVD and case discussion

I began the discussion by saying, "Of the graphs we worked with before break, some of those were of functions that had formulas. For example, we had a sine function, linear functions, and though we didn't specify it, there was also a quadratic function. But some of those graphs don't have an associated formula—like some of those yo-yo graphs I saw you draw in small groups. Of the functions we'll be discussing from the DVD and print cases, none of them have formulas. Instead, these functions are determined by data."

I showed the DVD. A third-grade class discussed the graph of temperature over time they had created based on data collected in Massachusetts from September to June. (Every Wednesday morning, the class recorded the outdoor temperature and added a point on the graph.) In a different segment from a fourth-grade class, the teacher drew a graph on the board, said that it showed the height of a plant over time, and students were to tell the story of what happened. They also created a corresponding table, which they related to their story.

Then participants turned to their small groups to discuss the DVD and print cases together. The small-group discussions were very fruitful, but I want to spend my time writing about what happened in the whole-group discussion.

When I brought everyone together for the discussion, I asked, "What are some of the mathematical ideas you see students getting from this work?" I held up a marker to indicate that I would make a list of their points.

Trudy was the first to speak, "One idea is that change can be measured."

Wow. That was a big idea to start off with. I asked Trudy to say more.

195

200

205

210

215

220

225

230

She explained, "In third and fourth grade, some students see the world and events happening to them. If they come to see that you can measure changes, you can have some sense of organization in the world that might not otherwise appear organized to you."

I said, "The idea that change can be measured is a big idea. Does anyone else want to say something about that?"

Ivan said, "I think they are noticing differences in rates of change."

When I asked Ivan for an example, he said, "Plants might grow in spurts. On the DVD, students talked about the different rates of growth of the plant."

Ariel said, "In line 177 of Case 29, Mario talks about how the candle is melting 1 centimeter every 30 seconds."

Ivan added, "In the first-grade case, Michael said it takes longer for the loose snow to melt completely."

I added, "Both Michael and Mario also recognize that the horizontal line means no change."

Violet said, "At line 138, Mario said the curved line means the candle is burning more slowly at the end."

Robin said, "We talked extensively about the temperature graph in Case 27 and how the students had the opportunity to look at data collected over a 10-month period. When they had just a slice of data, it gave you one impression, but when you could look at all of it, the kids could find trends."

I said, "There's an important difference between looking at particular points and looking at trends. But the weather graph also shows the difference between looking at local changes and the overall trends. Students noticed that the temperature might go up or down from one week to the next, but the overall trend from September to January was downward."

Sandy said, "I want to say something about my own experience here. Before I started this seminar, I thought of graphs as just a bunch of points. It's a completely new idea to see a graph as telling a story."

Georgeann said, "In Case 28 about melting snow and ice, the graph tells three different stories. You can compare the three stories to learn that something is true, something about how those substances melt."

Dina said, "You reach a different conclusion by comparing the graphs rather than looking at just one."

Ivan added, "What if the temperature graph were completed in Charleston, South Carolina, too? Then you could compare."

I said, "You'd be able to see what the high and low temperatures are in each location and when the seasons change. But once you make those comparisons, it also draws you into the question about what it is that makes the temperatures different at the different locations."

Yan said, "Something else the students have learned is that change can be shown in different modes. You can see it in graphs and also in tables."

I added Yan's point to the list we had been accumulating and stepped back to look at it.

- Change is something that can be measured.
- Differences in rates of change—how quickly or slowly something changes
- How different rates are represented:
  - constant rates
  - changing rates
- Describing trends vs. reading points
- Relating a graph to the story of the situation
- Comparing graphs leads to new information, hypotheses, and questions.
- Change can be represented in different ways.

Now I decided to shift the conversation, "You've identified some very powerful ideas here. What are some of the things you see teachers doing to help their students connect with these ideas?"

Dina said, "The teacher in the fourth-grade DVD asked students to tell the story of the graph. That guided the students to think about the overall story."

Mariam said, "Then she decided to go from the trends to look at specific numbers. So the students could analyze the change and calculate increases from day to day. She made the connection between those numbers and the graph."

I nodded and said, "She started with a qualitative graph, without any numbers. Then she went back and labeled the axes to provide numbers."

Violet said, "I liked when the third-grade teacher on the DVD asked, 'What would you tell a visitor about Massachusetts?' It encouraged students to say something general."

April said, "I'm thinking in all the cases, even just presenting the different models, moving from the table to the graph and back, and what a difference that makes in helping the kids see change. The teachers decide what experiences to bring to the students and what models they should use."

I added, "It's important to think about when to inform students about conventions and when to let students work on what those conventions might be."

Robin said, "I'm looking at the case about candles. Right at the beginning, the teacher asks students to make predictions. This isn't a cold shot. They've been looking at other graphs. Students need a lot of experience with these kinds of situations in order to make predictions."

I pointed out that in the third-grade class on the DVD, as well, the teacher indicated they had discussions about the temperature graph every few months. However, at this point, new kinds of observations were made. "Perhaps they needed all those prior discussions to be able to observe the general trends."

I concluded this discussion by saying, "You've identified important ideas the students in these cases are working on. It's also clear that these things don't just happen. The teachers in these cases have been thinking hard about how to bring their students into these ideas, and you've pointed to explicit places where they are making decisions. We could also look back at your student-thinking assignments to identify such decision points. But we engage in such exercises in order to learn to anticipate, so that you'll have a sense of a variety of moves that might be available to you, and you'll be able to make decisions to best support your students' learning."

Homework and exit cards

First, I distributed the chart that summarizes five categories of functions. I did not want participants to feel overwhelmed by it, so I emphasized that the course has focused mainly on linear functions. I suggested that as they look down that first column, most of that information may seem pretty familiar by now. I said, "You might think of this chart as a mini algebra textbook. It gives you lots of information about functions as a reference."

Then, I explained the homework. For this assignment, participants would go through the seminar materials to find examples of each type of function. I told them they should also write out whatever questions come up for them to discuss at our next session.

I also mentioned that the reading for next time is an essay that summarizes the ideas we have been working on throughout the seminar. "When you allot time for your homework, you should consider that this is a different kind of reading than your previous assignments. It's likely you'll need more time for it."

Then I posted the exit-card questions:

- What math ideas got clarified tonight?
- What ideas do you want to bring back to your students?

As always, it is helpful to see what participants report back about the ideas from the session that stood out for them.

NAZIR: What ideas got clarified? The idea that there is a story that can be told when reading a graph, that it's not just about the numbers. That even though the graphs may look different, they can still be saying the same thing.

SANDY: I tend to struggle with articulation of the mathematical ideas related to our work. Hearing about them helps, but being able to talk about them, identify them, and make connections to the reading was a powerful place for me today. In the past case discussions, I wasn't really sure about what I needed to discuss. But really being able to IDENTIFY SOME IDEAS enabled me to look deeper at what I was thinking and what students were thinking.

Ah Ha Moment: Graphs are more than points that need to be identi- 355
fied. They can tell a story. You can create a context that relates to the
graphs. And, WOW! There are all kinds of graphs: linear, quadratic,
exponential, all of which have meaning. I understand a lot more than
before.

TRUDY: Clarified idea—I am 80% clear. Graphs of constant change—
straight line. Graphs of not constant change—like the yo-yo. Loved the
yo-yo. I am slow to recognize the change may not be constant. I imme- 360
diately graph a diagonal line.

My own teaching—I have to build, create more opportunities to
measure change and provide different models (more than 1) to
compare.

JOY: Looking at a graph and being able to read it as a story has been
helpful. I never thought about this idea before. 365

Working with the students on graphs and then relating it to a table is
also an area that I'd like to work on more with my students.

I don't think I've ever thought about the difference between the steepness and slope. The ideas were clarified somewhat. Also that the slope
is negative if the line goes down, positive if the line goes up. 370

I was especially interested that Violet had something to say about the ideas
that were new for her.

VIOLET: Ideas clarified, many. What slope is, or more exactly, how slope
is measured.

Ideas about teaching: excited about these ideas in the early grades— 375
helping kids, or better, giving kids an opportunity to formalize what
they already notice and are interested in so they have images of ideas
that seem hard in the later grades.

I especially wanted to read the cards of the teachers who had been reporting
about their confusion. Tonight they seemed to be OK. 380

ELINOR: I am still thinking about what Trudy said about "Change can
be measured" and, by knowing this, it gives a sense of control.

During the DVD and in the cases, I'm paying attention to how the
teacher listens to students' ideas and statements and rephrases them.

I had meant to check in with Peggy during break today but did not get a 385
chance. From what I could see in small-group interactions, she was engaging
well in the content of the session.

PEGGY: How comparing graphs can show what is different. You possi-
bly can see any graph in a new way when it is looked at with another.

The difference in reading the trend or story of a graph rather than the 390
points.

How different rates of change can be represented. Constant rates—line. Changing rates—curve.

I would like to use the predicting graph (without labels or numbers) and then later have kids label it.

Responding to the seventh homework

I was actually quite moved as I read participants' homework about how their ideas about teaching and learning mathematics have been influenced by the seminar. Although not everybody put the same level of thought into their responses, many teachers thought very deeply. I wanted everyone to be able to read one another's writing, though, of course, that would be too much. Instead, I chose an excerpt from each person to include in a group response. I wrote:

Dear PFC Class,

I read with great interest your homework reflections on how your ideas about teaching and learning mathematics have been influenced by the seminar experience. What you wrote is so interesting and so varied, I thought the best way to respond back to all of you is to highlight some of the themes in your writing and to share some of the important things your classmates have to say.

What you're about to read includes a lot of important ideas condensed into a few pages. I suggest that you read it slowly and read it more than once. You'll find your own thought embedded among those of your colleagues. Take time to read and let the ideas of your colleagues sink in.

Many of you wrote about how the seminar work with tables and graphs has helped you make new mathematical connections and has also influenced what you bring to your students: "It was a really big idea that one point on a graph represents two values." "For some students [in my class] the table provided a new vantage point from which to view the predictable nature of patterns. The table gave added clarity to how both variables in a linear function change at a constant rate." "The experience I have had in working with different models in trying to make sense of functions has emphasized the importance to me of making sure students have experiences with a variety of models. Not only might different students find certain models help them make more sense of ideas than other models, but also by looking at the same idea through the varied lenses of models, they may begin to develop a deeper understanding of a concept."

Experience with this variety of models and representations led to productive work on articulating formulas that make sense in terms of the situation: "What I have discovered is that [in high school] I really didn't know what everything meant. I could say that I was solving for x, but what did x stand for? What was the context I was working with?... Reflecting on the way I have learned in this class has changed my teaching. I have been working with my students

400

405

410

415

420

425

430

differently since I have been learning differently.... By using a variety of models, the children are seeing relationships among the numbers that are helping them gain a better understanding of the formula for the situations....Whether we are working with a penny jar, a growing worm, or a staircase tower, thinking in terms of the situation helps to make the numbers represent something.... We have just recently started to focus more on naming the formula that could help us figure out the nth situation. We aren't writing it in algebraic terms, but in a way they can understand, in words that they say."

Others of you wrote about the discussions of teachers' moves and the assignment to plan a lesson. These experiences led to thinking about ways in which you can become clearer about your own mathematical agenda: "I am considering trying to think of questions beforehand, especially follow-up questions that I tend to think of at night after the class has ended." "Creating a goal for the lesson that all can explore (analysis), making conjectures about the initial analysis, creating visual models/diagrams to explore the conjecture, documenting the process, discussing the process, explaining the results, and justifying the results are all components of a mathematical classroom of inquiry. Wow! This is purposeful, planned, and practiced." "I have always been curious about how kids get stuck when learning math. But looking closely has led me to be even more curious about how students acquire math knowledge and what causes them to own the thinking. At the same time, I want to be effective in my teaching and not just curious for academic reasons. So learning how to use this knowledge is the ultimate goal."

Some of you who are coaches or who are in some way working with other teachers to support their learning wrote about how what you have learned in the course influences that work: "I decided to take this course because as a math coach, algebra was definitely an area of weakness for me. How could I assist teachers with asking the right questions when I did not know what the right questions were to ask?... I feel better equipped for this task, and better equipped to support students in their understanding of patterns, functions, and change." "The experience challenges me to try to nurture the learning of the teachers I work with so they feel safe and valued for the risks that they take when they question or ask for help. So many take a peek through the window and are afraid of the content they have to learn."

Many of you wrote about the way we functioned as a group in this course and how this supported your own mathematical learning: "[The] various groupings created a sense that we were all working collectively to gain understandings of content. No one person was esteemed better than another. In a classroom, this is often the major challenge." "The small groups provided the pondering and testing time needed to work on the problems. Group norms determined at the onset, groups could then proceed with a common understanding of what's important: 'struggle' time as well as talk

435

440

445

450

455

460

465

470

time." "[The seminar] is a place where the needs of all members of the class, held by the facilitator, matter.... I am struck by the respect for the learning and learning styles of all the members of the class. Learners, allowed to enter at the place they understand the ideas, are expected, without it ever being stated, to accept responsibility for their own learning and to work diligently to develop understanding." "[In this seminar], although I am allowed to struggle, I know that during the share time, I will be given another chance to solidify my ideas and maybe even catch hold of another idea or way of looking at the ideas that have come up. It makes me feel like a part of the community when I notice that I am not the only one struggling on a concept and that my idea is as valid as the ideas of others, though we may come at it from a different direction."

The way we worked as a group also provided ways of thinking about work with students: "Having the opportunity to listen to and work with colleagues from different backgrounds in both learning and teaching is priceless.... I can analyze these perspectives from the seminar and transfer what is occurring there directly into my work with students. Watching the ways my peers learn and grow, seeing what ideas help them make meaning of situations, and receiving ideas of how to work on situations in alternate ways provides a stronger foundation for me from which my students can draw." "[During one class, I told Maxine] how I was losing confidence in what I had figured out. She began telling me what I did know, how to see functions in tables and graphs. At the time, I felt somewhat soothed. Later I realized the value of her teaching strategy. It was as if she was laying out the firm ground which she knew that I had built. When I thought back about what she did, I was anxious to read the next chapter and try to add to what I already knew. I know how to employ the 'laying out the firm ground' strategy with my students but found new meaning experiencing it as a student."

Many of you wrote about how unfamiliar this content was at the beginning and how unsure you felt about implementing lessons with students: "Another point that hindered my own case writing was how new this math seemed to me.... [I] have struggled with fully comprehending all the pieces that we discuss each week." "[My students] loved the situations—Penny Jar, which is the best deal, bottle collection [but] ... I had no idea about where this math originated, where it would go next, ... what it could be used to build [and] ... what the misunderstanding of the big concept might be."

Some of you talked about how you are now noticing the opportunities for work on functions in many areas of content in your classrooms. For example, one of you wrote, "Creating a table to record the skip-counting number sequence that students hopped or skipped along a number line nudged them to think about how two quantities form a ratio relationship. As children shared their observations about the table, questions of whether this ratio relationship might help them predict larger numbers in the sequence arose. Intrigued by the uncertainty and challenge of the task, some students predicted that a

*doubling strategy could be used to identify larger numbers in the sequence."
Another of you said, "I am thinking about trying out some more growing pattern activities with kids and asking them to explain what they think is happening. I'm still curious to know what they think is changing and if they are
able to predict what would happen and why."*

*And many of you wrote about how you feel that, at the end of the course, you
are starting to make this content your own but still have further to go. For
example, one person talked about needing to gain more experience in visualizing whether a graph will be straight or curved, and another of you said,
"Looking at the rate of change and then the rate of change of the change is
new." Reflecting on how new some of these ideas still feel, one person concluded, "I feel that I would benefit from taking the seminar again."*

*I wish I could have you all back to do it again! We would all get more solid
and go deeper. Thank you all for these thoughts.*

Maxine

A few people wrote about mathematics that I needed to address, and so I
wrote a few individual responses, as well. In particular, I want to include here
what Peggy had written and my response.

Peggy

*During Session 6, I lost my balance in the PFC class and truly felt at sea.
I think I had felt secure with my interest in our explorations up to that time,
but I had not done the hard thinking that looks back and connects experiences. I went home from class and sat down to read the homework right away.
Luckily, the reading began with a review, which helped me to order my previous
experiences.*

*I noticed in Session 6 that my fellow teachers were associating cases with
kinds of functions. I decided to go back through the cases to find an example
for each kind of function. For linear function, I look at the lunch money model
in Case 6 of Chapter 2. This is a situation where each lunch cost $2. I know
this case well because I did it with my class. In working on this model, I made
a table and saw the kids make and interpret their tables. I also made a graph
and saw kids make and interpret their graphs. The variables in the situation
are the lunches and the cost. When the number of lunches goes up by 1, the
cost goes up by 2.*

*I reread the chapters looking for terms that related to my experience with the
$2 for a lunch situation. In Chapter 2, I noted, "The mathematical idea of
function involves a correspondence from one set to another." I thought about
how the set of number of lunches related to the set of cost of lunches. When
I make a table showing number of lunches in one column and corresponding
cost, I can see the correspondence between the two sets on any given line.
For example, 3 lunches cost $6. There is a correspondence between the sets of
2n (number of lunches) = cost (in dollars).*

520

525

530

535

540

545

550

555

In class, when Maxine talked about independent and dependent variables, I thought that the number of lunches was the independent variable. The cost of the lunches depended on the number of lunches, so it was the dependent variable. In showing the correspondence between the two sets, I put the independent variable, the number of lunches, on the x-axis. I put the dependent variable, the cost of lunches, on the y-axis.

From line to line in my table, I can see how the changing amount changes at a constant rate. Each successive line in the Number of Lunches column goes up by 1 as its corresponding cost goes up by 2. When I graphed the function between the two sets, it showed a series of correspondences, dots, which, when connected, form a line. It is my understanding that the line of the graph is the characteristic of a linear function.

When I worked on a similar lunch-money problem with my class, I hoped that they would make a table, but I did not show them how to make one. I think that I thought that some would make tables, and those who sat near them would have a chance to see how they made them. Maxine responded to my paper about the class by saying that I should not expect my students to discover how to make a table. In retrospect, I realized that I should have demonstrated how to make a table so that kids could use that tool to look at the correspondence between the two sets in the table format.

Reading and working on the problems in Chapter 6 introduced me to nonlinear functions. I think the table for "How Many Outfits?" shows a set of information that does not grow at a constant rate. The relationship between the sets is exponential. For example, if there are 4 colors, the corresponding outfits will be 4 to the 4th power or $4 \times 4 = 16$. A rule for this function might be to put the number of the color to that number's power to find the combinations.

Just now, I stopped to graph the correspondence between numbers of colors and possible number of combinations. For each additional color, the independent variable, there is a move of one box to the right on the x-axis. The corresponding combination goes up in increasing amounts, depending on the number to its own power. The ascent of the line is increasingly steep. I used a ruler to connect the dots and I think that it is not absolutely straight. The increase between the dots is not constant.

On the table for the combinations, I can see that the change is predictable but not constant. I enjoy trying to find patterns between the lines for the non-constant change, but I do not feel articulate in explaining what I see.

I know predicting what a graph will look like after I make a table will add to my fluency with functions. In the sharply ascending, nonlinear graph, I was inclined to imagine a curve that was doubling back. It was helpful when Maxine pointed out that the curve would only go back if the independent variable decreased. I like the idea of using my hand to show in the air what I think a graph will look like.

Reading Chapter 7, "Functions Without Formulas," helped to round out my picture of the possible correspondence between sets of variables. I will hold the graph of "Each Wednesday's Temperature" as my example of a function without a formula. The word "formula" is weighty for me because I have worked hard to swiftly describe how one set corresponds to another. In this case, the graph shows dots that move up and down as the weeks go on. Although there is not a formula for the movement from one line of the table to the next, it is possible to think about patterns in looking at the temperature over a series of weeks. Also, it is possible to look at the graph and predict what the weather might be in upcoming weeks.

In addition to my learning about functions, I also come away with some important ideas about how to work on functions with my class. For example, whenever I plan a lesson, I think about what I want my class to get out of what they will do. My understanding of focusing on the outcomes of lessons was jarred by my experience with "What's the Best Deal?" I had imagined that kids would have the opportunity to graph the results for each of the salary schemes, but in fact, they spent almost all of the hour computing the salary for each day. The idea of presenting calculators for the figuring had passed through my mind, but knowing that the class needed computation practice, I did not provide calculators. By holding back the calculators, I denied my class the chance to experience making graphs, which would have been very interesting to them.

A conversation at our PFC class really drove home the idea of planning lessons to focus on outcomes. In the future, I will get the desired activity firmly in mind and then tailor the classwork so that we get there.

During the last class, when I lost my balance, I asked Maxine a question about a graphic representation of a function. When I got some of what she explained, I went on to say how I was losing confidence in what I had figured out. She began telling me what I did know—how to see functions in tables and in graphs. At the time, I felt somewhat soothed. Later, I realized the value of her teaching strategy. It was as if she was laying out the firm ground that she knew I had built. When I thought back about what she did, I was anxious to read the next chapter and try to add to what I already knew. I know how to employ the "laying out the firm ground" strategy with my students, but found new meaning experiencing it as a student.

I spent one session with a small group of students who were looking at the tables and graphs of their classmates. As the students tried to read the work of their peers, I noticed that they were talking about how the ideas were communicated. Maxine spoke about thinking of having an audience as we do math; I think that reading each other's presentations is one way to get better at it.

I would like to try looking across the models that represent a function. I feel that others in the class are doing that and it is the next thing I would like to

605

610

615

620

625

630

635

640

645

tackle. When I do work with functions with my class I will keep it in mind that looking at all the possible models for a function holds the potential for interesting discoveries.

Wow. I thought it was so interesting that Peggy's response to feeling at sea was to use the homework assignment to go back over so much of what she had learned in the seminar. By reviewing parts of what she understood about linear functions, she could begin to sort out the ideas of nonlinear functions that were so difficult for her. Although some of her ideas are confused, she was making good headway. In my response, I wanted to offer Peggy encouragement, comment on her strengths, and also correct some of the mathematics she did not have quite right.

Dear Peggy,

During our last session (Session 7), I had been intending to check in with you after our discussion in Session 6. However, I didn't want to interrupt your work and didn't seem to find you during break. So I was very pleased to read your assignment and see that you had written about how you moved forward from our talk.

It was a very smart strategy on your part to go back over some of the ideas of the seminar and write out your understanding. It wasn't only a facilitator move to help you "lay out the firm ground"; you act on this as a learning move for yourself. I imagine that writing out these ideas for yourself helps you feel anchored, rather than being tossed about at sea. From there you can move into new learning.

I'm glad you did that writing before you were given Chapter 8 to read. That is, I'm glad you had the opportunity to write out those ideas for yourself before the chapter laid them out for you. However, my hope is that reading the ideas again made you feel firmly planted, even if there are still some ideas that require a stretch.

There is one place where I want to correct some of the words you use. When you wrote about the mathematics of the case "How Many Outfits?" you talked about it as an exponential function. In fact, it is a quadratic function, which is different from exponential. In that case, if there are 4 colors of shirts and shorts, then there are 4 × 4 outfits, which can be written as 4^2 and read as "four squared" or "four to the power of 2." The function rule for that context is $y = x^2$. (One characteristic of quadratic functions is that the independent variable is squared [taken to a power of 2].) You are right to say that as x increases by 1, the corresponding number of combinations goes up in increasing amounts. The corresponding value of the function is that number (x) times itself (not "to its own power").

"4 to the 4th power" means 4 × 4 × 4 × 4 and can be written as 4^4.

We did look at an exponential function. The example was in the case about folding paper. Each time you fold the paper, you double the number of sections.

650

655

660

665

670

675

680

685

The rule for that function is $y = 2^x$. That rule might look very similar to the quadratic function above, but in fact, it's quite different. After all, when $x = 10$, 2^x is already equal to 1,024, but x^2 is equal to 100. What characterizes an exponential function is that the independent variable is the exponent.

690

Of course, mixing up the vocabulary for quadratic and exponential functions does not detract from all the mathematics you learned in the seminar. Besides, you might have already sorted out these matters from reading Chapter 8.

Beyond the mathematics content itself, you participated in the seminar being very open to learning about learning and teaching. I appreciate all that you mentioned in your assignment.

695

Keep up all the good work.

Maxine

Detailed Agenda

Math activity: Stories and graphs

(75 minutes)

Small groups (40 minutes)

Whole group (35 minutes)

In this Math activity, participants work with qualitative graphing. They explain what each of a set of graphs indicates about movement of an object and draw graphs that match various stories. As they work with the stories and the graphs, they should articulate what the shape of the graph indicates about the rate of increase or decrease of the quantities involved. A main idea is that many of the same tools we use to examine graphs that represent functions defined by algebraic expressions are also useful when examining graphs that present qualitative representations of phenomena. For example, a horizontal segment indicates no change, a line sloping up indicates a steady increase, and a curving graph indicates a non-steady increase.

Organize participants into small groups and distribute "Math activity: Stories and graphs." Let participants know they will have 35 minutes to work in small groups on these questions. As participants work on the questions in Part I, they should articulate what the graphs indicate about the movement of the book-carrier. For instance, Graph 1 indicates the books are lifted at a steady rate, while Graph 6 indicates the book-carrier is moving slowly at first but then accelerates. Note that Graph 3 represents an impossible situation—that the book-carrier is at all heights at the same time. Participants' work on the graphs of Part I should provide them with the background to work on Part II, the dropping-keys situation. There are likely to be different (and still correct) graphs offered for questions in Part III, as different aspects of riding a Ferris wheel or playing with a yo-yo can be graphed.

Some participants may feel they need to have studied physics in order to answer these questions. Ask questions such as "What is the difference between falling from a tree limb just a few feet off the ground and falling from a tall building?" or " What is the difference between traveling on a ride that goes vertically up and down versus the circular path of the Ferris wheel?" in order to help them connect their own logic and experiences to these situations. (See "Maxine's Journal," pp. 241–248 for further examples of participants' comments on these situations.)

If your participants are mostly teachers of Grades K–5, base the work on Parts I, II, and III. If your group is predominantly from middle school, then include Part IV. Part IV is based on a single story, but participants are asked to make two graphs, one about speed and one about distance from home. You may want to challenge some participants to draw both graphs on the same set of axes and ask them to examine the connections between the two graphs. (See the Facilitator Note [pp. 237–240] for more detail on responses to Part IV.)

As you interact with the small groups, ask questions so that participants articulate the connections between the shape of the graphs and various aspects of their stories. Because the situations are open to interpretation, it is likely there will be a variety of graphs drawn for the situations in Part III. Encourage participants to compare graphs and suggest they explain the connections between the movement of the Ferris wheel or the yo-yo and the shape of the related graph. If there are a variety of graphs you want to use for the whole-group discussion, you might want to ask two or three participants to make a poster-sized version of their graphs. Note that the Ferris wheel graph is particularly important as it is the only example of a sine function in the seminar. Be sure every group has a chance to work on this problem.

After 15 minutes, announce that the whole-group discussion will be based on Parts II and III. Suggest that they spend the remaining time on these two parts. You might also announce that it is OK if they do not work with the yo-yo or the traveling-to-school situations if time does not permit.

The whole-group discussion should include two components:

■ Explanations of which of the three graphs represent the keys dropping situation in Part II
■ Examples of different graphs for Part III connected to what actions they represent

In this discussion, ask questions to help participants make connections between the shape of the graph and the action in the story contexts; for example, a steady increase is represented by a straight line; a non-steady increase is represented by a curved line.

Begin with a discussion of the dropping-keys situation. Solicit comments about what each graph shows and have participants present arguments to support which graph is most realistic. (*Note*: Graph 2 represents this situation as it shows the speed of the keys increasing over time.)

Display the various graphs your participants drew for the Ferris wheel situation and ask participants who did not draw a given graph to tell a story about the Ferris wheel that matches each of the graphs. Once graphs are offered and explained, introduce the term *periodic function* to describe motion that recurs in a regular way.

If your participants drew a variety of graphs for the yo-yo situation, and there is an adequate amount of time, you can display and discuss those as well.

Break

(15 minutes)

Functions Without Formulas

DVD discussion (10 minutes)

Whole group

The first DVD segment is of a third-grade class in Massachusetts examining a graph of temperatures over the course of a school year. Ask participants to take note of how students talk about the temperature, as well as the changes in the temperature and how those can be seen on the graph.

The second DVD segment is of a fourth-grade class examining both graphs and tables that represent plant growth. Suggest that participants note how students connect features of the graph to a story of how the plant grew and how they connected the graph and the story with information in the table.

Let participants know that they will view the DVD segments and then turn to the small-group case discussion. "In your small groups, discuss how students represent ideas of change using examples from both the DVD and the print cases."

Case discussion (70 minutes)

Small groups (35 minutes)
Whole group (35 minutes)

The cases in Chapter 7 present students creating and examining graphs of phenomena that change over time, specifically temperature, volume of snow and ice as they melt, and the height of a candle as it burns. The focus of the case discussion is on the connections the students make between the changes in the phenomena and the shape of the graph.

Organize the participants into groups of three or four and distribute the Focus Questions for Chapter 7. Inform the group they will have 35 minutes to work as a small group.

Question 1, based on Barbara's case about temperature, focuses on student thinking as they look to the graph to identify general trends. For instance, students note that while the weekly temperatures might involve both increases and decreases, the general trend from September through December is for the temperature to decrease. In discussing Focus Question 2, participants should examine the connections between the graph and the student comments about the melting snow and ice.

Focus Questions 3–5 are based on Maggie's case about the burning candle. In response to Focus Question 3, participants examine the graphs that represent the predictions of the students and what each graph indicates about the students' thinking. Focus Question 4 highlights the graphs of the data and the thinking of Drew and Mario. Participants discuss the connections the students are making, as well as the connections that they might be missing. When participants identify a connection that is missing, you might ask what next steps they would take to call the students' attention to that idea. Focus Question 5 is based on the table and the connections between the changes as seen in the table and as seen in the graphs.

The whole-group discussion should include two components:

- Examining examples of students looking at general trends in a graph as well as interpreting both change and the quantities represented on the graph
- A conversation about what these teachers are doing and what teachers can do, in general, to bring ideas about looking at change over time to their students

Begin the whole-group discussion by asking, "What are some of the mathematical ideas you see students in the cases and the DVD getting from this work?" If participants have difficulty engaging with this level of question, ask about how students in Case 27 began to look for trends in the temperature data. Then turn to Focus Questions 3–5 to solicit participants' comments on student thinking in the case about burning candles.

Use the last 10 minutes of the discussion time to turn to teacher moves. Ask, "What is it that you see teachers in these cases and the DVD doing to bring these ideas of change over time to their students?" Examples might include:

- Barbara collecting data over a long period and asking questions that focus both on specifics and long-range tendencies seen in the graph
- Theresa constructing the axes and graph for her young students so they could concentrate on the shape and meaning of the graph rather than being confused about how to create such a graph
- Maggie asking her students to predict the shape of the graphs before collecting the data

If there is time for further discussion ask, "What ideas about your own teaching do these cases bring up for you?"

Homework and exit cards

(10 minutes)

Whole group/individuals

Distribute the "Eighth Homework" and the chart detailing the five categories of functions (pp. 271–273). Take a few minutes to describe the nature of the chart and the essay in Chapter 8. Ask participants to read the homework directions. Then answer their questions about this assignment.

Use the last 5 minutes to pose two exit-card reflection questions:

- What mathematical ideas were clarified for you at this session?
- What ideas about your teaching do these cases bring up for you?

Before the next session...

In preparation for the next session, read participants' papers on their thinking about teaching and learning. You may write a single response that incorporates comments from the whole set of papers, or you may choose to write to each individual, commenting on his or her particular work. For more information, see the section in "Maxine's Journal" on responding to the seventh homework. Make copies of both the papers and your responses for your files before returning the work.

Possible Responses to Math Activity, Section IV: Speed and Distance Graphs for a Traveling-to-School Situation

The story about traveling to school is loosely sketched out. Because specific details are open to interpretation, participants might have graphs that differ from one another. Each graph for speed should have four sections corresponding to the four different speeds in the story: walking to school, hurrying home, "zero speed" while at home, and driving in a car. Participants may choose different ways to connect these horizontal segments, using longer or shorter intervals between the steady speeds. The graphs may differ in other ways. The graph for speed that follows starts with the person walking at a constant rate. Some participants, however, may draw a graph beginning at (0, 0), which would indicate the person starts at rest. Ask questions so that participants describe the assumptions they have made and explain how these assumptions are reflected in their graph.

There will be similar variations in the graph for distance from home. The graph drawn below also shows four sections, but only one is horizontal. In the first section, distance from home is increasing at a roughly steady pace; in the second, distance from home is decreasing; in the third, there is zero distance from home; and in the fourth, distance from home is increasing rapidly. In this case, unlike the sample graph drawn for speed, the graph begins at (0, 0) because this indicates the person begins at home. Ask questions so participants explain how various components of their graph match the details they are including in their version of the story.

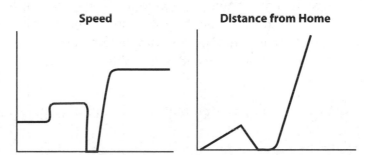

| **Speed** | **Distance from Home** |

Some participants may ask about the distinction between speed and velocity. Speed is always a positive, or zero, quantity. The term *velocity* indicates both speed and direction. A graph of velocity might indicate a positive value for the first segment, which shows the person walking to school, and a negative value for the second segment, in which the person runs in the opposite direction. The graph for speed is always at or above the x-axis, whether the person is moving away from home or toward home. The graph simply reports how fast the person is moving at a given time.

DVD Summary

Session 7: Functions Without Formulas

Third-grade class with teacher Deborah (5 minutes)

In this DVD segment, students are examining a graph of temperature over time. The graph was constructed from data collected once a week from September through June in Massachusetts.

First students discuss the increases and decreases in the temperature, describing the weekly changes from one measurement to another. Then they make comments about a more general trend of decreasing from September to January and increasing from January to June. Finally the teacher asks what this graph indicates about temperature in general in Massachusetts. Matthew summarizes what the shape of the graph indicates about temperature and changes in temperature.

Fourth-grade class with teacher Nancy (4 minutes)

In the first part of this segment, students examine a sketch of a graph representing plant growth over time. Max tells how the plant grew based on his observations from the graph.

In the next segment, the teacher has drawn a similar graph—this time on a set of axes that are labeled *Days* and *cm* and marked to indicate units. She solicits measurements from students to build a table based on the graph. She asks how they can tell when the plant is growing quickly by looking at the table. Students determine the amount of change by subtracting values and describing when the biggest change occurs. The teacher asks where that is—the place of fastest growth—on the graph, and Hannah points out the appropriate section of the graph. Then the teacher summarizes how to find the place of most growth on the graph and in the table.

Math activity: Stories and graphs (page 1)

I. In a small town, library books are moved from one level to another on a book-carrier that is operated by a rope on a pulley. The given graphs are supposed to represent the height (H) of the book-carrier as the operator pulls on the rope to lift the books over time (T). Explain what each graph would indicate about the way the book-carrier is moving. Which graph is most realistic? Which is least? Why?

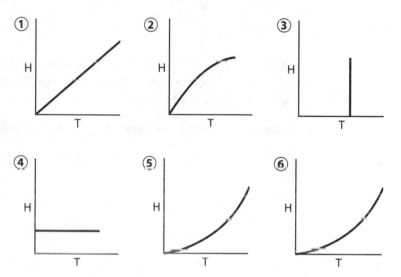

II. You accidentally drop your keys from the roof of a tall building. (Oops!) The given graphs represent the height of the keys as they fall. Explain what each graph would indicate about the movement of the keys. Which graph is most realistic? Which is least?

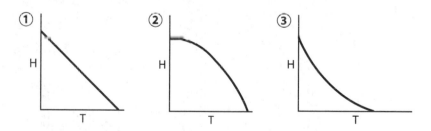

Math activity: Stories and graphs (page 2)

III. Make graphs for each of these situations. Depending on the details you add, you may make more than one graph for each situation.

1. A child is riding on a Ferris wheel. Make a graph to show the height of the child over time.

2. A child is playing with a yo-yo. Make a graph to show the height of the yo-yo over time.

IV. Consider this story.

I started walking to school at a steady pace and then realized I left my books at home, so I hurried back to get them. Then my mom drove me to school so I would not be late.

1. Draw a graph with speed on the y-axis and time on the x-axis.

2. Draw a graph with distance from home on the y-axis and time on the x-axis.

Focus Questions: Chapter 7

1. In Barbara's case, Case 27, students move from thinking about the graph of temperature in terms of a pattern to thinking about the graph as representing trends. Explain this distinction using examples from the case.

2. In Jessica's case, Case 28, lines 78–91, students draw conclusions about the melting ice and snow on the basis of the graphs. What are the conclusions, and how is each related to the shape of the graphs?

3. At the beginning of Maggie's case, Case 29, students offer predictions about the shape of the graph for the burning candle situation. Discuss the predictions in lines 124–139 (most students), lines 136–140 (Nathan), lines 142–145 (Amy), and lines 146–154 (Joseph). How does the shape of the predicted graph connect with each student's thinking about the candles?

4. Also in Case 29, consider the comments of Drew, lines 165–169, and Mario, lines 170–175, after graphing the data. What are the connections these students make between the shape of the graph and the candle situation? Are there connections you see they are missing?

5. In Case 29, lines 188–194, what connections does Crissy make among the table, the graph, and the situation? Are there connections you see that are not detailed in the case?

6. What do you see teachers in Cases 27–29 doing to bring ideas of change over time to their students?

Eighth Homework

Reading assignment: Casebook, Chapter 8

Read Chapter 8, the essay "The Mathematics of Patterns, Functions, and Change for the K–8 Classroom," by Stephen Monk, Deborah Schifter, and Tracy Noble.

Writing assignment

1. Reflecting on Chapter 8

Locate two or three points in the essay that particularly interest you. Write about each of those points. Explain what makes it interesting. What experiences have you had that led you to connect to these ideas?

Locate two or three points in the essay that you find confusing or which seem not to describe experiences you have had. Explain each of these. What is confusing or how is your own experience different from what is suggested?

Locate one or two points in the essay that suggest something you want to incorporate into your teaching practice. Explain each of these.

Bring two copies of this writing to the next session to support discussion of this chapter.

2. Reflecting on categories of functions

Look over the chart describing five categories of functions: linear, quadratic, exponential, hyperbolic, and sine. We have worked with specific examples of these functions in the seminar. However, we have concentrated on some types of functions, like linear, and other types we have worked with less extensively. For each type of function the chart presents an example with an equation and a table, provides two possible graphs that fit the category, and includes information about situations in which that type of function generally appears.

Review your work for the seminar, and locate examples for each type of function. What are the ways you think about each type? Fill out the lower sections of the chart, indicating examples from the seminar and how you characterize each category of functions. Then take notes on what makes sense to you about this chart and also what questions the information on the chart brings up. Bring these notes to the next session for discussion.

CATEGORIES OF FUNCTIONS

Name	Linear Functions	Quadratic Functions	Exponential Functions	Hyperbolic Functions	Sine Functions
Equation	$y = ax + b$	$y = ax^2 + bx + c$	$y = a^x$	$y = \frac{a}{x}$	$y = a \sin bx + c$
Example	$y = 3x + 4$	$y = x^2$	$y = 2^x$	$y = \frac{1}{x}$	$y = \sin x$

Linear Functions

x	y	Difference
-2	-2	
-1	1	3
0	4	3
1	7	3
2	10	3
3	13	3
4	16	3

As x increases by a constant amount, y increases by a constant amount.

Quadratic Functions

x	y	Difference
-2	4	
-1	1	-3
0	0	-1
1	1	1
2	4	3
3	9	5
4	16	7

As x increases by a constant amount, the differences between y values change linearly.

Exponential Functions

x	y	Difference
-2	$\frac{1}{4}$	
-1	$\frac{1}{2}$	$\frac{1}{4}$
0	1	$\frac{1}{2}$
1	2	1
2	4	2
3	8	4
4	16	8

As x increases by a constant amount, y is multiplied by a constant amount.

The differences form an exponential function.

Hyperbolic Functions

x	y
$\frac{1}{4}$	4
$\frac{1}{3}$	3
$\frac{1}{2}$	2
1	1
2	$\frac{1}{2}$
3	$\frac{1}{3}$
4	$\frac{1}{4}$

x and y are indirectly proportional.

The product of x and y is a constant.

Sine Functions

x	y
0	0
$0.25\pi = 0.79$	0.7071
$0.5\pi = 1.57$	1
$0.75\pi = 2.36$	0.7071
$\pi = 3.14$	0
$1.25\pi = 3.93$	-0.7071
$1.5\pi = 4.71$	-1
$1.75\pi = 5.50$	-0.7071
$2\pi = 6.28$	0
$2.25\pi = 7.07$	0.7071
$2.5\pi = 7.85$	1
$2.75\pi = 8.64$	0.7071
$3\pi = 9.42$	0

Name	Linear Functions	Quadratic Functions	Exponential Functions	Hyperbolic Functions	Sine Functions
Graphs	a is the slope; b is the y-intercept. The larger the value of $|a|$, the steeper the line. A change in the value of b moves the line up or down along the y-axis. *Note:* When $b = 0$, x and y are directly proportional. When $a > 0$, the line inclines from left to right.	When $a > 0$, the curve opens up; when $a < 0$, the curve opens down. A change in the value a makes the curve wider or narrower. Changes in b or c move the curve to the left or right and up or down.	When $a > 1$, the curve is increasing from left to right; when $a < 1$, the curve is decreasing from left to right. A change in the value of a stretches the curve out (or the opposite). The graph approaches but never touches the x-axis.	A change in the value of a moves the curve closer to or farther away from the axes. When $a > 0$, the curves are in quadrants I and III; When $a < 0$, the curves are in quadrants II and IV.	A change in the value of a changes the amplitude or height of the curve. A change in the value of b changes the frequency, stretching it or squeezing it. A change in the value of c raises or lowers the graph.
	When $a < 0$, the line declines from left to right.	$a > 0$, b and $c = 0$ $a < 0$, $b > 0$, $c > 0$	$a > 1$ $a < 1$	$a > 0$ $a < 0$	$a = 1$, $b = 1$, $c = 0$ a is positive and < 1. b is positive and > 1. $c = 0$

272

© Education Development Center

Name	Linear Functions	Quadratic Functions	Exponential Functions	Hyperbolic Functions	Sine Functions
Applications	When traveling at a constant velocity, distance traveled over time When an object is dropped from a height, velocity over time	The area of a square in relation to the length of a side The height of an object thrown in the air as a function of time	Growth when population doubles or triples regularly in a particular time interval. Amount of radiation over time; the half-life of a substance indicates how long it takes for half the quantity to decay	The size of each part when a given amount is divided into x equal parts To balance a seesaw, the distance from the fulcrum as a function of weight	Sitting in a Ferris wheel, your height above the ground as a function of time when the Ferris wheel rotates at a constant speed Sine functions are used in contexts of electricity, light, sound, and anything that travels as waves
Examples from my work in this seminar:					
What I associate with this type of function:					

Wrapping Up

Mathematical themes:

■ Examining different attributes of the same situation and seeing that they can result in different functions, each with different patterns of change

■ Examining some cubic functions

■ Recognizing that linear and quadratic functions belong to a larger category of functions called *polynomial functions*

Session Agenda

Chapter 8 discussion	Small groups	30 minutes
	Whole group	30 minutes
"Categories of Functions" discussion	Pairs	10 minutes
	Whole group	15 minutes
Break	Whole group	15 minutes
Math activity: Growing and painting cubes or Application problems	Small groups	55 minutes
	Whole group	20 minutes
Portfolio review and closing	Whole group	5 minutes

Background Preparation

Read

■ the Casebook, Chapter 8

■ "Maxine's Journal" for Session 8

■ the agenda for Session 8

Work through

■ the Math activity: Growing and painting cubes (pp. 309–310)

■ the Math activity: Application problems (pp. 311–312)

Materials

Duplicate

■ "Math activity: Growing and painting cubes" (pp. 309–310)

■ "Application problems" (pp. 311–312)

■ "Ninth Homework" (p. 313)

■ Evaluation Form (p. 314)

Obtain

■ graph paper

■ rulers

■ interlocking cubes

■ calculators

Cubic and Polynomial Functions

The Math activity in Session 8 introduces a new kind of function. By studying a cube, not only do participants work with a linear function (the perimeter of a face as a function of the length of an edge; $y = 4x$) and a quadratic function (the surface area of the cube as a function of the length of an edge; $y = 6x^2$), but also a cubic function (the volume of the cube as a function of the length of an edge; $y = x^3$).

A *cubic* function always has a term with the variable raised to the third power. Other examples are $y = 2x^3 + 3x^2 - 2x - 6$ or $y = {}^-5x^3 - 3$ or $y = 3x^3 - 3.6x^2$.

The tools developed through explorations of linear, quadratic, and exponential functions can be applied here as well. In particular, it is fruitful to examine the changes in the output variable as the input variable increases by 1.

Linear

For linear functions, we found that as the inputs increase by 1, the output is changed by a constant amount. The tables below show a specific example, $y = 4x$, and also examine what happens with the formula $y = ax + b$.

x	$y = 4x$	First Difference
1	4	
		4
2	8	
		4
3	12	
		4
4	16	

The difference is always 4.

x	$y = ax + b$	First Difference
1	$a + b$	
		a
2	$2a + b$	
		a
3	$3a + b$	
		a
4	$4a + b$	

The difference is always a.

Quadratic

For quadratic functions, we noted that the first differences do not produce a constant, but the second differences do. Consider this table for $y = 6x^2$.

x	$y = 6x^2$	First Difference	Second Difference
1	6		
		18	
2	24		12
		30	
3	54		12
		42	
4	96		12
		54	
5	150		12
		66	
6	216		

This pattern of constant second differences is true for all quadratic functions. Consider the quadratic $y = x^2 + 3x - 2$ and the general form $y = ax^2 + bx + c$ to see how this takes place.

x	$x^2 + 3x - 2$	First Difference	Second Difference
1	2		
		6	
2	8		2
		8	
3	16		2
		10	
4	26		2
		12	
5	38		2
		14	
6	52		

x	$ax^2 + bx + c$	First Difference	Second Difference
1	$a + b + c$		
		$3a + b$	
2	$4a + 2b + c$		$2a$
		$5a + b$	
3	$9a + 3b + c$		$2a$
		$7a + b$	
4	$16a + 4b + c$		$2a$
		$9a + b$	
5	$25a + 5b + c$		$2a$
		$11a + b$	
6	$36a + 6b + c$		

Cubic

Examine these tables to consider the two cubic functions from the Math activity in Session 8: $y = x^3$ and $y = (x - 2)^3 = x^3 - 6x^2 + 12x - 8$.

x	x^3	First Difference	Second Difference	Third Difference
1	1			
		7		
2	8		12	
		19		6
3	27		18	
		37		6
4	64		24	
		61		6
5	125		30	
		91		6
6	216		36	
		127		
7	343			

x	$(x-2)^3 =$ $x^3 - 6x^2 + 12x - 8$	First Difference	Second Difference	Third Difference
1	‑1			
		1		
2	0		0	
		1		6
3	1		6	
		7		6
4	8		12	
		19		6
5	27		18	
		37		6
6	64		24	
		61		
7	125			

With a cubic function, the changes become constant at the level of the third differences. This is true for all cubic functions, that is, any function such that the highest exponent is 3. (You might want to examine $y = ax^3 + bx^2 + cx + d$ to see what happens.)

In fact, this pattern of differences and changes continues for all *polynomial* functions. A polynomial function is one in which each term has the form ax^n, where n is some whole number and a is any number on the number line.

$y = 3x^5 + 2^4 - 5x^2 + 6x + 2$, $y = (\frac{1}{3})x^6 + 2x + 3$, and $y = x^5 + 3x^2 - x$ are examples of polynomial functions. The highest power of a polynomial function determines how many levels of differences are needed to produce a constant.

Maxine's Journal

May 12

We continued to work hard throughout Session 8, but the feel of it was more like a celebration. For most participants, all three activities—discussing the "Categories of Functions" chart, reflecting on Chapter 8, and working on more mathematics—felt like an affirmation of all they had learned in the last few months.

Categories of Functions

The discussion of the chart I handed out in the last session was an opportunity to clarify several points. As participants asked questions, I elaborated with examples.

Ivan pointed out that most of the functions we've worked with in this seminar go up as you move from left to right. But some examples in the chart go down. This felt especially important.

The Penny Jar context was about accumulating pennies. The number of pennies in the Penny Jar increases over time, and so the line goes up. Robin reminded us that in Session 7, we talked about a Penny Jar context in which you remove pennies each round. There, the line would go down. I picked a particular example—start with 15 pennies and remove 2 pennies each round—and we created a table and graph for it.

Number of Rounds	Number of Pennies
0	15
1	13
2	11
3	9
4	7

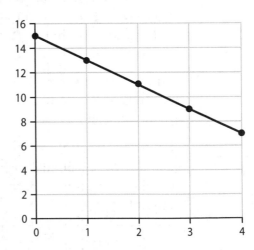

Lamis asked about the shape of a quadratic function. She said that in the chart, the graphs go up and down, but our examples only went up. In Session 6, I did show participants what quadratic functions look like over an extended domain, but I imagine many were too overwhelmed at that time to

05

10

15

20

take it in. So now I pointed out that the examples we considered in Session 6 used only positive values. However, if we look at the formulas over a larger domain—all the numbers on the number line—we get a different picture. We made up a table for the function $y = x^2$ and then created the corresponding graph.

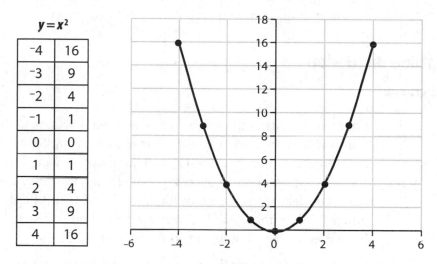

$y = x^2$	
⁻4	16
⁻3	9
⁻2	4
⁻1	1
0	0
1	1
2	4
3	9
4	16

Then I suggested we consider the function $y = {}^-x^2$.

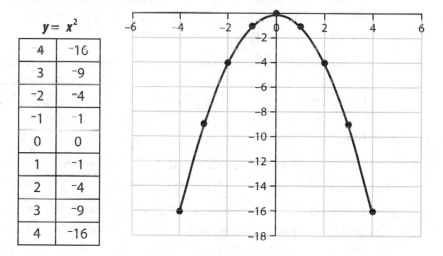

$y = {}^-x^2$	
⁻4	⁻16
⁻3	⁻9
⁻2	⁻4
⁻1	⁻1
0	0
1	⁻1
2	⁻4
3	⁻9
4	⁻16

Dina said that when she looks at this chart, she has an idea that is connected to the concept of landmarks. She said, "When we teach about computation, we encourage students to think in terms of landmark numbers. These numbers provide anchors as they work on their calculations. Does it make sense to think about landmark functions?"

I thought this was a very interesting idea. I said, "That's a nice way to think about it. When I look at a data table or a graph or formula, I do check out whether it has features that resemble one of these functions. That helps me think about what other characteristics this function ought to have."

I concluded this discussion by mentioning that we did not spend much time on the exponential, hyperbolic, or sine functions. I said, "At this point, it's not so important that you have in mind all the details about these functions, but just that you know they exist. And it's important that you know there are other categories, as well. This chart doesn't cover all possible functions."

Bill said, "Oh, great. Just when I feel that I've really figured something out, I come to see how much more there is to learn." Participants laughed. This was said in good humor.

Chapter 8 discussion

Small groups

I put participants into groups to discuss their reactions to the essay: what they found interesting, what confused them, and what ideas they would like to incorporate in their practice. Overall, participants were intrigued by the essay. I heard only one person, Flor, say that reading the essay distressed her. "I felt like I had learned so much in the course, and then I kept coming across language I didn't understand." Then she backed off and said, "Maybe I shouldn't have tried to read it when I was so exhausted."

As I listened to small groups, it seemed that many people were clarifying areas of confusion. One group graphed a quadratic and an exponential function in order to make comparisons. Another group talked about the power of the Phone-Plan problem.

I stopped by Peggy's table, and seeing that she had read my response to her homework, I took the opportunity to check in with her. After telling her that I was impressed with her work, I said, "I think you had the ideas right, but you were confusing some of the language about quadratic and exponential functions."

She gave me a big smile and said, "Yes, when I read the essay, I realized I had written about that incorrectly. I understand that now."

At her table, Dina was pointing to the line in the essay that mentions how important it is to have students working on the ideas of functions years before secondary school. She said, "When I think about my own learning in high school, I can remember it now, the teacher putting formulas on the board, and all these problems to practice. That was the experience. Once the course was over, whatever knowledge I had was gone. You don't really connect it to every-day things. Children need to make those connections earlier than high school."

Whole group

When we got together as a whole group, Bill began the discussion. "I thought this essay was a really nice summary. It helped me get a handle on what we were studying at different points in this seminar. It gave me names for things. To read about it out of the context of our lessons was really nice, a nice way to tie it all up."

April said, "I had a similar feeling. But I felt like I was missing student thinking and how they thought about functions. I was just wondering about that."

April had taken several other DMI seminars in which the concluding essay, called "Highlights of Related Research," summarized the ideas of the course through the lens of mathematics education research into student learning. This essay had a different flavor. I said, "April, I think I know what you're referring to. The issue is that it is a fairly recent idea to introduce the content of functions into the elementary grades and so there isn't yet a large body of research in which we get a reasonably fine-grained picture of how students engage with the conceptual issues. At this point, the main thing the different research studies indicate is that young children can productively work with the basic ideas of functions. Different studies give us examples, quite like the cases we have read in the last few months, though the essay does report on some findings of researchers. I wonder if anyone found that helpful."

Mariam responded, "Erick Smith has a quote about children using algebraic notation. That was so powerful, because for people who did so miserably, like me ... it's interesting that students make connections. I see myself in the learner's seat in this whole course because I was so busy repairing what happened in seventh grade. It all underscored that I'm a learner along with my kids. Also, I found it so helpful to have it spelled out what the conventions are."

Lamis said, "I didn't miss the research about students the way April did. I found that I was paying attention to my own thinking. Even the references to the cases the essay made, I felt, oh, I want to go back to that. So I felt like, because it's so new to me, I was happy to have it focus on just the mathematical ideas."

Elinor added, "This was all about me, like Lamis was saying. First this is about me understanding the content better. I found that with the essay I went back to my notes, and I found gaps in my notes, and I could fill in those gaps with vocabulary and information."

Most of the comments were about participants' responses to the essay, rather than content, until Ivan's question. He asked, "I noticed that the essay dedicated much more time to linear functions than any of the other functions. Is that because linear functions are more important?"

This was an interesting question, one that indicated Ivan, perhaps among others, was taking a step back to think about what the study of functions entails. I felt that it was worth a few minutes to provide some more background. I said, "I don't think we can rate the functions in terms of importance. The essay spent many more pages discussing the ideas of linear functions because that was the emphasis of our seminar. Linear functions are important because they are the most basic relationships between two quantities that are changing. They are also the easiest for us to think about, and so it makes sense to start there. During the seminar, we have come across many contexts in which the quantities are linearly related. Obviously there are many more, but there are also many, many functions that are not linear. But sometimes linear functions are used when the quantities aren't necessarily linearly related. Differential calculus is about using straight lines to study other functions close to a particular point on a graph. That is, by studying linear functions, we develop the ability to study more complicated functions. In statistics, sometimes there might be two quantities with points that appear all over the place on a graph, but show some kind of trend. Such data-based functions are often approximated by linear functions to study some of their properties."

I went on, "However, as we saw in the chart, there are other very important functions, too. In this seminar we mainly worked on two others. The exponential function has important applications in predicting population growth and in epidemiology. I'll also show you one very interesting mathematical feature of a particular exponential function." I drew a picture of an exponential function and a tangent line. "If you have a graph of this function and draw a line that is tangent, the slope of the tangent line is equal to the value of the point of tangency. That's true of any point you pick on this curve. It turns out that is an important trait.

"We also looked at quadratic functions. A quadratic function describes the height of an object in free fall as a function of time. You remember the story of Galileo dropping objects off the Leaning Tower of Pisa in the 1600s. It was Galileo who discovered this property, that no matter how large or how heavy the object, unless some other force interferes, all objects drop at the same speed, and the speed increases at a constant rate. That is, the effect of gravity is constant acceleration—and that results in movement according to a quadratic function."

Then I drew a picture of a sine curve.

I continued, "There are other very important functions, as well. What I've drawn here is a graph of a sine function. We looked at this with the Ferris wheel problem. If you sit on a Ferris wheel, once the wheel starts going at a constant rate, your height from the ground as a function of time is a sine curve. Anyway, it turns out that these kinds of functions are very important when you're working with light or sound."

I did not expect everyone to follow everything I had said. However, I thought Ivan's question was an interesting one that deserved attention. I also felt that now, at the end of the class, participants were in more of a position to situate my comments in a context—that is, in the context of everything they had learned in the last few months. I mentioned to participants that some of what I just explained appears on the third page of the chart "Categories of Functions."

Wrapping Up

Lamis then posed a different question: "I'm looking at this line in the last paragraph of the essay: 'But it is not simply a matter of tracking the particular values of input corresponding to particular values of output. Of equal interest is the way in which *changes in input correspond to changes in output.*' I need to hear more about that."

I said, "Let's first make sure we all know what the authors are talking about here and how this comment is related to what we studied. With all of our study of linear functions, when we talked about slope we were talking about the relationship of changes in output to changes in input. The slope gave us the rate of change. If we're saving pennies, it's just as important to know that we put 7 pennies in the jar each day as to know that we have 43 pennies on the 5th day.

"We also saw that when we had a quadratic function, the changes in output that correspond to equal changes in input weren't constant. But what we did see was that those changes in output formed a linear function. One way to characterize the different kinds of functions is how the changes in output behave.

"It might be that in some of our examples, the issue didn't seem so momentous. Let's think about applications that have greater consequence. We might say, for example, that it's not just that you have a certain amount of money in the bank, but that you are saving money at a certain rate. For another example, I'm thinking of my brother-in-law, who fell off his roof a few years ago, and it wasn't just that he had fallen a certain number of feet, but that he hit the ground at a certain speed. You can think of his speed as the change in the height function. (By the way, my brother-in-law is fine now.) Another example: It's not just that there are a certain number of people in the world, but that the number doubles every 20 years. Here is another example: Have you heard of the half-life of different radioactive substances? That's how long it takes for radiation emissions to be cut in half. We're not only concerned with what the current levels are but also with the rate of decay. These are all examples of concern about the changes."

I paused and took a breath, thinking we might be at the end of the discussion. Then Peggy spoke up: "What I liked is that there was enough information in the essay that I could recognize what I had done, and if there was something that I hadn't figured out yet, that I had enough information that I could work through it. I worked through a lot reading this paper, and it was a great experience."

I said, "I do want to point out that that means you have developed the tools to work through those ideas."

Peggy insisted, "But it wasn't just review, there was some new stuff. But there was enough there that I already understood and I could build on that to think through the new stuff."

I said, "That suggests to me that perhaps the essay could act as a reference to go back to later."

Robin added, "I'm going to teach sixth grade next year after years of being in Grade 5 or lower. I'll need to know all the content for that grade. I don't want to pick up some ratty old algebra textbook. I'd rather have it in this form and reference the case studies. And like Peggy, I was working through the mathematics as I read; I wasn't just reading it passively."

200

Then we took a break.

Math activity: Growing and painting cubes

I gave participants this last Math activity as an opportunity to act on all they had learned and also to give them an experience with a new kind of function, $y = x^3$. I thought they would move through the first part fairly quickly—given an $n \times n \times n$ cube, to find the formulas for the perimeter of a face, the surface area, and the volume as functions of the length of an edge. At first I was surprised that most groups spent quite a lot of time on this activity. I suppose they have never had much opportunity to think about the structure of a cube before. Now they were looking at the cube through this new lens of functions. However, once I listened carefully to their discussions, I realized there were quite a few new insights to explore with these basic functions.

205

210

Early on in their small-group work, I realized there was some confusion over the word *cube*, so I brought the group back together. I held up a multi-link cube and said, "We talk about this manipulative as a cube. Notice that it has 6 square faces. For the purposes of this activity, we'll refer to it as a unit cube—all the edges are 1 unit long. However, we can also use these cubes to build larger cubes. For example, how many unit cubes do we put together to create a cube that is $2 \times 2 \times 2$, that is, a cube whose edges are all 2 units long?"

215

220

Once it was confirmed that we need 8 unit cubes to create a $2 \times 2 \times 2$ cube, I explained what surface area is—the sum of the area of each of the 6 faces. The surface area of this cube is 24 square units.

225

Small groups

Eventually, all participants had a table of the three functions, but there were quite a few interesting discussions that went along with building the table.

Side Length	Perimeter	Surface Area	Volume
1	4	6	1
2	8	24	8
3	12	54	27
4	16	96	64
5	20	150	125

Wrapping Up

Ivan and Mariam looked at the differences between the values for surface area: 18, 30, 42, 54. Mariam said, "The differences of the differences are all 12." Ivan said, "So, if you take 54 + 12, you get 66. Add that to 150 and you should get the surface area for the 6 × 6 × 6." They did the calculations and got 216 both ways.

Ivan sat back and looked at the values in the table so far. He said, "I'm surprised that the surface area function is growing faster than the volume function."

Across the table, Sandy called out, "Just keep going. Volume catches up at the 6th cube and then starts growing faster."

April and Robin hadn't yet calculated the values for the 6th cube but decided to graph the first 5 points of the surface area and volume functions on the same pair of axes.

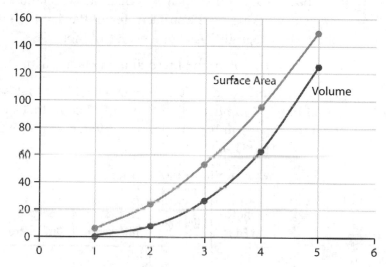

As I approached, they were discussing whether the two graphs would ever cross. Robin said, "It looks like it to me. The one at the bottom is starting to curve up at a faster rate."

I asked if they had found the formulas for the functions, and they showed me they had: $6x^2$ and x^3. Then I asked if they knew of any other ways to find the point of intersections.

April said, "Oh, yeah," and wrote $6x^2 = x^3$. She then went through the process of dividing both sides by x^2 to get $6 = x$. "Hmmm," she said. "It looks like this should happen for the 6 × 6 × 6." Then she took another look and laughed at herself. "Of course," she said. "When $x = 6$, you get 6 × 6 × 6 for both the surface area and volume."

When I stopped by to see how Peggy was doing, she looked up with a grin and said, "I'm absolutely thrilled. I can do this! Right now I'm finding a formula for the volume function. I think it's edge squared times edge. Yes, that's what it is."

I said, "So, it's edge squared times edge. Can you pull that edge squared apart?" I thought this would help her see it as edge × edge × edge. Instead, she interpreted my question differently.

Peggy said, "It's a layer! It's the area of one layer, and the edge matches the height. So if you find the area of one layer times the height, you get the whole shooting match!"

Not only was Peggy able to think about these functions, but she was sorting out how cubes can be decomposed, how the volume can be thought of as a stack of layers.

Peggy's partner, Dina, said, "Edge squared is edge times edge."

I pointed out that another way to write "edge squared times edge" is n^3, if n is the length of the edge.

I had assumed that Dina was clear on the relationships, but a minute later she was working on the surface area of the 4 × 4 × 4. Peggy said, "You have one face of 16, right? And you need 6 of those: 96."

Dina said, "Oh, right. I was thinking layers again. Layers is for volume."

Later I noticed that Trudy was looking at the first, second, and third differences of the volume function. She said, "I knew that's what would happen. It's 6 all the time. You have to find the differences one extra time for the volume function. That is so cool!"

This is what her table looked like:

Length of Edge	Volume	First Difference	Second Difference	Third Difference
1	1			
		7		
2	8		12	
		19		6
3	27		18	
		37		6
4	64		24	
		61		6
5	125		30	
		91		
6	216			

I asked her, "What kind of function do you get if you look at the second differences?"

Trudy looked at the second to last column of her calculations. She said, "The values increase at a constant rate, so it must be a linear function."

I asked, "What kind of function do you get if you look at the first differences?"

She looked at me quizzically, and so I said, "Actually, that function will be quadratic, since its differences are linear."

I had placed the middle-school teachers, Celeste, Ariel, and Violet, together, and they moved through the basic cube problem pretty quickly. Most of the time they worked on the functions of the Painted Cube problem, which had them find the number of unit-cubes with 0 faces painted, 1 face painted, 2 faces painted, and 3 faces painted for cubes of increasing size that are dropped into paint so that its surface is covered. This problem involves still more visualization of the structure of the cube.

After a while I asked the rest of the participants to move to that problem so that we could spend a little time discussing it.

Whole group

When we came together as a whole group, I pointed out that many participants had made very interesting observations in the context of one of the two problems. I told them that I wanted them to look over their work and identify one thing to share with all of us.

I gave them all a few minutes and said that we would start with all the things people have to share from the first problem. Peggy started us out by showing us how the function for volume can be written as $y = x^3$. I asked what the x stands for (the length of an edge) and what the y stands for (the volume), and then asked if anyone had any questions. There weren't any, and so we applauded Peggy's contribution.

We continued in this way, with different people volunteering an observation. Sometimes everyone in the group immediately recognized the person's point, and we all applauded. At other times, the observation led to more discussion.

When Trudy talked about looking at the differences of the volume function, she needed some help keeping track of when she was talking about the differences of the values of the function (first difference), when it was the differences of the differences (second difference), and when it was the differences of the differences of the differences (third difference). Eventually, we got her table on the board, and the group was intrigued.

When we got to the second problem, about the painted faces of the cube, we spent a bit of time considering the number of unit cubes that have 3 faces painted.

Flor said, "The cubes with 3 faces painted will always be the corners, and so there will always be 8."

Elinor asked, "Flor, how far did you have to go before you discovered that? I'm just curious about when you saw a pattern."

Flor said, "Well, we did a few, saw that each time it came out to 8, and then said, yeah, of course, it has to be like that. It will always be the cubes at each of the 8 vertices."

I added, "Sometimes you find something by looking for a pattern in the numbers, and sometimes you see it from thinking about the structure of the problem. There were a bunch of times today when I heard something similar to what Flor just said—that you made a discovery, perhaps based on a numerical pattern, and then looked at it from a different perspective and said, yeah, of course it has to come out that way."

April said, "We actually saw that right away. We didn't have to wait to see a pattern emerge since we knew there would always be those 8 corner pieces."

I said, "I think the table is pretty simple. I don't know if anyone graphed this. What would the graph look like?"

1	8
2	8
3	8
4	8
5	8

I quickly put a table up for us all to see. When I turned around, Sandy drew her hand across from left to right along a horizontal line.

I made a pair of axes and asked, "What would the x-axis be?"

People responded, "The length of an edge."

I asked, "And, the y-axis?"

Many responded, "The number of cubes."

I asked, "And where is my first point?"

Sandy said, "It's at 8. It's always 8."

I drew in a horizontal line through the points $(1, 8)$, $(2, 8)$, ... $(5, 8)$.

Bill asked, "Is it still a linear function? There is no change."

Georgeann said, "The slope is 0," and at the same time, Yan said, "The rate of change is 0."

I asked, "What is the equation of this line?"

Trudy started to say, "I forget, the change of y over the change of x. But, it's not changing. It's 0 divided by 0."

I said, "We have to be careful about how we think about this. The change of y is 0; what about the change of x? What if we go from the point $(2, 8)$ to $(4, 8)$? What is the change in y and what's the change in x?"

Trudy said, "Oh, yeah. The change in y is 0 and the change in x is 2, so when you do the division you get 0."

325

330

335

340

345

350

I nodded, "Trudy just went back to how we calculate slope. By looking at the change in y over the change in x, we find that the slope is 0. Several people already told us that. So how do we write the function that relates the x and y values?"

Bill said, "It's just $y = 8$."

I wrote "$y = 8$" on the board for everyone to look at, and asked, "What do you make of that?"

Sandy said, "I don't know. It looks different from the other linear functions we studied."

I nodded and said, "Yes, it does look different. But it's a line whose slope is equal to 0."

We spent a few more minutes looking at the function for the number of unit cubes with 1 face painted. We first looked at the table.

Length of Edge	Number of Unit Cubes with One Face Painted
2	0
3	6
4	24
5	54
6	96

Then Georgeann explained how to find the rule: $6(x - 2)^2$. She came up to the board and drew the face of a $5 \times 5 \times 5$ cube.

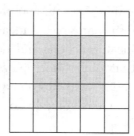

She said, "There's a square on each face with the unit cubes with one face painted. That's what I've shaded in here. That square sits inside a frame and the frame takes up one unit-face on each side. So the side of the square is $x - 2$. You square that to get the number for one face, and then you multiply it by 6 for the 6 faces."

Bill brought us back to the table, "If you look at the changes, you go from 0 to 6, and it changes 6, then it changes 18, and then it changes 30. The change of the change is constant—it's 12. So, you have a quadratic function." Bill finished his comments by gesturing with his hand, showing how the graph would curve up.

Length of Edge	Number of Unit Cubes with One Face Painted	First Difference
2	0	
		6
3	6	
		18
4	24	
		30
5	54	
		42
6	96	

I said, "Yep. So far, there are these two things that tell us we have a quadratic function. We see in the rule that the variable is squared. That exponent of 2 is one way to tell. The other, as Bill points out, is that the change of the changes is constant. That's another characteristic of a quadratic function. That means we know the graph will curve, like Bill was showing us.

"But I also want to back up a little bit. Let's look at the values in the table and see if there's anything there that tells us about that shape of the graph."

April said, "The change is increasing each time. So it curves up like that because the rate of change is increasing more and more."

After April's comment, I looked at the clock and pointed out that our time was almost up. I told the group that I wanted them to pause for just a moment, look at the material on the board and on their desks, and honor themselves for all they had learned in the past few months.

Saying goodbye

To close the seminar, I pointed out that in the Math activity we had just discussed, we worked with many of the ideas we had explored throughout the seminar. There were linear functions and nonlinear functions. Specifically, some of the functions that pertain to those cubes were quadratic functions, and we also saw they had learned how to interpret a new kind of function: a cubic function. Then I said, "To close, we're going to do a short exercise on functions without rules."

Feb 2   May 11

Wrapping Up

I drew a pair of axes and put the date of our first seminar meeting at the left on the horizontal axis, the current date on the right. As I did that, I heard murmuring and chuckling behind me.

I said, "You recognize that the horizontal axis is time, extending from when our seminar first got started until now. You can decide what you want the vertical axis to be, but I want you to graph some aspect of your experience in the seminar."

At first, participants looked a little confused about what they were being asked to do. So I talked some more. "There are quite a few things that changed throughout the course of these few months. You can pick one thing to show how it changed."

Even before I finished, it seemed that everyone was sketching something. Soon the room was buzzing as they wanted to share their graphs with neighbors and wanted to see what others had graphed.

At first I tried to pull the group together. I thought it would be fun to have some of them reproduce their graph on the board. However, when I tried to do that, it seemed that nobody heard me—they were so much into sharing their ideas in a less structured way. I decided that this activity was really for them, not for me, and so I didn't interfere. I let their discussions go for the rest of the time.

I passed out the last two assignments for them: a final reflection and an evaluation that I asked them to mail to me within two weeks. After that, many of us stood around for another 10 minutes or so, reluctant to say goodbye. Finally, it was time to go.

Final reflections

June 1

Over the last few weeks, participants have been sending me their final reflections and course evaluations. Now it is time for me to digest what they have been writing about and look back over the seminar as a whole.

Overall, participants wrote that the seminar experience was positive and powerful. This is true of those who reported painful secondary-school experiences with algebra, as well as those who enjoyed it.

Some teachers felt that they now had a grasp of the basic idea of what a function is. That does not necessarily mean that they now can state a formal definition. What they do have is the idea that a function involves a correspondence between two sets; they have an array of examples that they can make sense of; they can represent these functions in a variety of forms; and they have an idea of different categories of functions.

Flor reported that for her, finally understanding that each axis is identified by a different quantity, and that each point on the grid represents two values, opened up the possibility of making sense of this entire area of mathematics.

> *Understanding what a function even is felt very powerful. It made it simpler for me to understand why this type of math is even necessary to learn. Being able to explore the different types of functions with a better understanding of what the points on the grid mean felt helpful. I had done the same types of tasks in the past without having any understanding of what the points even represented or that it even had anything to do with change.*

Yan discovered that mysterious symbols whose meaning had always eluded her were not so mysterious after all.

> *The biggest change in my mathematical ideas is that algebra is not an elusive topic that considers the value of x using mysterious manipulation of equations. The ideas that I dealt with in this seminar were extremely interesting, sometimes captivating. I learned that x is just a symbol for a variable.*

> *I have a much clearer concept of what a function is—a relationship between quantities. Analyzing functions involves seeing patterns. There is logic that comes to light from organizing what I see. I need to consider the importance of a variety of representations, both concrete and abstract, to make connections in order to make my understanding deeper.*

> *Amazingly, the Penny Jar problems, when presented visually, are potent representations of functions and are connected to $y = mx + b$. $y = mx + b$ has meaning to me! The b is really the "start with" number and is called the y-intercept.*

Joy, who had always enjoyed her high-school math classes, was excited by the deeper meaning she could now bring to this content.

> *It was so important for me to explore the concepts and then have a way to explain the ideas in my own words. Finally seeing that connection to the algebraic formula made sense. The formulas weren't just math sentences with numbers and letters; the formulas actually mean something. These are ideas that I can now explain and/or represent in a different way—patterns in a table, visual representations, graphs, formulas. Seeing all these ideas connect (and being able to talk about them) has been very informative.*

Almost everyone felt very solid about the work we did on linear functions. They wrote about looking for the rate of change and the starting value as the two pieces of information they needed to establish what the function is. With that information, they could create a table, a graph, and an algebraic expression that defined the rule. They know when you can find the 10th value by doubling the 5th; and they know how to find the intersection of two functions.

Several people wrote about their realization that a graph can tell a story. They can look at a graph and from its shape—the high and low values, whether it is going up or down, straight or bending, and bending up or down—they can tell the story it represents. This makes them feel powerful.

440

445

450

455

460

465

470

475

Some people wrote about particular aspects of the way the seminar was conducted that were important to them. For example, one person wrote about how the preseminar assignment set them up to do the Math activity before reading the cases. They also highlighted the importance of doing any math activity before giving it to students.

Several participants wrote about the norms discussion we had on the first day.

From the initial class in which a tone of collaboration was set by just having all members of the seminar express what they could offer to the group and how they would like to be helped, I once again recognized how important it is for a teacher to validate and appreciate the fact that we all do have something to offer and that it is an expectation that we are all going to need assistance with learning in one form or another.

Robin wrote:

Speaking for myself, it was important that the facilitator was aware of and respectful of the anxiety many of us brought into the room and the need many of us had for a rich mix of both exploration and explicit instruction and explanation.

Some teachers elaborated on the idea that Robin began to discuss here, addressing how they were challenged to sort out ideas for themselves but were also given explicit information.

I was particularly aware in the whole-group discussions of what ideas you decided to bring up and follow through on, particularly when you decided to tell us information about functions, and when you left it to us to bring up and evaluate ideas ourselves. I felt powerful in making my own sense of the ideas, and the things you chose to tell us just added to what I had already figured out or perhaps gave a more formal name to an idea.

I was very interested in teachers' comments regarding what they learned about learning and teaching. Here, again, the issue of looking across multiple representations arose.

The importance of looking across representations seems extremely important in thinking about learning and teaching. It is through making these connections that students may develop the strongest understanding of functions (or really for that matter of other mathematical ideas). This is an area that I need to focus on as I work with students. I found that in reflecting back on my student-thinking assignments I often allowed us to get stuck in one representation—one time it was in just looking at a physical model with cubes, another time it was just looking at numbers in a table. In both situations, I realized that if I had given students more opportunities to look at their ideas using other representations, they might have made some new connections and it would have helped them move forward in their thinking.

Another issue was the movement toward multiplicative reasoning. April was most eloquent in her reflection.

As I read through my own papers and your responses to my work, the idea of students moving toward thinking about multiplicative relationships when working on linear functions stood out to me in some of your comments. Although we had talked about students moving towards making some generalizations about a function when they move from seeing what is happening in a problem as adding on some amount to multiplying, I hadn't really seen the importance of this. I remember a few other participants naming this as a goal in their work with students, and I wondered why they were pushing so hard on this idea.

In reading through a few comments you made about this idea and then looking back at my cases, I am beginning to understand the importance of multiplication in working with functions. You wrote, "In order to do this kind of reasoning, students may be moving from an additive way of looking at this situation, which requires them to always know the height of the previous tower in order to determine the next one, to a multiplicative view—each step has an increase of 2, no matter how many increases happen. You can multiply 2 by the number of steps to get the total increase over those steps." When I worked with a group of first and second graders, they seemed to grasp quite readily that they were adding on groups of 3 pennies and knew that if there was going to be 5 more days, they would need 5 more groups of 3. This is a pretty powerful understanding for a group of students who have not yet formally worked on multiplication! Their understanding of what was happening in the problem seemed pretty clear to me. When I worked with a group of third graders on the Growing Worm problem, their understanding of the multiplicative aspect of the problem seemed to be an important divide across which students moved into a new level of understanding. Students who noticed patterns in the numbers, but did not see they were adding on groups of 2, seemed in a different place from those who realized that if there were 5 more days they need to add on 5 more groups of 2. Why this multiplicative relationship is so important is still fuzzy to me, but I think I am beginning to make sense of it. Is it really the embodiment of the functional relationship, holding in mind the relationship between the two variables? The students who knew they needed to add on 5 days of 3 pennies each realized the important relationship between the days and the number of pennies added on. They didn't just see the days and the adding on of 3s as isolated.

Participants also wrote, more generally, about the importance of teaching with a clear mathematical agenda in mind, fully understanding the problems given to students, being prepared with questions but knowing that in the moment your questions will change, and working to understand students' ideas. They talked about reading some cases for the moves the teachers made or thinking about the moves they would make if they were the teacher. They discussed the power of writing their student-thinking assignments and receiving feedback from me about them. They also wrote about how important it was to plan to teach the same lesson as colleagues, with time to discuss their plans before teaching the lesson, and time to share results afterward.

Some teachers, writing about what they had learned about teaching in the PFC seminar, described ideas in contexts other than functions. Yan wrote about a student who solved 28×32 as $30 \times 30 - 4$ and the long discussion that ensued about why that works. "Many of the students were deeply involved. It was a powerful experience for us. I learned more about student thinking and more about my own thinking." Robin described a lesson on visualizing the structure of rectangular prisms.

Joy offered a different classroom example—one in which her students applied what they had learned in one lesson to a different context.

One activity students worked on was to figure out how many cookies they would have started with if each person's share was $\frac{11}{2}$ cookies. This was an open-ended question because they were not told how many people were sharing. The students created tables, used the pattern blocks to represent the cookies, and also referred to the ideas we have been focusing on in class. They tried doubling—when they figured out how many cookies there would have been for 5 people, they doubled it for 10. One child was going to check by completing the rest of the table, but his partner explained to him that you don't have to because she knew that it would work. She referred to the "Watch Them Grow" worm activity and said that we didn't have the extras like the head and tail. I thought her explanation of this was great. She was referring to the constant triangles in the worm, which were the head and tail. She was able to connect this idea to a new situation, one with fractions. We didn't have a constant to add on, just that each person gets $\frac{11}{2}$ cookies. The students were also looking across the table and comparing the columns, as well as looking down the column that shows the total number of cookies.

There were a few participants I had been concerned about in the course of the seminar. Peggy was one, after she missed part of Session 5 and then talked about feeling at sea in Session 6. However, she was now feeling solid.

Maxine's concern about how I was doing in math will resonate as I see kids struggle. Feeling that Maxine had confidence in me finding my balance and being able to do the work felt wonderful. I want to be sure that I put kids in that position, too.

I had also been concerned about Violet, a middle-school teacher who for some years had been teaching the content many of the participants were now learning. After several weeks of reading exit cards in which Violet indicated she was not learning much, I wrote to Violet about where to look for her own learning. Her final reflections addressed that. She said that although her ideas about functions have not changed much (though she did say that it was new to think about finding the intersection of two lines as the difference between the y-intercepts divided by the difference between the rates), her ideas about learning about functions changed significantly. By listening to participants who were sorting out these ideas for the first time, she came to realize what was difficult and what might be challenging to some of her students. For example, she had not thought about how students might need time to absorb the idea that a point on a graph represents two values. She wrote about how important it was to see how participants relied on contexts to sort out the mathematical ideas. She addressed how important it is for math learners to discover relationships for themselves.

Violet said that it was important for her to observe the various ways people approach the same problem and the great risks they take when doing the work in a group—to work so hard to understand the ideas while others watch and listen. She said that each time she was put in a new group, she felt there was a period of uneasiness. In some groups, that feeling never left.

That point helps me interpret some of the comments from other participants. Although they never named anyone, some participants wrote that some of the groupings did not work well for them. Specifically, they said, it was hard when some members of the group understood more than they did and they did not feel they had the opportunity to figure out the ideas for themselves.

Reading about this at the end of the seminar, I wonder whether there were other interventions I could have made. Perhaps I should have spent more time watching small-group dynamics. That is, I would have applied a different lens than seeing where everyone was with the mathematical ideas. I might have sat down with small groups to observe the interactions, to make sure that the small group provided a context to support each participant's learning. I might have returned to the norms discussion to give participants a chance to raise these issues, and perhaps I could have encouraged them to restructure the group or shift the dynamic if it was not working for them. These are issues for me to remember next time.

However, even though there are some things I will try to do better—and giving more attention to the elementary and middle-school heterogeneity is a big one—overall I feel very satisfied with what took place in this seminar on Patterns, Functions, and Change.

When asked about which ideas they are still puzzling over, the issue that came up repeatedly involved quadratic functions: The change in the dependent variable is not a constant rate, but the "change of the change" is. As I read what they have to say about this in their final reflections, it seems that this is a pattern people were able to recognize in the tables—they know this is a characteristic of quadratic functions—but they were not given enough contextual examples to feel satisfied with the meaning of this pattern.

For example, April first described an important aspect of learning how to learn mathematics.

I don't feel quite satisfied until I feel comfortable saying, "Ah, this is why it works." I found myself searching for this throughout our study of functions—if I found a pattern, I was not satisfied until I figured out why that

pattern was happening. I find I enjoy working through new ideas and don't — 650
feel uncomfortable being in a state where I am still figuring out an idea or
I am confused by an idea because I know that I will ultimately end up in a
place where I feel satisfied that I have a pretty good understanding of an idea.

April went on to explain that the idea of the change of the changes in a
quadratic function is one in which she is not yet satisfied. Joy, too, said that, — 655
each time she thinks about this idea, she goes back to the picture of Growing
Squares to identify the changes in the dependent variable and the changes of
those changes.

This is a good mathematical question for participants to be pondering
at the end of this seminar. I am pleased that they are looking for something — 660
deeper, beyond recognizing the pattern in the table. If they have an opportunity to take another mathematics class—an introductory calculus class, for
example, where the mathematics is situated in contexts—they will be well
positioned to engage with this question they are still working on. If they have
the opportunity to explore the relationship between distance, velocity, and — 665
acceleration, perhaps they will feel more satisfied. For now, they have the
pleasure of pondering this issue, knowing there is an idea out there that they
have yet to explore more deeply.

Detailed Agenda

There are two different options of Math activities available for this session, one focuses on cubic functions and one focuses on applications of the quadratic and exponential functions. The first, Growing and painted cubes, will extend participants' experience by introducing cubic functions. They will explore this new kind of function in a manner that is consistent with much of the work of the seminar, by encountering the function within a particular context, building models of the situation with manipulatives, and making connections between the models, the tables, the graphs, and the formulas. We expect most facilitators will choose "Math activity: Growing and painted cubes," and so "Maxine's Journal" and the agenda are written to describe this activity.

The second activity, Application problems, provides participants with examples of a few contexts in which quadratic and exponential functions are useful. The problems may seem more traditional in form, even though an important part of the work participants will do is making connections between the situations, the formulas, the tables, and the graphs. If many of your participants are curious about how their work in the seminar is applied and they are comfortable (or beginning to be comfortable) with more traditional algebraic notation, then you may want to choose this worksheet of application problems as the culminating experience for this session. The Facilitator's Note on page 304 presents possible answers to these problems.

Many participants continue to think about and work on the ideas in a DMI seminar even after it has concluded. For that reason, distribute the sheet you did not use at the end of the session, and let participants know they might find it interesting to look at this to continue to think about the ideas of the seminar.

Chapter 8 discussion

(60 minutes)

Small groups (30 minutes)

Whole group (30 minutes)

Organize participants in groups of 3 or 4. For this discussion, mixed grade-level groups are best. In their small-group discussion, participants will have the opportunity to share their reactions to the Chapter 8 essay and to talk over the terms they found unfamiliar. Tell them to read the work of all others in the group before beginning any conversation so they can talk about comments that they have in common.

Suggest they first talk about the points they found interesting and then turn to those that were confusing or with which they disagreed. They should also use this time to share information and to clarify any unfamiliar terms. Let them know they can call on you for help with terms they do not understand. There may be questions the essay brings up that are unresolved in the small-group work. Assure the groups they can bring these questions to the whole-group discussion. As you interact with the small groups, take note of themes and confusions so you can bring these up in the whole-group discussion.

Begin the whole-group discussion by asking participants for common themes they noticed among the points of interest. Then turn to what was confusing or the points of disagreement. If participants do not mention the points you noted during the small-group discussions, bring them up yourself. Clarify any terms that are unfamiliar and respond to the points of confusion. Use the last 10 minutes for comments about the connection between the essay and changes participants are considering in their own teaching practice.

End the discussion by mentioning that they may want to reread the essay in the future as they continue to work on bringing these kinds of ideas to their students.

"Categories of Functions" discussion (25 minutes)

Pairs (10 minutes)

Whole group (15 minutes)

The purpose of this discussion is to address any questions that arose from the Categories of Functions chart. Have participants turn to a neighbor and share their ideas and questions about the information in the chart. Then call the whole group together for a discussion. Begin by asking participants to share some of the notes they made for themselves about each of the categories. Then address their remaining questions. Use this discussion as an opportunity to highlight what participants have learned in the seminar and to indicate how that learning can be placed in the context of more formal mathematics.

Some of the questions that arise may have to do with seeing the full variety of functions included in the categories participants have worked on in the seminar. For example, most (though not all) of the linear functions that arose in the seminar have been increasing. It is important that participants recognize lines with negative slope as falling in the category of linear functions. Also, since most of the functions have had a domain of positive numbers, participants may be surprised to see the parabolic shape of quadratic functions when the domain is extended to include negative numbers.

For each category of functions, the chart provides information about how different values for the parameters in the formula are reflected in the graph. For instance, when the coefficient of the x^2 term of a quadratic function is positive, the graph opens upward; when the coefficient is negative, the graph opens downward. The intent of the chart is to offer a general view of five different kinds of functions. Assure participants it is not expected that they be familiar and comfortable with all these variations and the formal expressions on the information sheet; rather, they can use the sheet to see the way these functions are represented in more formal terms.

Let participants know it is fine for them to feel there is more for them to learn. In fact, in "Math activity: Growing and painted cubes," they will explore a function not included in the chart.

Break (15 minutes)

Math activity: Growing and painted cubes or Application problems (75 minutes)

Small groups (55 minutes)

Whole group (20 minutes)

Option 1: In this Math activity, participants will have an opportunity to work on a new problem and gain experience using the tools they have developed for analyzing mathematical situations. The activity is based on examining two situations. The first, Growing Cubes, is an extension of the Growing Squares problem. As participants work on Growing Cubes, they will examine three different relationships embedded in a single context: how the perimeter of the base of the cube changes as a function of the length of an edge, how the surface area of the cube changes as a function of the length of an edge, and how the volume of the cube changes as a function of the length of an edge. In relation to the length of an edge, the perimeter is an example of a linear function and the surface area is a quadratic function. Participants will also encounter a new nonlinear function, a cubic function ($y = x^3$), which represents the relationship between the length of an edge and the volume.

Cubes and Unit Cubes

A cube is a three-dimensional object with six square faces. In "Math activity: Growing and painted cubes," participants use interlocking cubes to build larger cubes. An edge of one interlocking cubic is one unit in length; a face is one square unit; the cube itself is one cubic unit. Thus, given a 2 × 2 × 2 cube, the perimeter of one face is 8 units, the surface area is 24 square units, and the volume is 8 cubic units.

The second context involves examining the structure of a cube by focusing on decomposing a painted cube into unit cubes and examining the number of painted faces on each of the unit cubes. As participants work on this problem, they first have to determine how many faces of the unit cubes might be painted. For cubes composed of more than one unit cube, each unit cube will have paint on 0, 1, 2, or 3 faces.

The main focus of these activities is to provide the opportunity for participants to examine relationships that are linear, quadratic, and cubic and to examine the connections between the shape of the graphs and these situations. Some participants may also choose to examine the formulas.

Ask questions so that *all* participants focus on connections:

- Between the shape of the graphs and the number patterns in the tables
- Between the number patterns in the tables and the structure of the cube
- Between the changes (first, second, and third differences) in the output and the shape of the graphs

Organize participants into small groups and distribute the first page of "Math activity: Growing and painting cubes." Mention that this activity provides participants an opportunity to use the various tools they have developed for examining mathematical relationships—symbols, tables, and graphs. You should also let them know when they complete the first page of this activity, they should contact you to share their conclusions and to obtain the second page of the activity sheet.

Possible responses for the tables from Question 1:

Length of an Edge in Linear Units	Perimeter of the Base in Linear Units	Surface Area in Square Units	Volume in Cubic Units
1	4	6	1
2	8	24	8
3	12	54	27
4	16	96	64
...	...	...	...
n	$4n$	$6n^2$	n^3

Refer to "Maxine's Journal," pp. 284–290 for an example of the points that participants might examine.

As you work with the small groups on Question 2, encourage them to build and decompose cubes in order to develop a picture of what is happening with the painted cubes. When the $2 \times 2 \times 2$ cube is decomposed into 8 cubes, each of the 8 unit cubes will have 3 faces painted. With the $3 \times 3 \times 3$ cube, there will be a total of 27 unit cubes. The 8 corner pieces will have 3 faces painted. There will be 12 unit cubes with 2 faces painted. There will be 6 cubes with 1 face painted. That leaves 1 cube unaccounted for. This unit cube is embedded within the larger cube and will have no faces painted. (See the Facilitator's Note on pp. 302–304 for more detail on the Painted Cube math activity.)

The whole-group discussion should have a celebratory feel—a way for participants to note the progress they have made as mathematical thinkers. Ask each group to share something they have figured out in the context of working on these problems. After each group shares, invite other participants to celebrate what they accomplished.

It is likely that participants will have more to explore about the Painted Cube math activity than can be discussed in the allotted time. Let participants know they can continue to think about and talk about this problem even after the seminar is over. You might suggest that leaving the seminar experience with an interesting math problem to explore and a sense of owning the tools to explore it is a good way to end the seminar.

Option 2: Some facilitators may choose to have their participants work with the Application problems instead of Growing and painted cubes. Similar to the activity described above, have participants work in small groups and then have groups present something they learned.

Portfolio review and closing
(5 minutes)

Distribute and explain the "Final Reflection" assignment that participants are to do as homework. This assignment has two purposes: One is to provide participants with the opportunity to examine how their own thinking has changed over the course of the seminar. The other is to provide you, the facilitator, with information about what your participants have learned.

Announce the date by which you wish the assignment to be completed and the process for returning it to you. If you are using a seminar evaluation form, distribute that form and make clear how they will return it and by what date. Providing a stamped, self-addressed envelope for the final reflection and the seminar evaluation form may be helpful.

Distribute "Application Problems" (or, alternately, the "Growing and painted cubes" problems) and explain that participants may choose to work on them at any time. These problems are given as a gift and are not required for the seminar.

You should end the session by sharing what you have learned by participating in this experience with them.

The Painted Cube

One way to picture the relationships involved in the Painted Cube work is to consider a $3 \times 3 \times 3$ cube. Look at a single face of the cube that is a 3×3 square.

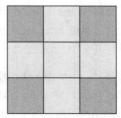

    The dark shaded squares are part of the corner cubes, each of which has 3 faces painted. Therefore, in the $3 \times 3 \times 3$ cube each of the 8 corners will have 3 faces painted. The lightly shaded squares are part of the unit cubes, which have 2 faces painted. However, if we count 4 unit cubes per face of the larger

---

cube times 6 faces of the larger cube, we obtain 24; this is exactly twice as many as we want because we have counted each cube twice. Therefore, there are 12 cubes with 2 faces painted. The middle square on each face represents a cube with a single face painted and there are 6 of those.

To summarize for a 3 × 3 × 3 cube, of the 27 unit cubes, 8 have 3 faces with paint, 12 have 2 faces with paint, 6 have one face with paint, and 1 has no face with paint.

As small groups complete their work on Question 2, listen to their explanations for determining the number of unit cubes with a given number of faces painted. Ask questions so participants connect the number patterns they notice in the table with the square faces of the cubes. Distribute page 2 of "Math acitivity: Growing and painted cubes" as the small groups complete page 1. If many groups reach this point at the same time, you might want to have a short whole-group conversation to establish the values for the 2 × 2 × 2 and 3 × 3 × 3 cubes instead of working with each group individually.

As participants work on Question 3, help them articulate the connections between the tables of values and what they predict for the graphs. For instance, the graph for 2 faces painted will be linear because the table illustrates a constant increase of 12 as the edge length increases by 1. The graph for 1 face painted will be a quadratic, the kind of graph associated with growing squares, because the changes are not constant but linear. The graph for 3 faces painted is a horizontal line. The remaining two relationships, number of unit cubes with 0 faces painted and the total number of cubes, are cubic functions similar to the graph in Question 1.

Participant responses for the tables for Question 3 might look like this:

Dimensions	0 Faces Painted	1 Face Painted	2 Faces Painted	3 Faces Painted	Total Number of Unit Cubes
2 x 2 x 2	0	0	0	8	8
3 x 3 x 3	1	6 = (6 x 1)	12 = (6 x 2)	8	27
4 x 4 x 4	8	24 = (6 x 4)	24 = (6 x 4)	8	64
5 x 5 x 5	27	54 = (6 x 9)	36 = (6 x 6)	8	125
6 x 6 x 6	64	96 = (6 x 16)	48 = (6 x 8)	8	216

You should also encourage participants to examine how the number patterns they see in the table are connected to the structure of the cube. You might consider questions such as: Why are the values in the 0-faces-painted column the same as those in the total-number-of-unit-cubes column? Why are the values in the 1 face painted 6 times the square numbers? Why do the values in the 2 faces painted increase by 12 each time?

As participants discuss such questions, they might recognize that each larger cube contains within it an inner cube with dimensions 2 less than the larger cube. This inner cube contains all of the unit cubes with no faces painted. The outer cube then is made up of a shell plus this inner cube.

Consider the case of a $5 \times 5 \times 5$ cube. The inner cube will be $3 \times 3 \times 3$. One way to understand the other relationships is to examine one face of the outer cube.

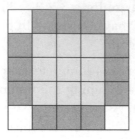

The lightly shaded square in the middle of the face of the outer cube, the $5 \times 5 \times 5$, corresponds to one of the faces of the inner cube, the $3 \times 3 \times 3$. Each of these unit cubes will have 1 face painted. In this example, these form a square, 3×3, on each of the faces of the outer cube. Because there are 6 faces, the total number of unit cubes with 1 face painted will be 6×9. As participants notice such relationships, ask how the diagram can support their thinking about a $6 \times 6 \times 6$ cube or an $n \times n \times n$ cube to help them develop general rules for 0 faces painted, $(n - 2)^3$, and 1 face painted, $6(n - 2)^2$.

The darkly shaded squares correspond to the unit cubes of the outer cube with 2 faces painted. On each edge of the cube, there are $(n - 2)$ such unit cubes. (In the picture, when $n = 5$, there are 3 unit cubes at each edge with 2 faces painted.) Since there are 12 edges in a cube, there are $12(n - 2)$ unit cubes with 2 faces painted.

To summarize the general expressions for each of the categories,

Dimensions	0 Faces Painted	1 Face Painted	2 Faces Painted	3 Faces Painted	Total Number of Unit Cubes
$n \times n \times n$	$(n - 2)^3$	$6(n - 2)^2$	$2(n - 2)$	8	n^3

Note: An implication of this work is that $(n - 2)^3 + 6(n - 2)^2 + 12(n - 2) + 8 = n^3$. If you have participants who are ready to accept such a challenge, you can suggest they work to show how the left side of this equation can be shown to be equal to n^3. It is not necessary that all participants do this.

Possible Answers to Optional Application Problems

This note provides the answers to the "Application Problems" math activity.

<u>Dropped and Tossed Objects</u>

1. If a penny is dropped from a height of 150 feet, its height changes over time according to this formula: $h = 150 - 16t^2$, where t is measured in seconds.

From the table below, we see that the penny hits the ground between 3 and 4 seconds after it is dropped and much closer to 3 than 4. This can also be seen in the graph. While the graph is shown in all four quadrants, in this situation, only the first quadrant is applicable.

t	$150 - 16t^2$
1	134
2	86
3	6
4	⁻106 (Not applicable in this situation)
5	⁻250 (Not applicable)

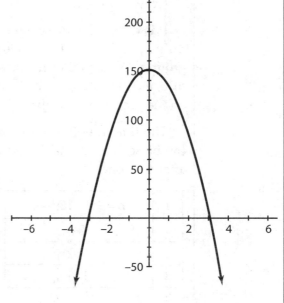

2. The second part of this formula ($^-16t^2$) tells how much height the penny has lost since it began falling. To land at exactly 1 seconds, the penny must have started out at $16(4^2)$ feet high.

3. If the penny is dropped from a height of 1,050 feet, the formula will be $h = 1,050 - 16t^2$. The penny will land between 8 and 9 seconds after it is dropped. A table and graph for this quadratic function looks like this:

t	$1,050 - 16t^2$
1	1,034
2	986
3	906
4	794
5	650
...	
8	26
9	⁻246 (Not applicable in this situation)

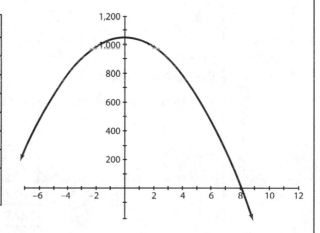

4. In the formula, $h = 96t - 16t^2 + 4$, each one of the three terms has a meaning associated with the situation; the sum of these three values at any time indicates how high the penny is above the ground.

- **4** At $t = 0$, the penny is 4 feet above the ground. This indicates the height of the penny before it is tossed upward.
- **$-16t^2$** If the penny were dropped with no initial upward velocity, $-16t^2$ indicates the number of feet the penny would travel downward.
- **96t** If there were no gravity, $96t$ indicates the distance the penny would travel upward.

It is the sum of these three terms at any time t that indicates the height of the penny. For instance, when $t = 1$, $h = 96 - 16 + 4$, the penny is 84 feet above ground. On the other hand, when $t = 10$, $h = 960 - 1,600 + 4$, which equals -636, indicating a position below ground level. This means the penny landed on the ground in less than 10 seconds.

The time it will take to hit the ground is the value of t when $h = 0$. This can be seen on the table and graph. The penny lands on the ground a little after 6 seconds.

t	$h = 96t - 16t^2 + 4$
1	84
2	132
3	148
4	132
5	84
6	4
7	-108 (Not applicable in this situation)

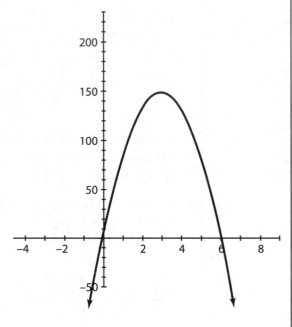

Population

This table shows the population of a small, mythical country for various years.

Year	Population
1825	200
1850	252
1875	318
1900	401
1925	504
1950	635
1975	800

1. Graph:

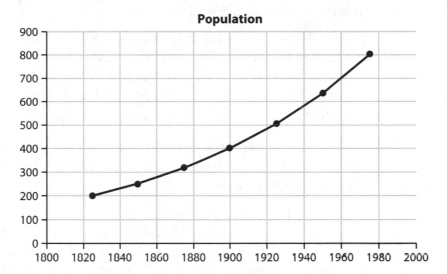

Population

2. The table indicates that the population doubles approximately each 75-year period; for example, from 1850 to 1925 or 1900 to 1975. Thus, the situation can be approximated by an exponential function that represents doubling every 75 years. The actual population will not be determined by the formula, but if the trend continues, the formula provides approximate values.

3. In 2000, the population should be double what it was in 1925, so about 1,008. Using the same logic in 2050, the population would be 1,600.

To determine the population in the year 3000, we need to calculate how many periods of 75 years to add to a known data point. Because $\frac{3000 - 1950}{75} =$ 14, there are 14 periods of 75 years between 1950 and 3000. The population will double 14 times over that period. $2^{14} = 16,384$; therefore, the population in 3000 will be 635(16,384) or 10,403,840.

4. If we extend the table or the graph until the years 2000, 2050, or 3000, we could read the data from the table or the graph.

5. I. $P = 200(2)^{\frac{t}{75}}$ II. $P = 200(2)^{\frac{r-1825}{75}}$ III. $P = 401(2)^{\frac{n-1900}{75}}$

For all versions of the function, there are differences between the actual data in the table and values determined by the formula. This is because the formula is an approximation for the situation.

Version I. This is based on the year 1825 and the population of 200 at that time. The variable t represents the number of years after 1825; that is, $t = 0$ matches the data point with a population of 200, and $t = 25$ matches a population of 252 and the year 1850. Because the population doubles every 75 years, t is divided by 75 in the formula in order to determine the number of 75-year periods—the appropriate exponent for 2. The product of 200 and $2^{\frac{t}{75}}$ indicates the population t years after 1825. For instance, if the date is

1975, $t = 150(1975 - 1825)$. So $\frac{t}{75} = 2$. The population will double 2 times from an original number of 200, $200(2)^2 = 800$.

Version II. This is also based on the year 1825 and the original population of 200. However, the variable r is the actual year. $(r - 1825)$ determines the number of years since 1825. Note that $(r - 1825)$ is the same as t in the previous formulation. So, when $r = 1975$, the exponent is calculated by $\frac{1975 - 1825}{2} = \frac{150}{75} = 2$. The formula becomes $200(2)^2 = 800$.

Version III. This formula is based on the year 1900 and a population of 401. For $n = 1975$, the exponent becomes $\frac{75}{75}$, or 1; i.e., from 1900 to 1975, the population will double 1 time. $401 \times 2 = 802$.

Note that each formula allows for non-integral values in the exponent. It is likely that most participants' intuitive definitions of exponents are based on repeated multiplication that requires integers. A different definition of exponent is used to define exponentiation over all of the numbers on the number line.

Carbon Dating

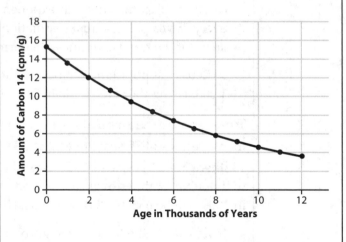

Age in Thousands of Years	Amount of Carbon 14 (cpm/g)
0	15.3
1	13.5558
2	12.0104
3	10.6412
4	9.4281
5	8.3533
6	7.401
7	6.5573
8	5.8098
9	5.1475
10	4.5606
11	4.0407
12	3.5801

1. Both the table and the graph show the half-life is somewhat less than 6,000 years.

2. For a 4,000-year-old object, $a = 9.4281$.

3. If $a = 2.34$, the age of an object is between 15,000 and 16,000 years.

PATTERNS, FUNCTIONS, AND CHANGE

Math activity: Growing and painted cubes (page 1)

In past sessions, we have explored growth patterns for various 2-dimensional tile arrangements. In this session, we will look at a specific kind of 3-dimensional object, a cube.

A cube is a rectangular structure in which all three dimensions are the same. Start with a unit cube, that is, a cube that is 1 unit of length on each edge. We will examine 3 different aspects of this cube: the perimeter of the base, the area of all 6 faces, and the volume.

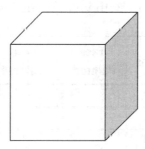

For a cube with edge lengths of 1 unit, the perimeter of the base is 4 units, the surface area is 6 square units, and the volume is 1 cubic unit. What would these values be for a cube with edge lengths of 2 units or 3 units or 4 units?

1. Make tables for perimeter, for surface area, and for volume as the edge lengths of the cube increase. Examine the tables to predict the shape of the graph for each of the three relationships. Explain your predictions. Make the graphs for perimeter vs. edge length, surface area vs. edge length, and volume vs. edge length and compare them with your predictions.

2. Now imagine a new scenario. Start with a cube that is 2 × 2 × 2. Dip the cube into a tub of paint so that the entire surface is coated. Imagine that you can break apart the 2 × 2 × 2 cube into unit cubes, that is, cubes with dimensions of 1 × 1 × 1. You will have 8 of the unit cubes. Imagine looking at each of the 8 unit cubes to see how many of its surfaces will have paint on them. What is possible? Can one of the unit cubes have no faces with paint? 1 face? 2 faces? 3 faces? 4 faces? 5 faces? 6 faces? Once you have determined the possibilities, count the number of cubes in each of these categories: no sides painted, 1 side painted, 2 sides painted, etc.

Explore this for the 2 × 2 × 2 cube and then consider the same question for a 3 × 3 × 3 cube. Once you have examined the 2 × 2 × 2 and the 3 × 3 × 3 cubes, explain your conclusions to the facilitator and then obtain Question 3.

Math activity: Growing and painting cubes (page 2)

3. Now consider cubes with dimensions $4 \times 4 \times 4$, $5 \times 5 \times 5$, and so on.

For each case, investigate the number of unit cubes with a given number of faces painted.

Complete the table below to show how many unit cubes have 0 faces painted, 1 face painted, 2 faces painted, and 3 faces painted as the dimensions of the cube increase. Examine the tables to predict the shape of the graph for each of the four possibilities. Explain your predictions. Make the 4 graphs and compare them with your predictions.

Dimensions	0 Faces Painted	1 Face Painted	2 Faces Painted	3 Faces Painted	Total Number of Unit Cubes
2 x 2 x 2					
3 x 3 x 3					
4 x 4 x 4					
5 x 5 x 5					
6 x 6 x 6					

Application problems (page 1)

Applications of quadratic functions: Dropped and tossed objects

Dropped Objects

1. If a penny is dropped from a height of 150 feet, its height changes over time according to this formula: $h = 150 - 16t^2$, where t is measured in seconds. Use the mathematical tools (numerical analysis, tables, and graphs) you have developed to determine how long it will take for the penny to hit the ground. What does the graph of height over time look like? What connections do you see between the graph and the table?

2. Suppose you wanted the penny to land after exactly 4 seconds. From what height would you need to drop it? Explain how you figured this out.

3. Suppose you dropped the penny from the top of the Empire State Building (1,050 feet high). How long will it take to hit the ground? What does the graph of height over time look like? What connections do you see between the graph and the table?

A Tossed Object

4. Suppose a super hero tosses the penny in the air so that at the instant he lets go of it, it is traveling with a velocity of 96 ft/s. The formula for height is given by $h = 96t - 16t^2 + 4$. Why might that make sense? How long will it take to hit the ground? What does the graph of height over time look like? What connections do you see among the graph, the table, the situation, and the formula?

Applications of exponential functions: Population and carbon dating

Population

This table shows the population (in thousands) of a small mythical country for various years.

Year	Population
1825	200
1850	252
1875	318
1900	401
1925	504
1950	635
1975	800

1. What does a graph of this data look like?

2. About how long does it take for the population to double?

Application problems (page 2)

3. What would you expect the population to be in 2000? 2050? 3000?

4. How can you see the answers to Questions 2 and 3 in the table? In the graph? By calculation?

5. Here are three different formulas that can be used to determine population in this situation:

   I. $P = 200(2)^{\frac{t}{75}}$ II. $P = 200(2)^{\frac{r - 1825}{75}}$ III. $P = 401(2)^{\frac{n - 1900}{75}}$

   a. Explain what t, r, and n each represent.

   b. Explain how each formula fits the table and the situation and how each one can give the correct answer.

   c. What connections do you see among the table, the graph, the situation, and the formula?

Carbon Dating

In living organisms, the ratio of normal carbon (carbon 12) to radioactive carbon (carbon 14) is nearly constant. When plants and animals die, the amount of carbon 14 decreases by radioactive decay. A Geiger counter can measure the amount of carbon 14 in a sample by counting disintegrations per minute. Thus, the ratio of counts per minute to the weight of a sample of carbon is a function of how long the sample has been dead. The function can be represented as $a = 15.3(0.886)^t$ where a is counts per minute per gram (cpm/g) and t is measured in thousands of years.

1. Make a table and graph for this function. Use $t = 1, 2, 3, 4 \ldots$ representing 1,000 years, 2,000 years, 3,000 years, ... along the horizontal axis. How long does it take for the amount of carbon 14 present in an object to be halved? (This is called the half-life of carbon 14.)

2. If a sample from Stonehenge were known to be 4,000 years old, what would be the value of a?

3. Charcoal from the famous Lascaux Cave in France is determined to have $a = 2.34$. What age would that indicate?

Ninth Homework
Final Reflection Questions

This is an opportunity for you to think about your experiences in the seminar. Read through the collection of your assignments, facilitator's responses, and your math work to get a sense of how your ideas have changed. Use this body of work to guide your responses to the following questions.

1. How have your mathematical ideas changed over the course of the seminar? Be specific about the ideas that have changed.

2. How have your ideas about learning changed? Be specific.

3. How have your ideas about teaching changed? Be specific.

4. It is likely that there are issues, mathematical and pedagogical, that arose during the seminar that still puzzle you. Pick one issue that is still "alive" for you. Explain what it is and your current thinking about it.

Evaluation Form

Please respond to the following questions and return your responses in the self-addressed and stamped envelope.

1. What worked for you about the way the seminar was conducted? Be specific.

2. What did not work for you?

3. What changes would you suggest if this seminar were to be offered again?

4. What else would you like to tell the seminar facilitator(s) about this experience?